# A Short Table of Integrals

## FOURTH EDITION

*by* B. O. PEIRCE

*Late Hollis Professor of Mathematics and*
*Natural Philosophy in Harvard University*

*Revised by* RONALD M. FOSTER

*Professor of Mathematics*
*Polytechnic Institute of Brooklyn*

## Ginn and Company

Boston · New York · Chicago · Atlanta · Dallas · Columbus
San Francisco · Toronto · London

# Preface

THE CONTINUED SUCCESS of this book is due to the excellent work of its author, B. O. Peirce, late Hollis Professor of Mathematics and Natural Philosophy at Harvard University. At this time it has seemed advisable to prepare a revision of the work, and it is hoped that the book will have ahead of it many more years of useful life.

In the preparation of this fourth revision of Peirce's tables, advantage has been taken of the opportunity to insert in their appropriate places the numerous additions that had been made in previous editions. With this exception the table of indefinite integrals remains practically unchanged, aside from minor corrections. On the other hand, certain substantial changes have been made in the remainder of the work. These include the addition of a number of definite integrals, the revision of the section on Bessel functions, the addition of certain information concerning other transcendental functions, the addition of a table of natural values of the gamma function, and the substitution of much more ample tables of the exponential and hyperbolic functions, as well as of squares, cubes, roots, and reciprocals.

*Ronald M. Foster*

# Contents

vi

# A Short Table
# of Integrals

# Introduction

IT IS PRESUMED that the user of these tables is familiar with the standard forms of the indefinite integral (or anti-derivative) of the principal elementary functions, as well as with the elementary operations involving indefinite integrals. These fundamental forms are collected for ready reference in the first section of the table. Many integrals not found directly in the table can be obtained by a simple change of variable. Thus particular attention is directed to Formula 22, —the use of which is often imperative in order to make full use of the subsequent formulas. It should also be noted that an arbitrary constant is to be added to all the formulas for indefinite integrals given in the table.

In the following tables the inverse trigonometric functions are to be understood as restricted to their *principal values*. These are indicated by the accompanying figures.

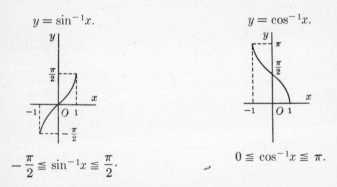

$y = \sin^{-1}x.$

$$-\frac{\pi}{2} \leqq \sin^{-1}x \leqq \frac{\pi}{2}.$$

$y = \cos^{-1}x.$

$$0 \leqq \cos^{-1}x \leqq \pi.$$

The curves representing the functions $\tan^{-1}x$ and $\operatorname{ctn}^{-1}x$ extend indefinitely in both directions.

$$y = \tan^{-1}x.$$

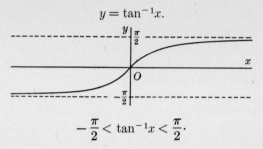

$$-\frac{\pi}{2} < \tan^{-1}x < \frac{\pi}{2}.$$

The principal value of $\operatorname{ctn}^{-1}x$ is connected with the principal value of $\tan^{-1}x$ by the relation $\tan^{-1}x + \operatorname{ctn}^{-1}x = \frac{1}{2}\pi$.

$$y = \operatorname{ctn}^{-1}x.$$

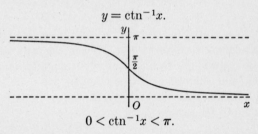

$$0 < \operatorname{ctn}^{-1}x < \pi.$$

The tables are adapted to the use of the hyperbolic functions, and graphs of three of the inverse hyperbolic functions follow.

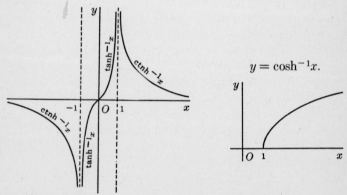

$$y = \cosh^{-1}x.$$

It should be noted that the notation $\sin^{-1}x$ is used for the inverse sine function in preference to the notation arc sin $x$, and similarly for the other inverse functions in the tables.

In certain trigonometric formulas, notably those in which the integration has been effected by means of the substitution $z = \tan \frac{1}{2} x$, there is a hidden use of the principal value, over and above the principal value of the function occurring explicitly in the formula, and so restrictions on the independent variable are necessary. See, for example, Formula 309.

The formula

$$\log (x + yi) = \tfrac{1}{2} \log (x^2 + y^2) + i \tan^{-1} \frac{y}{x}$$

is treacherous, since the values of the multiple-valued function on the left cannot be expressed in terms of the principal value of $\tan^{-1}y/x \pm k\pi$. Sometimes an even multiple of $\pi$ must be added, and sometimes an odd multiple. The formula which is correct in all cases is the following:

$$\log (x + yi) = \log r + \phi i,$$
$$x = r \cos \phi, \quad y = r \sin \phi, \quad r = \sqrt{x^2 + y^2}.$$

Thus, if complex quantities are being used, the integral of $1/x$ can always be written simply as $\log x$. If, on the other hand, the problem is restricted to the use of real quantities only, the result should be written $\log | x |$. In the tables the absolute value signs are not used. The notation $\log x$ is used throughout for the natural logarithm. Many authors in these days use the notation $\ln x$ for the natural logarithm. However, it is well to become accustomed to the use of $\log x$, a usage which is almost universal in higher mathematics.

The imaginary unit $\sqrt{-1}$ is designated by $i$, despite the large use of $j$ by electrical engineers.

# PART I

# Indefinite Integrals

## FUNDAMENTAL FORMS

**1.** $\int a\,dx = ax$

**2.** $\int af(x)dx = a\int f(x)dx$

**3.** $\int \dfrac{dx}{x} = \log x*$

**4.** $\int x^m dx = \dfrac{x^{m+1}}{m+1}$, when $m$ is different from $-1$

**5.** $\int e^x dx = e^x$

**6.** $\int a^x \log a\,dx = a^x$

**7.** $\int \dfrac{dx}{1+x^2} = \tan^{-1}x$, or $-\operatorname{ctn}^{-1}x$

**8.** $\int \dfrac{dx}{\sqrt{1-x^2}} = \sin^{-1}x$, or $-\cos^{-1}x$

**9.** $\int \dfrac{dx}{x\sqrt{x^2-1}} = \sec^{-1}x$, or $-\csc^{-1}x$

*See discussion on page 3.

**10.** $\int \dfrac{dx}{\sqrt{2\,x - x^2}} = \text{versin}^{-1}x,$ or $-\text{coversin}^{-1}x$

**11.** $\int \cos x\,dx = \sin x,$ or $-\text{coversin}\,x$

**12.** $\int \sin x\,dx = -\cos x,$ or $\text{versin}\,x$

**13.** $\int \text{ctn}\,x\,dx = \log \sin x$

**14.** $\int \tan x\,dx = -\log \cos x$

**15.** $\int \tan x \sec x\,dx = \sec x$

**16.** $\int \sec^2 x\,dx = \tan x$

**17.** $\int \csc^2 x\,dx = -\text{ctn}\,x$

In the following formulas, $u$, $v$, $w$, and $y$ represent any functions of $x$:

**18.** $\int (u + v + w + \text{etc.})dx = \int u\,dx + \int v\,dx + \int w\,dx + \text{etc.}$

**19.** $\int u\,dv = uv - \int v\,du$

**20.** $\int u\dfrac{dv}{dx}\,dx = uv - \int v\dfrac{du}{dx}\,dx$

**21.** $\int f(y)dx = \int \dfrac{f(y)dy}{\dfrac{dy}{dx}}$

**22.** $\int f(ax + b)dx = \dfrac{1}{a}\int f(ax + b)d(ax + b)$

## RATIONAL ALGEBRAIC FUNCTIONS

### *Expressions Involving* $(a + bx)$

The substitution of $y$ or $z$ for $x$, where $y \equiv a + bx$, $z \equiv (a + bx)/x$, gives

**23.** $\displaystyle \int (a + bx)^m dx = \frac{1}{b} \int y^m dy$

**24.** $\displaystyle \int x(a + bx)^m dx = \frac{1}{b^2} \int y^m (y - a) dy$

**25.** $\displaystyle \int x^n (a + bx)^m dx = \frac{1}{b^{n+1}} \int y^m (y - a)^n dy$

**26.** $\displaystyle \int \frac{x^n dx}{(a + bx)^m} = \frac{1}{b^{n+1}} \int \frac{(y - a)^n dy}{y^m}$

**27.** $\displaystyle \int \frac{dx}{x^n (a + bx)^m} = -\frac{1}{a^{m+n-1}} \int \frac{(z - b)^{m+n-2} dz}{z^m}$

Whence

**28.** $\displaystyle \int \frac{dx}{a + bx} = \frac{1}{b} \log (a + bx)$

**29.** $\displaystyle \int \frac{dx}{(a + bx)^2} = -\frac{1}{b(a + bx)}$

**30.** $\displaystyle \int \frac{dx}{(a + bx)^3} = -\frac{1}{2\,b(a + bx)^2}$

**31.** $\displaystyle \int \frac{x\,dx}{a + bx} = \frac{1}{b^2} \left[ a + bx - a \log (a + bx) \right]$

**32.** $\displaystyle \int \frac{x\,dx}{(a + bx)^2} = \frac{1}{b^2} \left[ \log (a + bx) + \frac{a}{a + bx} \right]$

**33.** $\displaystyle \int \frac{x\,dx}{(a + bx)^3} = \frac{1}{b^2} \left[ -\frac{1}{a + bx} + \frac{a}{2(a + bx)^2} \right]$

**34.** $\displaystyle \int \frac{x^2 dx}{a + bx} = \frac{1}{b^3} \left[ \tfrac{1}{2} (a + bx)^2 - 2\,a(a + bx) + a^2 \log (a + bx) \right]$

**35.** $\displaystyle\int \frac{x^2 dx}{(a+bx)^2} = \frac{1}{b^3}\left[a+bx-2a\log(a+bx)-\frac{a^2}{a+bx}\right]$

**36.** $\displaystyle\int \frac{dx}{x(a+bx)} = -\frac{1}{a}\log\frac{a+bx}{x}$

**37.** $\displaystyle\int \frac{dx}{x^2(a+bx)} = -\frac{1}{ax}+\frac{b}{a^2}\log\frac{a+bx}{x}$

**38.** $\displaystyle\int \frac{dx}{x(a+bx)^2} = \frac{1}{a(a+bx)}-\frac{1}{a^2}\log\frac{a+bx}{x}$

**39.** $\displaystyle\int \frac{(a+bx)dx}{a'+b'x} = \frac{bx}{b'}+\frac{ab'-a'b}{b'^2}\log(a'+b'x)$

**40.** $\displaystyle\int (a+bx)^n(a'+b'x)^m dx$

$$= \frac{1}{(m+n+1)b}\left((a+bx)^{n+1}(a'+b'x)^m - m(ab'-a'b)\int(a+bx)^n(a'+b'x)^{m-1}dx\right)$$

**41.** $\displaystyle\int \frac{(a+bx)^n dx}{(a'+b'x)^m}$

$$= -\frac{1}{(m-1)(ab'-a'b)}\left(\frac{(a+bx)^{n+1}}{(a'+b'x)^{m-1}}+(m-n-2)b\int\frac{(a+bx)^n dx}{(a'+b'x)^{m-1}}\right)$$

$$= -\frac{1}{(m-n-1)b'}\left(\frac{(a+bx)^n}{(a'+b'x)^{m-1}}+n(ab'-a'b)\int\frac{(a+bx)^{n-1}dx}{(a'+b'x)^m}\right)$$

$$= -\frac{1}{(m-1)b'}\left(\frac{(a+bx)^n}{(a'+b'x)^{m-1}}-nb\int\frac{(a+bx)^{n-1}dx}{(a'+b'x)^{m-1}}\right)$$

**42.** $\displaystyle\int \frac{dx}{(a+bx)(a'+b'x)} = \frac{1}{ab'-a'b} \cdot \log \frac{a'+b'x}{a+bx}$

**43.** $\displaystyle\int \frac{dx}{(a+bx)^n(a'+b'x)^m}$
$$= \frac{1}{(m-1)(ab'-a'b)}\left( \frac{-1}{(a+bx)^{n-1}(a'+b'x)^{m-1}} - (m+n-2)b \int \frac{dx}{(a+bx)^n(a'+b'x)^{m-1}} \right)$$

**44.** $\displaystyle\int \frac{x\,dx}{(a+bx)(a'+b'x)} = \frac{1}{ab'-a'b}\left( \frac{a}{b} \log (a+bx) - \frac{a'}{b'} \log (a'+b'x) \right)$

**45.** $\displaystyle\int \frac{dx}{(a+bx)^2(a'+b'x)} = \frac{1}{ab'-a'b}\left( \frac{1}{a+bx} + \frac{b'}{ab'-a'b} \log \frac{a'+b'x}{a+bx} \right)$

**46.** $\displaystyle\int \frac{x\,dx}{(a+bx)^2(a'+b'x)} = \frac{-a}{b(ab'-a'b)(a+bx)} - \frac{a'}{(ab'-a'b)^2} \log \frac{a'+b'x}{a+bx}$

**47.** $\displaystyle\int \frac{x^2dx}{(a+bx)^2(a'+b'x)} = \frac{a^2}{b^2(ab'-a'b)(a+bx)}$
$$+ \frac{1}{(ab'-a'b)^2}\left[ \frac{a'^2}{b'} \log (a'+b'x) + \frac{a(ab'-2\,a'b)}{b^2} \log (a+bx) \right]$$

## Expressions Involving $(a + bx^n)$

**48.** $\displaystyle\int \frac{dx}{c^2 + x^2} = \frac{1}{c}\tan^{-1}\frac{x}{c} = \frac{1}{c}\sin^{-1}\frac{x}{\sqrt{x^2 + c^2}}$

**49.** $\displaystyle\int \frac{dx}{c^2 - x^2} = \frac{1}{2\,c}\log\frac{c + x}{c - x} = \frac{1}{c}\tanh^{-1}\frac{x}{c},\ \text{or } \frac{1}{c}\operatorname{ctnh}^{-1}\frac{x}{c}$

**50.** $\displaystyle\int \frac{dx}{a + bx^2} = \frac{1}{\sqrt{ab}}\tan^{-1}\frac{x\sqrt{ab}}{a}$

**51.** $\displaystyle\int \frac{dx}{a + bx^2} = \frac{1}{2\sqrt{-ab}}\log\frac{a + x\sqrt{-ab}}{a - x\sqrt{-ab}},$

$\quad$ or $\dfrac{1}{\sqrt{-ab}}\tanh^{-1}\dfrac{x\sqrt{-ab}}{a},$

$\quad$ or $\dfrac{1}{\sqrt{-ab}}\operatorname{ctnh}^{-1}\dfrac{x\sqrt{-ab}}{a}$

**52.** $\displaystyle\int \frac{dx}{(a + bx^2)^2} = \frac{x}{2\,a(a + bx^2)} + \frac{1}{2\,a}\int \frac{dx}{a + bx^2}$

**53.** $\displaystyle\int \frac{dx}{(a + bx^2)^{m+1}} = \frac{1}{2\,ma}\cdot\frac{x}{(a + bx^2)^m} + \frac{2\,m - 1}{2\,ma}\int \frac{dx}{(a + bx^2)^m},$

where $m \neq 0$

**54.** $\displaystyle\int \frac{x\,dx}{a + bx^2} = \frac{1}{2\,b}\log\left(x^2 + \frac{a}{b}\right)$

**55.** $\displaystyle\int \frac{x\,dx}{(a + bx^2)^{m+1}} = \frac{1}{2}\int \frac{dz}{(a + bz)^{m+1}},\ \text{where } z = x^2$

**56.** $\displaystyle\int \frac{dx}{x(a + bx^2)} = \frac{1}{2\,a}\log\frac{x^2}{a + bx^2}$

**57.** $\displaystyle\int \frac{x^2\,dx}{a + bx^2} = \frac{x}{b} - \frac{a}{b}\int \frac{dx}{a + bx^2}$

**58.** $\displaystyle\int \frac{dx}{x^2(a+bx^2)} = -\frac{1}{ax} - \frac{b}{a}\int \frac{dx}{a+bx^2}$

**59.** $\displaystyle\int \frac{x^2\,dx}{(a+bx^2)^{m+1}} = \frac{-x}{2\,mb(a+bx^2)^m} + \frac{1}{2\,mb}\int \frac{dx}{(a+bx^2)^m}$

**60.** $\displaystyle\int \frac{dx}{x^2(a+bx^2)^{m+1}} = \frac{1}{a}\int \frac{dx}{x^2(a+bx^2)^m} - \frac{b}{a}\int \frac{dx}{(a+bx^2)^{m+1}}$

**61.** $\displaystyle\int \frac{dx}{x^4+a^4}$
$$= \frac{1}{4\,a^3\sqrt{2}}\left[\log\left(\frac{x^2+ax\sqrt{2}+a^2}{x^2-ax\sqrt{2}+a^2}\right) + 2\tan^{-1}\left(\frac{ax\sqrt{2}}{a^2-x^2}\right)\right]$$

**62.** $\displaystyle\int \frac{dx}{x^4-a^4} = \frac{1}{4\,a^3}\left[\log\left(\frac{x-a}{x+a}\right) - 2\tan^{-1}\left(\frac{x}{a}\right)\right]$

**63.** $\displaystyle\int \frac{dx}{a+bx^3} = \frac{k}{3\,a}\left[\tfrac{1}{2}\log\left(\frac{(k+x)^2}{k^2-kx+x^2}\right) + \sqrt{3}\tan^{-1}\frac{2\,x-k}{k\sqrt{3}}\right]$,
where $bk^3 = a$

**64.** $\displaystyle\int \frac{x\,dx}{a+bx^3} = \frac{1}{3\,bk}\left[\tfrac{1}{2}\log\left(\frac{k^2-kx+x^2}{(k+x)^2}\right) + \sqrt{3}\tan^{-1}\frac{2\,x-k}{k\sqrt{3}}\right]$,
where $bk^3 = a$

**65.** $\displaystyle\int \frac{dx}{x(a+bx^n)} = \frac{1}{an}\log\frac{x^n}{a+bx^n}$

**66.** $\displaystyle\int \frac{dx}{(a+bx^n)^{m+1}} = \frac{1}{a}\int \frac{dx}{(a+bx^n)^m} - \frac{b}{a}\int \frac{x^n\,dx}{(a+bx^n)^{m+1}}$

**67.** $\displaystyle\int \frac{x^m dx}{(a+bx^n)^{p+1}} = \frac{1}{b}\int \frac{x^{m-n}dx}{(a+bx^n)^p} - \frac{a}{b}\int \frac{x^{m-n}dx}{(a+bx^n)^{p+1}}$

**68.** $\displaystyle\int \frac{dx}{x^m(a+bx^n)^{p+1}} = \frac{1}{a}\int \frac{dx}{x^m(a+bx^n)^p} - \frac{b}{a}\int \frac{dx}{x^{m-n}(a+bx^n)^{p+1}}$

**69.** $\displaystyle\int x^{m-1}(a+bx^n)^p dx = \frac{1}{b(m+np)}\left[x^{m-n}(a+bx^n)^{p+1} - (m-n)a\int x^{m-n-1}(a+bx^n)^p dx\right]$

$\displaystyle= \frac{1}{m+np}\left[x^m(a+bx^n)^p + npa\int x^{m-1}(a+bx^n)^{p-1}dx\right]$

$\displaystyle= \frac{1}{ma}\left[x^m(a+bx^n)^{p+1} - (m+np+n)b\int x^{m+n-1}(a+bx^n)^p dx\right]$

$\displaystyle= \frac{1}{an(p+1)}\left[-x^m(a+bx^n)^{p+1} + (m+np+n)\int x^{m-1}(a+bx^n)^{p+1}dx\right]$

## Expressions Involving $(a + bx + cx^2)$

Let $X = a + bx + cx^2$ and $q = 4ac - b^2$; then

**70.** $\displaystyle\int \frac{dx}{X} = \frac{2}{\sqrt{q}} \tan^{-1} \frac{2cx + b}{\sqrt{q}}$

**71.** $\displaystyle\int \frac{dx}{X} = \frac{1}{\sqrt{-q}} \log \frac{2cx + b - \sqrt{-q}}{2cx + b + \sqrt{-q}},$

$\qquad$ or $\dfrac{-2}{\sqrt{-q}} \tanh^{-1} \dfrac{2cx + b}{\sqrt{-q}}$, or $\dfrac{-2}{\sqrt{-q}} \operatorname{ctnh}^{-1} \dfrac{2cx + b}{\sqrt{-q}}$

**72.** $\displaystyle\int \frac{dx}{X^2} = \frac{2cx + b}{qX} + \frac{2c}{q} \int \frac{dx}{X}$

**73.** $\displaystyle\int \frac{dx}{X^3} = \frac{2cx + b}{q} \left( \frac{1}{2X^2} + \frac{3c}{qX} \right) + \frac{6c^2}{q^2} \int \frac{dx}{X}$

**74.** $\displaystyle\int \frac{dx}{X^{n+1}} = \frac{2cx + b}{nqX^n} + \frac{2(2n-1)c}{qn} \int \frac{dx}{X^n}$

**75.** $\displaystyle\int \frac{x\,dx}{X} = \frac{1}{2c} \log X - \frac{b}{2c} \int \frac{dx}{X}$

**76.** $\displaystyle\int \frac{x\,dx}{X^2} = -\frac{bx + 2a}{qX} - \frac{b}{q} \int \frac{dx}{X}$

**77.** $\displaystyle\int \frac{x\,dx}{X^{n+1}} = -\frac{2a + bx}{nqX^n} - \frac{b(2n-1)}{nq} \int \frac{dx}{X^n}$

**78.** $\displaystyle\int \frac{x^2}{X}\,dx = \frac{x}{c} - \frac{b}{2c^2} \log X + \frac{b^2 - 2ac}{2c^2} \int \frac{dx}{X}$

**79.** $\displaystyle\int \frac{x^2}{X^2}\,dx = \frac{(b^2 - 2ac)x + ab}{cqX} + \frac{2a}{q} \int \frac{dx}{X}$

**80.** $\displaystyle\int \frac{x^m\,dx}{X^{n+1}} = -\frac{x^{m-1}}{(2n - m + 1)cX^n} - \frac{n - m + 1}{2n - m + 1} \cdot \frac{b}{c} \int \frac{x^{m-1}\,dx}{X^{n+1}}$

$\qquad\qquad + \dfrac{m - 1}{2n - m + 1} \cdot \dfrac{a}{c} \displaystyle\int \frac{x^{m-2}\,dx}{X^{n+1}}$

**81.** $\displaystyle\int \frac{dx}{xX} = \frac{1}{2a}\log\frac{x^2}{X} - \frac{b}{2a}\int\frac{dx}{X}$

**82.** $\displaystyle\int \frac{dx}{x^2X} = \frac{b}{2a^2}\log\frac{X}{x^2} - \frac{1}{ax} + \left(\frac{b^2}{2a^2} - \frac{c}{a}\right)\int\frac{dx}{X}$

**83.** $\displaystyle\int \frac{dx}{x^mX^{n+1}} = -\frac{1}{(m-1)ax^{m-1}X^n} - \frac{n+m-1}{m-1}\cdot\frac{b}{a}\int\frac{dx}{x^{m-1}X^{n+1}} - \frac{2n+m-1}{m-1}\cdot\frac{c}{a}\int\frac{dx}{x^{m-2}X^{n+1}}$

**84.** $\displaystyle\int X^n dx = \frac{1}{2(2n+1)c}\left((b+2cx)X^n + nq\int X^{n-1}dx\right)$

**85.** $\displaystyle\int \frac{dx}{xX^n} = \frac{1}{2a(n-1)X^{n-1}} - \frac{b}{2a}\int\frac{dx}{X^n} + \frac{1}{a}\int\frac{dx}{xX^{n-1}}$

**86.** $\displaystyle\int \frac{dx}{(a'+b'x)X} = \frac{1}{2(ab'^2 - a'bb' + a'^2c)}\left(b'(\log(a'+b'x)^2 - \log X) + (2a'c - bb')\int\frac{dx}{X}\right)$

**87.** $\displaystyle\int (a'+b'x)X^n dx = \frac{b'X^{n+1}}{2(n+1)c} + \frac{2a'c-bb'}{2c}\int X^n dx$

**88.** $\displaystyle\int \frac{(a'+b'x)dx}{X^n} = -\frac{b'}{2(n-1)cX^{n-1}} + \frac{2a'c-bb'}{2c}\int\frac{dx}{X^n}$

**89.** $\int (a' + b'x)^m X^n dx$

$$= \frac{1}{(m+2n+1)c} \left( b'(a' + b'x)^{m-1} X^{n+1} + (m+n)(2a'c - bb') \int (a' + b'x)^{m-1} X^n dx \right.$$
$$\left. - (m-1)(ab'^2 - a'bb' + ca'^2) \int (a' + b'x)^{m-2} X^n dx \right)$$

**90.** $\int \dfrac{(a' + b'x)^m dx}{X^n} = \dfrac{1}{q(n-1)} \left( \dfrac{(b + 2cx)(a' + b'x)^m}{X^{n-1}} - 2(m - 2n + 3)c \displaystyle\int \dfrac{(a' + b'x)^m dx}{X^{n-1}} \right.$

$$\left. + m(2a'c - bb') \int \frac{(a' + b'x)^{m-1} dx}{X^{n-1}} \right)$$

$$= \frac{1}{(m - 2n + 1)c} \left( \frac{b'(a' + b'x)^{m-1}}{X^{n-1}} + (m-n)(2a'c - bb') \int \frac{(a' + b'x)^{m-1} dx}{X^n} \right.$$
$$\left. - (m-1)(ab'^2 - a'bb' + ca'^2) \int \frac{(a' + b'x)^{m-2} dx}{X^n} \right)$$

**91.** $\int \dfrac{X^n dx}{(a' + b'x)^m}$

$$= \frac{1}{b'^2(m-1)} \left( \frac{-b'X^n}{(a' + b'x)^{m-1}} + n(bb' - 2a'c) \int \frac{X^{n-1}dx}{(a' + b'x)^{m-1}} + 2nc \int \frac{X^{n-1}dx}{(a' + b'x)^{m-2}} \right)$$

$$= -\frac{1}{(m - 2n - 1)b'^2} \left( \frac{b'X^n}{(a' + b'x)^{m-1}} + 2n(ab'^2 - a'bb' + ca'^2) \int \frac{X^{n-1}dx}{(a' + b'x)^m} \right.$$
$$\left. + n(bb' - 2a'c) \int \frac{X^{n-1}dx}{(a' + b'x)^{m-1}} \right)$$

**92.** $\displaystyle\int \frac{dx}{(a'+b'x)^m X^n}$

$\displaystyle = -\frac{1}{(m-1)(ab'^2-a'bb'+ca'^2)}\left(\frac{b'}{(a'+b'x)^{m-1}X^{n-1}} + (m+n-2)(bb'-2ca')\int \frac{dx}{(a'+b'x)^{m-1}X^n}\right.$

$\displaystyle \left. + (m+2n-3)c\int \frac{dx}{(a'+b'x)^{m-2}X^n}\right)$

$\displaystyle = \frac{1}{2(ab'^2-a'bb'+ca'^2)}\left(\frac{b'}{(n-1)(a'+b'x)^{m-1}X^{n-1}}\right.$

$\displaystyle + (2a'c-bb')\int \frac{dx}{(a'+b'x)^{m-1}X^n}$

$\displaystyle \left. + \frac{(m+2n-3)b'^2}{n-1}\int \frac{dx}{(a'+b'x)^m X^{n-1}}\right).$

**93.** If $ab'^2 - a'bb' + ca'^2 = 0$,

$\displaystyle\int \frac{dx}{(a'+b'x)^m X^n}$

$\displaystyle = \frac{-1}{(m+n-1)(bb'-2a'c)}\left(\frac{b'}{(a'+b'x)^m X^{n-1}} + (m+2n-2)c\int \frac{dx}{(a'+b'x)^{m-1}X^n}\right)$

## Rational Fractions

Every proper fraction can be represented by the general form:

$$\frac{f(x)}{F(x)} = \frac{g_1 x^{n-1} + g_2 x^{n-2} + g_3 x^{n-3} + \cdots + g_n}{x^n + k_1 x^{n-1} + k_2 x^{n-2} + \cdots + k_n}$$

If $a$, $b$, $c$, etc., are the roots of the equation $F(x) = 0$, so that

$$F(x) = (x-a)^p (x-b)^q (x-c)^r \cdots,$$

then

$$\frac{f(x)}{F(x)} = \frac{A_1}{(x-a)^p} + \frac{A_2}{(x-a)^{p-1}} + \frac{A_3}{(x-a)^{p-2}} + \cdots + \frac{A_p}{x-a}$$
$$+ \frac{B_1}{(x-b)^q} + \frac{B_2}{(x-b)^{q-1}}$$
$$+ \frac{B_3}{(x-b)^{q-2}} + \cdots + \frac{B_q}{x-b}$$
$$+ \frac{C_1}{(x-c)^r} + \frac{C_2}{(x-c)^{r-1}} + \frac{C_3}{(x-c)^{r-2}} + \cdots + \frac{C_r}{x-c}$$
$$+ \cdots \qquad \cdots \qquad \cdots \qquad \cdots \quad \cdots,$$

where the numerators of the separate fractions may be determined by the equations

$$A_m = \frac{\phi_1^{[m-1]}(a)}{(m-1)!}, \quad B_m = \frac{\phi_2^{[m-1]}(b)}{(m-1)!}, \quad \text{etc., etc.}$$

$$\phi_1(x) = \frac{f(x)(x-a)^p}{F(x)}, \quad \phi_2(x) = \frac{f(x)(x-b)^q}{F(x)}, \quad \text{etc., etc.}$$

If $a$, $b$, $c$, etc., are single roots, then $p = q = r = \cdots = 1$, and

$$\frac{f(x)}{F(x)} = \frac{A}{x-a} + \frac{B}{x-b} + \frac{C}{x-c} \cdots,$$

where

$$A = \frac{f(a)}{F'(a)}, \quad B = \frac{f(b)}{F'(b)}, \quad \text{etc.}$$

The simpler fractions, into which the original fraction is thus divided, may be integrated by means of the formulas:

**94.** $\int \dfrac{h\,dx}{(mx+n)^l} = \int \dfrac{h\,d(mx+n)}{m(mx+n)^l} = \dfrac{h}{m(1-l)(mx+n)^{l-1}}$

**95.** $\int \dfrac{h\,dx}{mx+n} = \dfrac{h}{m} \log(mx+n)$

If any of the roots of the equation $f(x) = 0$ are imaginary, the parts of the integral which arise from conjugate roots can be combined and the integral brought into a real form.

The identities given below are sometimes convenient:

$$\frac{1}{(a+bx^2)(a'+b'x^2)} \equiv \frac{1}{a'b-ab'} \cdot \left[\frac{b}{a+bx^2} - \frac{b'}{a'+b'x^2}\right],$$

$$\frac{m+nx}{(k+lx)(a+bx+cx^2)} \equiv \left[\frac{1}{al^2+ck^2-bkl}\right]$$
$$\cdot \left[\frac{l(ml-nk)}{k+lx} + \frac{c(nk-ml)x+(aln+ckm-blm)}{a+bx+cx^2}\right],$$

$$\frac{l+mx^n}{(a+bx^n)(a'+b'x^n)} \equiv \frac{1}{a'b-ab'} \cdot \left[\frac{bl-am}{a+bx^n} + \frac{a'm-b'l}{a'+b'x^n}\right],$$

$$\frac{1}{(x+a)(x+b)(x+c)} \equiv \frac{A}{x+a} + \frac{B}{x+b} + \frac{C}{x+c}, \text{ where}$$

$$A = \frac{1}{(a-b)(a-c)}, \quad B = \frac{1}{(b-c)(b-a)}, \quad C = \frac{1}{(c-a)(c-b)},$$

$$\frac{1}{(x+a)(x+b)(x+c)(x+g)} \equiv \frac{A}{x+a} + \frac{B}{x+b} + \frac{C}{x+c} + \frac{G}{x+g},$$

where

$$A = \frac{1}{(b-a)(c-a)(g-a)}, \quad B = \frac{1}{(a-b)(c-b)(g-b)}, \quad \text{etc.}$$

## IRRATIONAL ALGEBRAIC FUNCTIONS

### *Expressions Involving* $\sqrt{a+bx}$

The substitution of a new variable of integration, $y = \sqrt{a+bx}$, gives

**96.** $\displaystyle\int \sqrt{a+bx}\, dx = \frac{2}{3\,b} \sqrt{(a+bx)^3}$

**97.** $\displaystyle\int x\sqrt{a+bx}\, dx = -\frac{2(2\,a - 3\,bx)\sqrt{(a+bx)^3}}{15\,b^2}$

**98.** $\displaystyle\int x^2\sqrt{a+bx}\, dx = \frac{2(8\,a^2 - 12\,abx + 15\,b^2x^2)\sqrt{(a+bx)^3}}{105\,b^3}$

**99.** $\displaystyle\int \frac{\sqrt{a+bx}}{x}\, dx = 2\sqrt{a+bx} + a\int \frac{dx}{x\sqrt{a+bx}}$

**100.** $\displaystyle\int \frac{dx}{\sqrt{a+bx}} = \frac{2\sqrt{a+bx}}{b}$

**101.** $\displaystyle\int \frac{x\,dx}{\sqrt{a+bx}} = -\frac{2(2\,a - bx)}{3\,b^2} \sqrt{a+bx}$

**102.** $\displaystyle\int \frac{x^2\,dx}{\sqrt{a+bx}} = \frac{2(8\,a^2 - 4\,abx + 3\,b^2x^2)}{15\,b^3} \sqrt{a+bx}$

**103.** $\displaystyle\int \frac{dx}{x\sqrt{a+bx}} = \frac{1}{\sqrt{a}} \log \frac{\sqrt{a+bx} - \sqrt{a}}{\sqrt{a+bx} + \sqrt{a}},$

$$\text{or } \frac{-2}{\sqrt{a}} \tanh^{-1}\frac{\sqrt{a+bx}}{\sqrt{a}}, \quad \text{or } \frac{-2}{\sqrt{a}} \operatorname{ctnh}^{-1}\frac{\sqrt{a+bx}}{\sqrt{a}}$$

**104.** $\displaystyle\int \frac{dx}{x\sqrt{a+bx}} = \frac{2}{\sqrt{-a}}\tan^{-1}\sqrt{\frac{a+bx}{-a}}$

**105.** $\displaystyle\int \frac{dx}{x^2\sqrt{a+bx}} = -\frac{\sqrt{a+bx}}{ax} - \frac{b}{2\,a}\int \frac{dx}{x\sqrt{a+bx}}$

**106.** $\displaystyle\int (a+bx)^{\pm\frac{n}{2}}dx = \frac{2}{b}\int y^{1\pm n}dy = \frac{2(a+bx)^{\frac{2\pm n}{2}}}{b(2\pm n)}$

**107.** $\displaystyle\int x(a+bx)^{\pm\frac{n}{2}}dx = \frac{2}{b^2}\left[\frac{(a+bx)^{\frac{4\pm n}{2}}}{4\pm n} - \frac{a(a+bx)^{\frac{2\pm n}{2}}}{2\pm n}\right]$

**108.** $\displaystyle\int \frac{x^m dx}{\sqrt{a+bx}} = \frac{2\,x^m\sqrt{a+bx}}{(2\,m+1)b} - \frac{2\,ma}{(2\,m+1)b}\int \frac{x^{m-1}dx}{\sqrt{a+bx}}$

**109.** $\displaystyle\int \frac{dx}{x^n\sqrt{a+bx}} = -\frac{\sqrt{a+bx}}{(n-1)ax^{n-1}} - \frac{(2\,n-3)b}{(2\,n-2)a}\int \frac{dx}{x^{n-1}\sqrt{a+bx}}$

**110.** $\displaystyle\int \frac{(a+bx)^{\frac{n}{2}}dx}{x} = b\int (a+bx)^{\frac{n-2}{2}}dx + a\int \frac{(a+bx)^{\frac{n-2}{2}}}{x}dx$

**111.** $\displaystyle\int \frac{dx}{x(a+bx)^{\frac{m}{2}}} = \frac{1}{a}\int \frac{dx}{x(a+bx)^{\frac{m-2}{2}}} - \frac{b}{a}\int \frac{dx}{(a+bx)^{\frac{m}{2}}}$

## Expressions Involving Both $\sqrt{a+bx}$ and $\sqrt{a'+b'x}$

Let $u = a+bx$, $v = a'+b'x$, and $k = ab' - a'b$, then

**112.** $\displaystyle\int \sqrt{uv}\,dx = \frac{k+2\,bv}{4\,bb'}\sqrt{uv} - \frac{k^2}{8\,bb'}\int \frac{dx}{\sqrt{uv}}$

**113.** $\displaystyle\int \frac{\sqrt{v}\,dx}{\sqrt{u}} = \frac{1}{b}\sqrt{uv} - \frac{k}{2\,b}\int \frac{dx}{\sqrt{uv}}$

**114.** $\displaystyle\int \frac{x\,dx}{\sqrt{uv}} = \frac{\sqrt{uv}}{bb'} - \frac{ab'+a'b}{2\,bb'}\int \frac{dx}{\sqrt{uv}}$

$$115. \int \frac{dx}{\sqrt{uv}} = \frac{2}{\sqrt{bb'}} \log\left(\sqrt{bb'}\,u + b\sqrt{v}\right), \text{ or } \frac{2}{\sqrt{bb'}}\tanh^{-1}\sqrt{\frac{b'u}{bv}} \quad [bb' > 0]$$

$$= \frac{2}{\sqrt{-bb'}}\tan^{-1}\sqrt{-\frac{b'u}{bv}}, \text{ or } -\frac{1}{\sqrt{-bb'}}\sin^{-1}\frac{2\,bb'x + a'b + ab'}{|k|} \quad [bb' < 0]$$

$$116. \int \frac{dx}{v\sqrt{u}} = \frac{1}{\sqrt{kb'}}\log\frac{b'\sqrt{u}-\sqrt{kb'}}{b'\sqrt{u}+\sqrt{kb'}} = \frac{2}{\sqrt{-kb'}}\tan^{-1}\frac{b'\sqrt{u}}{\sqrt{-kb'}}$$

$$117. \int \frac{dx}{v\sqrt{uv}} = -\frac{2\sqrt{u}}{k\sqrt{v}}$$

$$118. \int v^m\sqrt{u}\,dx = \frac{1}{(2m+3)b'}\left(2\,v^{m+1}\sqrt{u} + k\int\frac{v^m dx}{\sqrt{u}}\right)$$

$$119. \int \frac{\sqrt{u}\,dx}{v^m} = -\frac{1}{(2m-3)b'}\left(\frac{2\sqrt{u}}{v^{m-1}} + k\int\frac{dx}{v^m\sqrt{u}}\right) = \frac{1}{(m-1)b'}\left(-\frac{\sqrt{u}}{v^{m-1}} + \frac{1}{2}b\int\frac{dx}{v^{m-1}\sqrt{u}}\right)$$

$$120. \int \frac{v^m dx}{\sqrt{u}} = \frac{2}{(2m+1)b}\left(v^m\sqrt{u} - mk\int\frac{v^{m-1}dx}{\sqrt{u}}\right)$$

$$121. \int \frac{dx}{v^m\sqrt{u}} = -\frac{1}{(m-1)k}\left(\frac{\sqrt{u}}{v^{m-1}} + \left(m-\tfrac{3}{2}\right)b\int \frac{dx}{v^{m-1}\sqrt{u}}\right)$$

$$122. \int v^m u^{n-\frac{1}{2}}dx = \frac{1}{(2m+2n+1)b'}\left(2v^{m+1}u^{n-\frac{1}{2}} + (2n-1)k\int v^m u^{n-\frac{3}{2}}dx\right)$$

$$123. \int v^m u^{-(n+\frac{1}{2})}dx = \frac{1}{(2n-1)k}\left(2v^{m+1}u^{-(n-\frac{1}{2})} - (2m-2n+3)b'\int v^m u^{-(n-\frac{1}{2})}dx\right)$$

$$= \frac{2}{(2n-1)b}\left(-v^m u^{-(n-\frac{1}{2})} + mb'\int v^{m-1}u^{-(n-\frac{1}{2})}dx\right)$$

$$124. \int v^{-m}u^{(n-\frac{1}{2})}dx = \frac{-1}{(2m-2n-1)b'}\left(2u^{n-\frac{1}{2}}v^{-(m-1)} + (2n-1)k\int u^{n-\frac{3}{2}}v^{-m}dx\right)$$

$$= \frac{1}{(m-1)b'}\left(-u^{n-\frac{1}{2}}v^{-(m-1)} + \left(n-\tfrac{1}{2}\right)b\int u^{n-\frac{3}{2}}v^{-(m-1)}dx\right)$$

$$125. \int v^{-m}u^{-(n+\frac{1}{2})}dx = \frac{1}{(2n-1)k}\left(2v^{-(m-1)}u^{-(n-\frac{1}{2})} + (2m+2n-3)b'\int v^{-m}u^{-(n-\frac{1}{2})}dx\right)$$

*Expressions Involving $\sqrt{x^2 \pm a^2}$ or $\sqrt{a^2 - x^2}$*

**126.** $\int \sqrt{x^2 \pm a^2}\, dx = \frac{1}{2}[x\sqrt{x^2 \pm a^2} \pm a^2 \log (x + \sqrt{x^2 \pm a^2})]$*

**127.** $\int \sqrt{a^2 - x^2}\, dx = \frac{1}{2}\left(x\sqrt{a^2 - x^2} + a^2 \sin^{-1}\frac{x}{a}\right)$

**128.** $\int \dfrac{dx}{\sqrt{x^2 + a^2}} = \log (x + \sqrt{x^2 + a^2}),$ or $\sinh^{-1}\dfrac{x}{a}$*

**129.** $\int \dfrac{dx}{\sqrt{x^2 - a^2}} = \log (x + \sqrt{x^2 - a^2}),$ or $\cosh^{-1}\dfrac{x}{a}$*

**130.** $\int \dfrac{dx}{\sqrt{a^2 - x^2}} = \sin^{-1}\dfrac{x}{a},$ or $-\cos^{-1}\dfrac{x}{a}$

**131.** $\int \dfrac{dx}{x\sqrt{x^2 - a^2}} = \dfrac{1}{a}\cos^{-1}\dfrac{a}{x}$

**132.** $\int \dfrac{dx}{x\sqrt{a^2 \pm x^2}} = -\dfrac{1}{a}\log\left(\dfrac{a + \sqrt{a^2 \pm x^2}}{x}\right)$*

**133.** $\int \dfrac{\sqrt{a^2 \pm x^2}}{x}\, dx = \sqrt{a^2 \pm x^2} - a \log \dfrac{a + \sqrt{a^2 \pm x^2}}{x}$*

**134.** $\int \dfrac{\sqrt{x^2 - a^2}}{x}\, dx = \sqrt{x^2 - a^2} - a \cos^{-1}\dfrac{a}{x}$

**135.** $\int \dfrac{x\, dx}{\sqrt{a^2 \pm x^2}} = \pm \sqrt{a^2 \pm x^2}$

**136.** $\int \dfrac{x\, dx}{\sqrt{x^2 - a^2}} = \sqrt{x^2 - a^2}$

*See Formulas 703–704.

**137.** $\int x\sqrt{x^2 \pm a^2}\,dx = \frac{1}{3}\sqrt{(x^2 \pm a^2)^3}$

**138.** $\int x\sqrt{a^2 - x^2}\,dx = -\frac{1}{3}\sqrt{(a^2 - x^2)^3}$

**139.** $\int \sqrt{(x^2 \pm a^2)^3}\,dx$

$$= \frac{1}{4}\left[x\sqrt{(x^2 \pm a^2)^3} \pm \frac{3\,a^2 x}{2}\sqrt{x^2 \pm a^2} + \frac{3\,a^4}{2}\log(x + \sqrt{x^2 \pm a^2})\right]^*$$

**140.** $\int \sqrt{(a^2 - x^2)^3}\,dx$

$$= \frac{1}{4}\left[x\sqrt{(a^2 - x^2)^3} + \frac{3\,a^2 x}{2}\sqrt{a^2 - x^2} + \frac{3\,a^4}{2}\sin^{-1}\frac{x}{a}\right]$$

**141.** $\int \dfrac{dx}{\sqrt{(x^2 \pm a^2)^3}} = \dfrac{\pm\,x}{a^2\sqrt{x^2 \pm a^2}}$

**142.** $\int \dfrac{dx}{\sqrt{(a^2 - x^2)^3}} = \dfrac{x}{a^2\sqrt{a^2 - x^2}}$

**143.** $\int \dfrac{x\,dx}{\sqrt{(x^2 \pm a^2)^3}} = \dfrac{-1}{\sqrt{x^2 \pm a^2}}$

**144.** $\int \dfrac{x\,dx}{\sqrt{(a^2 - x^2)^3}} = \dfrac{1}{\sqrt{a^2 - x^2}}$

**145.** $\int x\sqrt{(x^2 \pm a^2)^3}\,dx = \frac{1}{5}\sqrt{(x^2 \pm a^2)^5}$

**146.** $\int x\sqrt{(a^2 - x^2)^3}\,dx = -\frac{1}{5}\sqrt{(a^2 - x^2)^5}$

*See Formulas 703–704.

**147.** $\displaystyle\int x^2\sqrt{x^2 \pm a^2}\,dx$

$$= \frac{x}{4}\sqrt{(x^2 \pm a^2)^3} \mp \frac{a^2}{8}x\sqrt{x^2 \pm a^2} - \frac{a^4}{8}\log(x + \sqrt{x^2 \pm a^2})^*$$

**148.** $\displaystyle\int x^2\sqrt{a^2 - x^2}\,dx$

$$= -\frac{x}{4}\sqrt{(a^2 - x^2)^3} + \frac{a^2}{8}\left(x\sqrt{a^2 - x^2} + a^2\sin^{-1}\frac{x}{a}\right)$$

**149.** $\displaystyle\int \frac{\sqrt{a^2 \pm x^2}\,dx}{x^3} = -\frac{\sqrt{a^2 \pm x^2}}{2\,x^2} \pm \frac{1}{2}\int \frac{dx}{x\sqrt{a^2 \pm x^2}}$

**150.** $\displaystyle\int x^3\sqrt{a^2 \pm x^2}\,dx = (\pm\tfrac{1}{5}x^2 - \tfrac{2}{15}a^2)\sqrt{(a^2 \pm x^2)^3}$

**151.** $\displaystyle\int \frac{dx}{x^3\sqrt{a^2 \pm x^2}} = -\frac{\sqrt{a^2 \pm x^2}}{2\,a^2x^2} \mp \frac{1}{2\,a^2}\int \frac{dx}{x\sqrt{a^2 \pm x^2}}$

**152.** $\displaystyle\int \frac{dx}{x^3\sqrt{x^2 - a^2}} = \frac{\sqrt{x^2 - a^2}}{2\,a^2x^2} + \frac{1}{2\,a^3}\cos^{-1}\frac{a}{x}$

**153.** $\displaystyle\int \frac{x^2\,dx}{\sqrt{x^2 \pm a^2}} = \frac{x}{2}\sqrt{x^2 \pm a^2} \mp \frac{a^2}{2}\log(x + \sqrt{x^2 \pm a^2})^*$

**154.** $\displaystyle\int \frac{x^2\,dx}{\sqrt{a^2 - x^2}} = -\frac{x}{2}\sqrt{a^2 - x^2} + \frac{a^2}{2}\sin^{-1}\frac{x}{a}$

**155.** $\displaystyle\int \frac{dx}{x^2\sqrt{x^2 \pm a^2}} = \mp\frac{\sqrt{x^2 \pm a^2}}{a^2x}$

**156.** $\displaystyle\int \frac{dx}{x^2\sqrt{a^2 - x^2}} = -\frac{\sqrt{a^2 - x^2}}{a^2x}$

*See Formulas 703–704.

**157.** $\int \dfrac{\sqrt{x^2 \pm a^2}\, dx}{x^2} = -\dfrac{\sqrt{x^2 \pm a^2}}{x} + \log\,(x + \sqrt{x^2 \pm a^2})^*$

**158.** $\int \dfrac{\sqrt{a^2 - x^2}}{x^2}\, dx = -\dfrac{\sqrt{a^2 - x^2}}{x} - \sin^{-1}\dfrac{x}{a}$

**159.** $\int \dfrac{x^2\, dx}{\sqrt{(x^2 \pm a^2)^3}} = \dfrac{-x}{\sqrt{x^2 \pm a^2}} + \log\,(x + \sqrt{x^2 \pm a^2})^*$

**160.** $\int \dfrac{x^2\, dx}{\sqrt{(a^2 - x^2)^3}} = \dfrac{x}{\sqrt{a^2 - x^2}} - \sin^{-1}\dfrac{x}{a}$

**161.** $\int \dfrac{f(x^2)dx}{\sqrt{a + cx^2}} = g \int f\left(\dfrac{au^2}{g^2 - cu^2}\right) \dfrac{du}{(g^2 - cu^2)},$
where $u = \dfrac{gx}{\sqrt{a + cx^2}}$

**162.** $\int \dfrac{xf(x^2)dx}{\sqrt{a + cx^2}} = \dfrac{1}{c} \int f\left(\dfrac{u^2 - a}{c}\right) du,$
where $u^2 = a + cx^2$

**163.** $\int \dfrac{x\sqrt{a + bx^2}}{\sqrt{a' + b'x^2}}\, dx = \dfrac{1}{b'\sqrt{b'}} \int \sqrt{ab' - a'b + by^2} \cdot dy,$
where $y^2 = a' + b'x^2$

**164.** $\int \sqrt{\dfrac{ax^2 + b}{a'x^2 + b'}}\, dx$ and $\int \dfrac{dx}{\sqrt{(ax^2 + b)(a'x^2 + b')}}$ are elliptic
integrals.
[See the section on elliptic integrals, pages 71–77.]

*See Formulas 703–704.

## Expressions Involving $\sqrt{a + bx + cx^2}$

Let $X = a + bx + cx^2$, $q = 4\,ac - b^2$, and $k = 4\,c/q$. In order to rationalize the function $f(x, \sqrt{a + bx + cx^2})$ we may put $\sqrt{a + bx + cx^2} = \sqrt{\pm c}\,\sqrt{A + Bx \pm x^2}$, according as $c$ is positive or negative, and then substitute for $x$ a new variable $z$,

$z = \sqrt{A + Bx + x^2} \pm x$, if $c > 0$.

$z = (\sqrt{A + Bx - x^2} - \sqrt{A})/x$, if $c < 0$ and $-a/c > 0$.

$z = \sqrt{(x - \beta)/(\alpha - x)}$, where $\alpha$ and $\beta$ are the roots of the equation $A + Bx - x^2 = 0$, if $c < 0$ and $\dfrac{a}{-c} < 0$.

**165.** $\displaystyle\int \frac{dx}{\sqrt{X}} = \frac{1}{\sqrt{c}}\,\sinh^{-1}\left(\frac{2\,cx + b}{\sqrt{q}}\right)^{*}$

**166.** $\displaystyle\int \frac{dx}{\sqrt{X}} = \frac{-1}{\sqrt{-c}}\,\sin^{-1}\left(\frac{2\,cx + b}{\sqrt{-q}}\right)$

**167.** $\displaystyle\int \frac{dx}{X\sqrt{X}} = \frac{2(2\,cx + b)}{q\sqrt{X}}$

**168.** $\displaystyle\int \frac{dx}{X^2\sqrt{X}} = \frac{2(2\,cx + b)}{3\,q\sqrt{X}}\left(\frac{1}{X} + 2\,k\right)$

**169.** $\displaystyle\int \frac{dx}{X^n\sqrt{X}} = \frac{2(2\,cx + b)\sqrt{X}}{(2\,n - 1)qX^n} + \frac{2\,k(n - 1)}{2\,n - 1}\int \frac{dx}{X^{n-1}\sqrt{X}}$

**170.** $\displaystyle\int \sqrt{X}\,dx = \frac{(2\,cx + b)\sqrt{X}}{4\,c} + \frac{1}{2\,k}\int \frac{dx}{\sqrt{X}}$

**171.** $\displaystyle\int X\sqrt{X}\,dx = \frac{(2\,cx + b)\sqrt{X}}{8\,c}\left(X + \frac{3}{2\,k}\right) + \frac{3}{8\,k^2}\int \frac{dx}{\sqrt{X}}$

**172.** $\displaystyle\int X^2\sqrt{X}\,dx$

$\qquad = \dfrac{(2\,cx + b)\sqrt{X}}{12\,c}\left(X^2 + \dfrac{5\,X}{4\,k} + \dfrac{15}{8\,k^2}\right) + \dfrac{5}{16\,k^3}\int \dfrac{dx}{\sqrt{X}}$

*See Formula 703.

**173.** $\int X^n \sqrt{X}\, dx = \dfrac{(2\,cx+b)X^n\sqrt{X}}{4(n+1)c} + \dfrac{2\,n+1}{2(n+1)k}\int \dfrac{X^n dx}{\sqrt{X}}$

**174.** $\int \dfrac{x\, dx}{\sqrt{X}} = \dfrac{\sqrt{X}}{c} - \dfrac{b}{2\,c}\int \dfrac{dx}{\sqrt{X}}$

**175.** $\int \dfrac{x\, dx}{X\sqrt{X}} = -\dfrac{2(bx+2\,a)}{q\sqrt{X}}$

**176.** $\int \dfrac{x\, dx}{X^n\sqrt{X}} = -\dfrac{\sqrt{X}}{(2\,n-1)cX^n} - \dfrac{b}{2\,c}\int \dfrac{dx}{X^n\sqrt{X}}$

**177.** $\int \dfrac{x^2\, dx}{\sqrt{X}} = \left(\dfrac{x}{2\,c} - \dfrac{3\,b}{4\,c^2}\right)\sqrt{X} + \dfrac{3\,b^2-4\,ac}{8\,c^2}\int \dfrac{dx}{\sqrt{X}}$

**178.** $\int \dfrac{x^2\, dx}{X\sqrt{X}} = \dfrac{(2\,b^2-4\,ac)x+2\,ab}{cq\sqrt{X}} + \dfrac{1}{c}\int \dfrac{dx}{\sqrt{X}}$

**179.** $\int \dfrac{x^2\, dx}{X^n\sqrt{X}}$

$= \dfrac{(2\,b^2-4\,ac)x+2\,ab}{(2\,n-1)cq\, X^{n-1}\sqrt{X}} + \dfrac{4\,ac+(2\,n-3)b^2}{(2\,n-1)cq}\int \dfrac{dx}{X^{n-1}\sqrt{X}}$

**180.** $\int \dfrac{x^3\, dx}{\sqrt{X}}$

$= \left(\dfrac{x^2}{3\,c} - \dfrac{5\,bx}{12\,c^2} + \dfrac{5\,b^2}{8\,c^3} - \dfrac{2\,a}{3\,c^2}\right)\sqrt{X} + \left(\dfrac{3\,ab}{4\,c^2} - \dfrac{5\,b^3}{16\,c^3}\right)\int \dfrac{dx}{\sqrt{X}}$

**181.** $\int x\sqrt{X}\, dx = \dfrac{X\sqrt{X}}{3\,c} - \dfrac{b}{2\,c}\int \sqrt{X}\, dx$

**182.** $\int xX\sqrt{X}\, dx = \dfrac{X^2\sqrt{X}}{5\,c} - \dfrac{b}{2\,c}\int X\sqrt{X}\, dx$

**183.** $\int \dfrac{xX^n\, dx}{\sqrt{X}} = \dfrac{X^n\sqrt{X}}{(2\,n+1)c} - \dfrac{b}{2\,c}\int \dfrac{X^n\, dx}{\sqrt{X}}$

**184.** $\int x^2\sqrt{X}\, dx = \left(x - \dfrac{5\,b}{6\,c}\right)\dfrac{X\sqrt{X}}{4\,c} + \dfrac{5\,b^2-4\,ac}{16\,c^2}\int \sqrt{X}\, dx$

**185.** $\int \dfrac{x^2 X^n\, dx}{\sqrt{X}} = \dfrac{x X^n \sqrt{X}}{2(n+1)c} - \dfrac{(2\,n+3)b}{4(n+1)c} \int \dfrac{x X^n dx}{\sqrt{X}}$

$$- \dfrac{a}{2(n+1)c} \int \dfrac{X^n dx}{\sqrt{X}}$$

**186.** $\int x^3 \sqrt{X}\, dx = \left( x^2 - \dfrac{7\,bx}{8\,c} + \dfrac{35\,b^2}{48\,c^2} - \dfrac{2\,a}{3\,c} \right) \dfrac{X\sqrt{X}}{5\,c}$

$$+ \left( \dfrac{3\,ab}{8\,c^2} - \dfrac{7\,b^3}{32\,c^3} \right) \int \sqrt{X}\, dx$$

**187.** $\int \dfrac{dx}{x\sqrt{X}} = - \dfrac{1}{\sqrt{a}} \log \left( \dfrac{\sqrt{X}+\sqrt{a}}{x} + \dfrac{b}{2\sqrt{a}} \right)$, if $a > 0$

**188.** $\int \dfrac{dx}{x\sqrt{X}} = \dfrac{1}{\sqrt{-a}} \sin^{-1} \left( \dfrac{bx+2\,a}{x\sqrt{-q}} \right)$, or $\dfrac{-1}{\sqrt{a}} \sinh^{-1} \dfrac{2\,a+bx}{x\sqrt{q}}$

**189.** $\int \dfrac{dx}{x\sqrt{X}} = - \dfrac{2\sqrt{X}}{bx}$, if $a = 0$

**190.** $\int \dfrac{dx}{x X^n \sqrt{X}}$

$$= \dfrac{\sqrt{X}}{(2\,n-1)a X^n} + \dfrac{1}{a} \int \dfrac{dx}{x X^{n-1}\sqrt{X}} - \dfrac{b}{2\,a} \int \dfrac{dx}{X^n \sqrt{X}}$$

**191.** $\int \dfrac{dx}{x^2 \sqrt{X}} = - \dfrac{\sqrt{X}}{ax} - \dfrac{b}{2\,a} \int \dfrac{dx}{x\sqrt{X}}$

**192.** $\int \dfrac{\sqrt{X}\, dx}{x} = \sqrt{X} + \dfrac{b}{2} \int \dfrac{dx}{\sqrt{X}} + a \int \dfrac{dx}{x\sqrt{X}}$

**193.** $\int \dfrac{X^n\, dx}{x\sqrt{X}} = \dfrac{X^n}{(2\,n-1)\sqrt{X}} + a \int \dfrac{X^{n-1}dx}{x\sqrt{X}} + \dfrac{b}{2} \int \dfrac{X^{n-1}dx}{\sqrt{X}}$

**194.** $\int \dfrac{\sqrt{X}\, dx}{x^2} = - \dfrac{\sqrt{X}}{x} + \dfrac{b}{2} \int \dfrac{dx}{x\sqrt{X}} + c \int \dfrac{dx}{\sqrt{X}}$

**195.** $\int \dfrac{x^m\, dx}{X^n \sqrt{X}} = \dfrac{1}{c} \int \dfrac{x^{m-2}\, dx}{X^{n-1}\sqrt{X}} - \dfrac{b}{c} \int \dfrac{x^{m-1}\, dx}{X^n \sqrt{X}} - \dfrac{a}{c} \int \dfrac{x^{m-2}\, dx}{X^n \sqrt{X}}$

**196.** $\displaystyle\int\frac{x^m X^n dx}{\sqrt{X}} = \frac{x^{m-1}X^n\sqrt{X}}{(2\,n+m)c} - \frac{(2\,n+2\,m-1)b}{2\,c(2\,n+m)}\int\frac{x^{m-1}X^n dx}{\sqrt{X}}$

$$- \frac{(m-1)a}{(2\,n+m)c}\int\frac{x^{m-2}X^n dx}{\sqrt{X}}$$

**197.** $\displaystyle\int\frac{dx}{x^m X^n\sqrt{X}}$

$$= -\frac{\sqrt{X}}{(m-1)ax^{m-1}X^n} - \frac{(2\,n+2\,m-3)b}{2\,a(m-1)}\int\frac{dx}{x^{m-1}X^n\sqrt{X}}$$

$$- \frac{(2\,n+m-2)c}{(m-1)a}\int\frac{dx}{x^{m-2}X^n\sqrt{X}}$$

**198.** $\displaystyle\int\frac{X^n dx}{x^m\sqrt{X}} = -\frac{X^{n-1}\sqrt{X}}{(m-1)x^{m-1}} + \frac{(2\,n-1)b}{2(m-1)}\int\frac{X^{n-1}dx}{x^{m-1}\sqrt{X}}$

$$+ \frac{(2\,n-1)c}{m-1}\int\frac{X^{n-1}dx}{x^{m-2}\sqrt{X}}$$

**199.** $\displaystyle\int f(x,\,\sqrt{(x-a)(x-b)})\,dx$

$$= 2(a-b)\int f\left[\frac{bu^2-a}{u^2-1},\frac{u(b-a)}{u^2-1}\right]\frac{u\,du}{(u^2-1)^2},$$

where $u^2(x-b) = x-a$

## Expressions Involving $(a' + b'x)$ and $\sqrt{a + bx + cx^2}$

Let $X = a + bx + cx^2$, $\quad v = a' + b'x$, $\quad q = 4\,ac - b^2$,

$\beta = bb' - 2\,a'c$, $\qquad k = ab'^2 - a'bb' + ca'^2$, then

**200.** $\displaystyle\int\frac{dx}{v\sqrt{X}} = \frac{1}{\sqrt{k}}\log\frac{2\,k+\beta v - 2\,b'\sqrt{kX}}{v}$

$$\text{or } \frac{1}{\sqrt{-k}}\tan^{-1}\frac{2\,k+\beta v}{2\,b'\sqrt{-kX}}$$

$$\text{or } \frac{1}{\sqrt{-k}}\sin^{-1}\frac{2\,k+\beta v}{b'v\sqrt{-q}}, \text{ if } k \neq 0$$

**201.** $\int \dfrac{dx}{v\sqrt{X}} = -\dfrac{2\,b'\sqrt{X}}{\beta v}$, if $k = 0$:

thus, $\int \dfrac{dx}{(x \pm 1)\sqrt{x^2 - 1}} = \pm \sqrt{\dfrac{x \mp 1}{x \pm 1}}$

**202.** $\int \dfrac{dx}{v^2\sqrt{X}} = -\dfrac{b'\sqrt{X}}{kv} - \dfrac{\beta}{2\,k}\int \dfrac{dx}{v\sqrt{X}}$

**203.** $\int \dfrac{dx}{v^2\sqrt{X}} = -\dfrac{2\,b'\sqrt{X}}{3\,\beta v^2} - \dfrac{2\,c}{3\,\beta}\int \dfrac{dx}{v\sqrt{X}}$, if $k = 0$

**204.** $\int \dfrac{dx}{vX\sqrt{X}} = \dfrac{1}{k}\left(\dfrac{b'}{\sqrt{X}} - \tfrac{1}{2}\,\beta\int \dfrac{dx}{X\sqrt{X}} + b'^2\int \dfrac{dx}{v\sqrt{X}}\right)$

**205.** $\int \dfrac{v\,dx}{X\sqrt{X}} = -\dfrac{2(2\,k + \beta v)}{b'q\sqrt{X}}$

**206.** $\int \dfrac{v\,dx}{\sqrt{X}} = \dfrac{b'\sqrt{X}}{c} - \dfrac{\beta}{2\,c}\int \dfrac{dx}{\sqrt{X}}$

**207.** $\int v\sqrt{X}\,dx = \dfrac{b'X\sqrt{X}}{3\,c} - \dfrac{\beta}{2\,c}\int \sqrt{X}\,dx$

**208.** $\int \dfrac{v\,dx}{X^n\sqrt{X}} = -\dfrac{b'\sqrt{X}}{(2\,n - 1)cX^n} - \dfrac{\beta}{2\,c}\int \dfrac{dx}{X^n\sqrt{X}}$

**209.** $\int \dfrac{vX^n\,dx}{\sqrt{X}} = \dfrac{b'X^n\sqrt{X}}{(2\,n + 1)c} - \dfrac{\beta}{2\,c}\int \dfrac{X^n\,dx}{\sqrt{X}}$

**210.** $\int \dfrac{dx}{v^m\sqrt{X}} = -\dfrac{b'\sqrt{X}}{(m - 1)kv^{m-1}} - \dfrac{(2\,m - 3)\beta}{2(m - 1)k}\int \dfrac{dx}{v^{m-1}\sqrt{X}}$

$-\dfrac{(m - 2)c}{(m - 1)k}\int \dfrac{dx}{v^{m-2}\sqrt{X}}$, if $k \neq 0$

**211.** $\int \dfrac{dx}{v^m\sqrt{X}} = -\dfrac{2\,b'\sqrt{X}}{(2\,m - 1)\beta v^m}$

$-\dfrac{2(m - 1)c}{(2\,m - 1)\beta}\int \dfrac{dx}{v^{m-1}\sqrt{X}}$, if $k = 0$

**212.** $\displaystyle \int \frac{\sqrt{X}\,dx}{v^m} = -\frac{b'X\sqrt{X}}{(m-1)kv^{m-1}} - \frac{(2m-5)\beta}{2(m-1)k}\int\frac{\sqrt{X}\,dx}{v^{m-1}} - \frac{(m-4)c}{(m-1)k}\int\frac{\sqrt{X}\,dx}{v^{m-2}}$

$\displaystyle = \frac{1}{(m-1)b'^2}\left(-\frac{b'\sqrt{X}}{v^{m-1}} + \tfrac12\beta\int\frac{dx}{v^{m-1}\sqrt{X}} + c\int\frac{dx}{v^{m-2}\sqrt{X}}\right)$

$\displaystyle = \frac{1}{(m-2)b'^2}\left(-\frac{b'\sqrt{X}}{v^{m-1}} - k\int\frac{dx}{v^m\sqrt{X}} - \tfrac12\beta\int\frac{dx}{v^{m-1}\sqrt{X}}\right)$

**213.** $\displaystyle \int v^m\sqrt{X}\,dx = \frac{1}{(m+2)c}\left(b'v^{m-1}X\sqrt{X} - (m+\tfrac12)\beta\int v^{m-1}\sqrt{X}\,dx - (m-1)k\int v^{m-2}\sqrt{X}\,dx\right)$

**214.** $\displaystyle \int\frac{dx}{v^m X^n\sqrt{X}} = -\frac{1}{(m-1)k}\left(\frac{b'\sqrt{X}}{v^{m-1}X^n} + (m+n-\tfrac32)\beta\int\frac{dx}{v^{m-1}X^n\sqrt{X}}\right.$

$\displaystyle \left. + (m+2n-2)c\int\frac{dx}{v^{m-2}X^n\sqrt{X}}\right)$, if $k\neq 0$

**215.** $\displaystyle \int\frac{dx}{v^m X^n\sqrt{X}} = \frac{-2}{(2m+2n-1)\beta}\left(\frac{b'\sqrt{X}}{v^m X^n} + (m+2n-1)c\int\frac{dx}{v^{m-1}X^n\sqrt{X}}\right)$, if $k=0$

**216.** $\displaystyle \int\frac{X^n dx}{v^m\sqrt{X}} = -\frac{1}{(m-1)k}\left(\frac{b'X^{n-1}\sqrt{X}}{v^{m-1}} + (m-n-\tfrac32)\beta\int\frac{X^n dx}{v^{m-1}\sqrt{X}} + (m-2n-2)c\int\frac{X^n dx}{v^{m-2}\sqrt{X}}\right)$

$\displaystyle = -\frac{1}{(m-2n)b'^2}\left(\frac{b'X^{n-1}\sqrt{X}}{v^{m-1}} + (2n-1)k\int\frac{X^{n-1}dx}{v^m\sqrt{X}} + (n-\tfrac12)\beta\int\frac{X^{n-1}dx}{v^{m-1}\sqrt{X}}\right)$

$\displaystyle = -\frac{1}{(m-1)b'^2}\left(-\frac{b'X^{n-1}\sqrt{X}}{v^{m-1}} + (n-\tfrac12)\beta\int\frac{X^{n-1}dx}{v^{m-1}\sqrt{X}} + (2n-1)c\int\frac{X^{n-1}dx}{v^{m-2}\sqrt{X}}\right)$

**217.** $\displaystyle\int \frac{v^m X^n dx}{\sqrt{X}} = \frac{1}{(m+2n)c}\left(b'v^{m-1}X^n\sqrt{X} - (m+n-\tfrac{1}{2})\beta\int\frac{v^{m-1}X^n dx}{\sqrt{X}} - (m-1)k\int\frac{v^{m-2}X^n dx}{\sqrt{X}}\right)$

**218.** $\displaystyle\int \frac{v^m dx}{X^n\sqrt{X}} = \frac{1}{(m-2n)c}\left(\frac{b'v^{m-1}\sqrt{X}}{X^n} - (m-n-\tfrac{1}{2})\beta\int\frac{v^{m-1}dx}{X^n\sqrt{X}} - (m-1)k\int\frac{v^{m-2}dx}{X^n\sqrt{X}}\right)$

The identities given below are sometimes convenient:

$$\frac{1}{(x+a)(x+b)\sqrt{X}} \equiv \frac{1}{(b-a)(x+a)\sqrt{X}} + \frac{1}{(a-b)(x+b)\sqrt{X}}$$

$$\frac{1}{\sqrt{a+bx+cx^2}\pm\sqrt{a'+b'x+c'x^2}} \equiv \frac{\sqrt{a+bx+cx^2}\mp\sqrt{a'+b'x+c'x^2}}{a-a'+(b-b')x+(c-c')x^2}$$

$$\frac{\sqrt{X}}{(x+a)(x+b)} \equiv \frac{\sqrt{X}}{(b-a)(x+a)} + \frac{\sqrt{X}}{(a-b)(x+b)}$$

$$\frac{(x+a)\sqrt{X}}{x+b} \equiv \sqrt{X} + \frac{(a-b)\sqrt{X}}{x+b}$$

## MISCELLANEOUS ALGEBRAIC EXPRESSIONS

**219.** $\int \sqrt{2\,ax - x^2} \cdot dx = \dfrac{x - a}{2} \sqrt{2\,ax - x^2} + \dfrac{a^2}{2} \sin^{-1} \dfrac{x - a}{a}$

**220.** $\int \dfrac{dx}{\sqrt{2\,ax - x^2}} = \operatorname{versin}^{-1} \dfrac{x}{a}$

$\qquad = \cos^{-1} \left(1 - \dfrac{x}{a}\right) = 2 \sin^{-1} \sqrt{\dfrac{x}{2\,a}}$

**221.** $\int \dfrac{x^n dx}{\sqrt{2\,ax - x^2}} = - \dfrac{x^{n-1}\sqrt{2\,ax - x^2}}{n}$

$\qquad\qquad - \dfrac{a(1 - 2\,n)}{n} \int \dfrac{x^{n-1} dx}{\sqrt{2\,ax - x^2}}$

**222.** $\int \dfrac{dx}{x^n \sqrt{2\,ax - x^2}} = \dfrac{\sqrt{2\,ax - x^2}}{a(1 - 2\,n)x^n}$

$\qquad\qquad + \dfrac{n - 1}{(2\,n - 1)a} \int \dfrac{dx}{x^{n-1}\sqrt{2\,ax - x^2}}$

**223.** $\int x^n \sqrt{2\,ax - x^2} \cdot dx = - \dfrac{x^{n-1}\sqrt{(2\,ax - x^2)^3}}{n + 2}$

$\qquad\qquad + \dfrac{(2\,n + 1)a}{n + 2} \int x^{n-1}\sqrt{2\,ax - x^2} \cdot dx$

**224.** $\int \dfrac{\sqrt{2\,ax - x^2} \cdot dx}{x^n} = \dfrac{\sqrt{(2\,ax - x^2)^3}}{(3 - 2\,n)ax^n}$

$\qquad\qquad + \dfrac{n - 3}{(2\,n - 3)a} \int \dfrac{\sqrt{2\,ax - x^2} \cdot dx}{x^{n-1}}$

**225.** $\displaystyle\int \frac{dx}{x\sqrt{x^n - a^2}} = \frac{2}{an}\cos^{-1}\frac{a}{x^{\frac{n}{2}}}$

**226.** $\displaystyle\int \frac{dx}{x\sqrt{x^n + a^2}} = \frac{1}{an}\log\frac{\sqrt{a^2 + x^n} - a}{\sqrt{a^2 + x^n} + a}$

**227.** $\displaystyle\int \frac{x^{\frac{1}{2}}\,dx}{\sqrt{a^3 - x^3}} = \frac{2}{3}\sin^{-1}\left(\frac{x}{a}\right)^{\frac{3}{2}}$

**228.** $\displaystyle\int \frac{dx}{(a + bx^2)\sqrt{x}} = \frac{1}{b\delta^3\sqrt{2}}\left[\log\left(\frac{x + \delta^2 + \sqrt{2}\,\delta^2 x}{\sqrt{a + bx^2}}\right) + \tan^{-1}\left(1 + \frac{\sqrt{2}\,x}{\delta}\right) - \tan^{-1}\left(1 - \frac{\sqrt{2}\,x}{\delta}\right)\right],$

where $b\delta^4 = a$

**229.** $\displaystyle\int \frac{\sqrt{x}\cdot dx}{a + bx^2} = \frac{1}{b\delta\sqrt{2}}\left[\tan^{-1}\left(1 + \frac{\sqrt{2}\,x}{\delta}\right) - \tan^{-1}\left(1 - \frac{\sqrt{2}\,x}{\delta}\right) - \log\left(\frac{x + \delta^2 + \sqrt{2}\,\delta^2 x}{\sqrt{a + bx^2}}\right)\right],$

where $b\delta^4 = a$

230. $\int \dfrac{x^{\frac{3}{2}} \cdot dx}{a + bx^2} = \dfrac{2\sqrt{x}}{b} - \dfrac{a}{b} \int \dfrac{dx}{(a + bx^2)\sqrt{x}}$

231. $\int \dfrac{dx}{(a + bx^2)^2 \sqrt{x}} = \dfrac{\sqrt{x}}{2a(a + bx^2)} + \dfrac{3}{4a} \int \dfrac{dx}{(a + bx^2)\sqrt{x}}$

232. $\int \dfrac{\sqrt{x} \cdot dx}{(a + bx^2)^2} = \dfrac{x^{\frac{3}{2}}}{2a(a + bx^2)} + \dfrac{1}{4a} \int \dfrac{\sqrt{x} \cdot dx}{(a + bx^2)}$

233. $\int (a + bx)^n dx = \dfrac{n}{(n + 1)b} (a + bx)^{\frac{n+1}{n}}$, where $n \neq -1$

234. $\int \dfrac{dx}{(a + bx)^n} = \dfrac{n}{(n - 1)b} (a + bx)^{\frac{n-1}{n}}$, where $n \neq 1$

235. $\int f(x, \sqrt[n]{a + bx}) dx = \dfrac{n}{b} \int f\left(\dfrac{z^n - a}{b}, z\right) z^{n-1} dz$, where $z^n = a + bx$

236. $\int (a + bx)^{\frac{m}{n}} dx = \dfrac{n(a + bx)^{\frac{m+n}{n}}}{b(m + n)}$

**237.** $\int f(x, (a+bx)^{\frac{m}{n}}, (a+bx)^{\frac{p}{q}}, \cdots)dx$

$$= \frac{s}{b}\int f\left(\frac{y^s-a}{b}, y^{\frac{ms}{n}}, y^{\frac{ps}{q}}, \cdots\right)y^{s-1}dy,$$

where $y^s = a + bx$, and $s$ is the least common multiple of $n$, $q$, etc.

If $a_1$, $a_2$, $a_3$, etc., are the roots of the equation

$$p_0x^n + p_1x^{n-1} + p_2x^{n-2} + \cdots + p_n = 0,$$

the integrand in the expression

$$\int \frac{(q_0x^m + q_1x^{m-1} + \cdots + q_n)dx}{(p_0x^n + p_1x^{n-1} + \cdots + p_n)\sqrt{a+bx+cx^2}},$$

where $m < n$, may be expressed as the sum of a number of partial fractions of the form $\dfrac{A}{(x-a_k)^r\sqrt{a+bx+cx^2}}$, and these can be integrated by the aid of equations given above. Thus,

**238.** $\int \dfrac{(px+q)dx}{(x-a')(x-b')\sqrt{a+bx+cx^2}}$

$$= \frac{q+a'p}{a'-b'}\int \frac{dx}{(x-a')\sqrt{a+bx+cx^2}}$$

$$- \frac{q+b'p}{a'-b'}\int \frac{dx}{(x-b')\sqrt{a+bx+cx^2}}$$

**239.** $\int \dfrac{dx}{(a'+c'x^2)\sqrt{a+cx^2}}$

$$= \frac{1}{a'}\sqrt{\frac{a'}{ac'-a'c}}\tan^{-1}x\sqrt{\frac{ac'-a'c}{a'(a+cx^2)}},$$

or $\dfrac{1}{2a'}\sqrt{\dfrac{a'}{a'c-ac'}}\log\dfrac{\sqrt{a+cx^2}+x\sqrt{(a'c-ac')/a'}}{\sqrt{a+cx^2}-x\sqrt{(a'c-ac')/a'}}$

**240.** $\int \dfrac{x \, dx}{(a' + c'x^2)\sqrt{a + cx^2}}$

$$= \frac{1}{c'} \sqrt{\frac{c'}{a'c - ac'}} \, \tan^{-1} \sqrt{\frac{c'(a + cx^2)}{a'c - ac'}},$$

$$\text{or} \; \frac{1}{2 \, c'} \sqrt{\frac{c'}{ac' - a'c}} \, \log \frac{\sqrt{a + cx^2} - \sqrt{(ac' - a'c)/c'}}{\sqrt{a + cx^2} + \sqrt{(ac' - a'c)/c'}}$$

**241.** $\int f\left[x, \; \sqrt[n]{\dfrac{a + bx}{a' + b'x}}\right] dx$

$$= n(a'b - ab') \int f\left(\frac{a - a'z^n}{b'z^n - b}, z\right) \cdot \frac{z^{n-1} dz}{(b'z^n - b)^2},$$

where $z^n(a' + b'x) = a + bx$

**242.** $\int f(x, \; \sqrt[n]{c + \sqrt[m]{a + bx}}) dx$

$$= \frac{mn}{b} \int f\left[\frac{(z^n - c)^m - a}{b}, z\right] (z^n - c)^{m-1} z^{n-1} dz,$$

where $z^n = c + \sqrt[m]{a + bx}$

**243.** $\int f\left[x, \left(\dfrac{a + bx}{a' + b'x}\right)^{\frac{m}{n}}, \left(\dfrac{a + bx}{a' + b'x}\right)^{\frac{p}{q}}, \cdots\right] dx$

$$= s(a'b - ab') \int f\left[\frac{a'y^s - a}{b - b'y^s}, y^{\frac{ms}{n}}, y^{\frac{ps}{q}}, \cdots\right] \frac{y^{s-1} dy}{(b - b'y^s)^2},$$

where $y^s(a' + b'x) = a + bx$ and $s$ is the least common multiple of $n$, $q$, etc.

**244.** $\int f(x, \; \sqrt{a + bx + x^2}) dx$

$$= 2 \int f\left(\frac{2\sqrt{a} \cdot z - b}{1 - z^2}, \frac{z^2\sqrt{a} - bz + \sqrt{a}}{1 - z^2}\right) \cdot \frac{(z^2\sqrt{a} - bz + \sqrt{a}) dz}{(1 - z^2)^2},$$

where $xz + \sqrt{a} = \sqrt{a + bx + x^2}$

**245.** $\int f(x, \sqrt{a + bx + x^2})dx$

$$= \int f\left(\frac{u^2 - a}{b - 2\,u}, \frac{u^2 - bu + a}{2\,u - b}\right) \frac{2(bu - a - u^2)du}{(b - 2\,u)^2},$$

where $u = \sqrt{a + bx + x^2} - x$

# TRANSCENDENTAL FUNCTIONS

## *General Expressions*

**246.** $\int \sin x \cdot f(\cos x)dx = -\int f(\cos x)d\cos x$

**247.** $\int \cos x \cdot f(\sin x)dx = \int f(\sin x)d\sin x$

**248.** $\int \sin x \cdot f(\sin x, \cos x)dx = -\int f(\sqrt{1 - z^2}, z)dz,$

where $z = \cos x$

**249.** $\int f(\sin x)dx = -\int f\left(\cos\left(\frac{\pi}{2} - x\right)\right) d\left(\frac{\pi}{2} - x\right)$

**250.** $\int f(\tan x)dx = -\int f\left(\operatorname{ctn}\left(\frac{\pi}{2} - x\right)\right) d\left(\frac{\pi}{2} - x\right)$

**251.** $\int f(\sec x)dx = -\int f\left(\csc\left(\frac{\pi}{2} - x\right)\right) d\left(\frac{\pi}{2} - x\right)$

**252.** $\int \dfrac{\sin x \cdot f(\sin^2 x)dx}{\sqrt{1 - k^2 \sin^2 x}} = \int \dfrac{f(z)dz}{2\sqrt{(1 - z)(1 - k^2 z)}},$

where $z = \sin^2 x$

**253.** $\int \dfrac{\cos x \cdot f(\cos^2 x)dx}{\sqrt{1 - k^2 \sin^2 x}} = \int \dfrac{f(1 - z)dz}{2\sqrt{z(1 - k^2 z)}},$ where $z = \sin^2 x$

**254.** $\int \dfrac{\tan x \cdot f(\tan^2 x)dx}{\sqrt{1 - k^2 \sin^2 x}} = \int f\left(\dfrac{z}{1-z}\right) \dfrac{dz}{2(1-z)\sqrt{1-k^2 z}},$

where $z = \sin^2 x$.

**255.** $\int \sec^{n+2} x \cdot f(\tan x)dx = \int (1 + z^2)^{\frac{n}{2}} f(z)dz; \quad z = \tan x$

**256.** $\int f(\sin x, \cos x)dx$

$$= -\int f\left[\cos\left(\dfrac{\pi}{2}-x\right), \sin\left(\dfrac{\pi}{2}-x\right)\right] d\left(\dfrac{\pi}{2}-x\right)$$

**257.** $\int f(x) \cdot \sin^{-1} x \cdot dx = \sin^{-1} x \cdot \phi(x) - \int \dfrac{\phi(x)dx}{\sqrt{1-x^2}},$

where $\phi(x) = \int f(x)dx$

**258.** $\int f(x) \cdot \cos^{-1} x \, dx = \cos^{-1} x \cdot \phi(x) + \int \dfrac{\phi(x)dx}{\sqrt{1-x^2}}$

**259.** $\int f(x) \cdot \tan^{-1} x \, dx = \tan^{-1} x \cdot \phi(x) - \int \dfrac{\phi(x)dx}{1+x^2}$

**260.** $\int f(x) \cdot \text{ctn}^{-1} x \, dx = \text{ctn}^{-1} x \cdot \phi(x) + \int \dfrac{\phi(x)dx}{1+x^2}$

**261.** $\int f(x, \cos x)dx = -\int f\left(\dfrac{\pi}{2}-z, \sin z\right) dz,$

where $z = \dfrac{\pi}{2} - x$

**262.** $\int \dfrac{\sin x \cdot f(\cos x)dx}{a+b\cos x} = -\dfrac{1}{b}\int f\left(\dfrac{z-a}{b}\right) \dfrac{dz}{z},$

where $z = a + b\cos x$

**263.** $\int f(x, \log x)dx = \int f(e^z, z)e^z \, dz,$ where $z = \log x$

**264.** $\int \dfrac{f(\log x)dx}{x} = \int f(z)dz,$ where $z = \log x$

**265.** $\int x^m f(\log x)dx = \int e^{(m+1)z} f(z)dz$

**266.** $\int f(\sin x,\ \cos x,\ \tan x,\ \text{ctn } x,\ \sec x,\ \csc x)dx$

$$= \int f\left(\frac{2z}{1+z^2},\ \frac{1-z^2}{1+z^2},\ \frac{2z}{1-z^2},\ \frac{1-z^2}{2z},\ \frac{1+z^2}{1-z^2},\ \frac{1+z^2}{2z}\right)\frac{2\,dz}{1+z^2},$$

where $z = \tan\dfrac{x}{2}$;

$$= \int f\left(z,\ \sqrt{1-z^2},\ \frac{z}{\sqrt{1-z^2}},\ \frac{\sqrt{1-z^2}}{z},\ \frac{1}{\sqrt{1-z^2}},\ \frac{1}{z}\right)\frac{dz}{\sqrt{1-z^2}},$$

where $z = \sin x$;

$$= \int f\left(\frac{z}{\sqrt{1+z^2}},\ \frac{1}{\sqrt{1+z^2}},\ z,\ \frac{1}{z},\ \sqrt{1+z^2},\ \frac{\sqrt{1+z^2}}{z}\right)\frac{dz}{1+z^2},$$

where $z = \tan x$;

$$= \int f\left(\sqrt{z},\ \sqrt{1-z},\ \sqrt{\frac{z}{1-z}},\ \sqrt{\frac{1-z}{z}},\ \frac{1}{\sqrt{1-z}},\ \frac{1}{\sqrt{z}}\right)\frac{dz}{2\sqrt{z(1-z)}},$$

where $z = \sin^2 x$;

$$= \int f\left(\sqrt{\frac{z}{1+z}},\ \frac{1}{\sqrt{1+z}},\ \sqrt{z},\ \frac{1}{\sqrt{z}},\ \sqrt{1+z},\ \sqrt{\frac{1+z}{z}}\right)\frac{dz}{2(1+z)\sqrt{z}},$$

where $z = \tan^2 x$.

## Expressions Involving Trigonometric Functions*

**267.** $\int \sin x\, dx = -\cos x$

**268.** $\int \sin^2 x\, dx = -\frac{1}{2}\cos x \sin x + \frac{1}{2} x = \frac{1}{2} x - \frac{1}{4}\sin 2x$

**269.** $\int \sin^3 x\, dx = -\frac{1}{3}\cos x(\sin^2 x + 2)$

**270.** $\int \sin^n x\, dx = -\dfrac{\sin^{n-1} x \cos x}{n} + \dfrac{n-1}{n}\int \sin^{n-2} x\, dx.$

*See also the special list of integrals useful in the theory of alternating currents, on pages 121–124.

**271.** $\int \cos x \, dx = \sin x$

**272.** $\int \cos^2 x \, dx = \frac{1}{2} \sin x \cos x + \frac{1}{2} x = \frac{1}{2} x + \frac{1}{4} \sin 2x$

**273.** $\int \cos^3 x \, dx = \frac{1}{3} \sin x (\cos^2 x + 2)$

**274.** $\int \cos^n x \, dx = \frac{1}{n} \cos^{n-1} x \sin x + \frac{n-1}{n} \int \cos^{n-2} x \, dx$

**275.** $\int \sin x \cos x \, dx = \frac{1}{2} \sin^2 x$

**276.** $\int \sin^2 x \cos^2 x \, dx = - \frac{1}{8} (\frac{1}{4} \sin 4x - x)$

**277.** $\int \sin x \cos^m x \, dx = - \frac{\cos^{m+1} x}{m+1}$

**278.** $\int \sin^m x \cos x \, dx = \frac{\sin^{m+1} x}{m+1}$

**279.** $\int \cos^m x \sin^n x \, dx$

$$= \frac{\cos^{m-1} x \sin^{n+1} x}{m+n} + \frac{m-1}{m+n} \int \cos^{m-2} x \sin^n x \, dx$$

**280.** $\int \cos^m x \sin^n x \, dx$

$$= - \frac{\sin^{n-1} x \cos^{m+1} x}{m+n} + \frac{n-1}{m+n} \int \cos^m x \sin^{n-2} x \, dx$$

**281.** $\int \dfrac{\sin^n x \, dx}{\cos^m x} = \dfrac{1}{n-m} \left( - \dfrac{\sin^{n-1} x}{\cos^{m-1} x} + (n-1) \int \dfrac{\sin^{n-2} x \, dx}{\cos^m x} \right)$

$$= \frac{1}{m-1} \left( \frac{\sin^{n+1} x}{\cos^{m-1} x} - (n-m+2) \int \frac{\sin^n x \, dx}{\cos^{m-2} x} \right)$$

$$= \frac{1}{m-1} \left( \frac{\sin^{n-1} x}{\cos^{m-1} x} - (n-1) \int \frac{\sin^{n-2} x \, dx}{\cos^{m-2} x} \right)$$

**282.** $\int \dfrac{\cos^m x \, dx}{\sin^n x} = -\dfrac{\cos^{m+1} x}{(n-1)\sin^{n-1} x} - \dfrac{m-n+2}{n-1} \int \dfrac{\cos^m x \, dx}{\sin^{n-2} x}$

$$= \dfrac{\cos^{m-1} x}{(m-n)\sin^{n-1} x} + \dfrac{m-1}{m-n} \int \dfrac{\cos^{m-2} x \, dx}{\sin^n x}$$

$$= -\dfrac{1}{n-1} \dfrac{\cos^{m-1} x}{\sin^{n-1} x} - \dfrac{m-1}{n-1} \int \dfrac{\cos^{m-2} x \, dx}{\sin^{n-2} x}$$

**283.** $\int \dfrac{\sin^m x \, dx}{\cos^n x} = -\int \dfrac{\cos^m\left(\dfrac{\pi}{2} - x\right) d\left(\dfrac{\pi}{2} - x\right)}{\sin^n\left(\dfrac{\pi}{2} - x\right)}$

**284.** $\int \dfrac{dx}{\sin x \cos x} = \log \tan x$

**285.** $\int \dfrac{dx}{\cos x \sin^2 x} = \log \tan \left(\dfrac{\pi}{4} + \dfrac{x}{2}\right) - \csc x$

**286.** $\int \dfrac{dx}{\sin^m x \cos^n x}$

$$= \dfrac{1}{n-1} \cdot \dfrac{1}{\sin^{m-1} x \cdot \cos^{n-1} x} + \dfrac{m+n-2}{n-1} \int \dfrac{dx}{\sin^m x \cdot \cos^{n-2} x}$$

$$= -\dfrac{1}{m-1} \cdot \dfrac{1}{\sin^{m-1} x \cdot \cos^{n-1} x} + \dfrac{m+n-2}{m-1} \int \dfrac{dx}{\sin^{m-2} x \cdot \cos^n x}$$

**287.** $\int \dfrac{dx}{\sin^m x} = -\dfrac{1}{m-1} \cdot \dfrac{\cos x}{\sin^{m-1} x} + \dfrac{m-2}{m-1} \int \dfrac{dx}{\sin^{m-2} x}$

**288.** $\int \dfrac{dx}{\cos^n x} = \dfrac{1}{n-1} \cdot \dfrac{\sin x}{\cos^{n-1} x} + \dfrac{n-2}{n-1} \int \dfrac{dx}{\cos^{n-2} x}$

**289.** $\int \tan x \, dx = -\log \cos x$

**290.** $\int \tan^2 x \, dx = \tan x - x$

**291.** $\int \tan^n x \, dx = \dfrac{\tan^{n-1} x}{n-1} - \int \tan^{n-2} x \, dx$

**292.** $\int \text{ctn } x \, dx = \log \sin x$

**293.** $\int \text{ctn}^2 x \, dx = -\text{ctn } x - x$

**294.** $\int \text{ctn}^n x \, dx = -\dfrac{\text{ctn}^{n-1}x}{n-1} - \int \text{ctn}^{n-2}x \, dx$

**295.** $\int \sec x \, dx = \log \tan \left(\dfrac{\pi}{4} + \dfrac{x}{2}\right) = \tfrac{1}{2} \log \dfrac{1+\sin x}{1-\sin x}$

$\qquad = \log (\sec x + \tan x)$

$\qquad = \log \dfrac{\cos x}{1 - \sin x}$

$\qquad = \log \dfrac{1 + \sin x}{\cos x}$

$\qquad = -\log (\sec x - \tan x)$

**296.** $\int \sec^2 x \, dx = \tan x$

**297.** $\int \sec^n x \, dx = \int \dfrac{dx}{\cos^n x} = \dfrac{\sin x}{(n-1)\cos^{n-1}x} + \dfrac{n-2}{n-1} \int \dfrac{dx}{\cos^{n-2}x}$

$\qquad = \dfrac{\sin x}{(n-1)\cos^{n-1}x} + \dfrac{n-2}{n-1} \int \sec^{n-2}x \, dx$

**298.** $\int \csc x \, dx = \log \tan \tfrac{1}{2} x = \tfrac{1}{2} \log \dfrac{1-\cos x}{1+\cos x}$

$\qquad = \log (\csc x - \text{ctn } x)$

$\qquad = \log \dfrac{\sin x}{1 + \cos x} = \log \dfrac{1 - \cos x}{\sin x}$

$\qquad = -\log (\csc x + \text{ctn } x)$

**299.** $\int \csc^2 x \, dx = -\text{ctn } x$

**300.** $\int \csc^n x \, dx = -\dfrac{\cos x}{(n-1)\sin^{n-1}x} + \dfrac{n-2}{n-1} \int \csc^{n-2}x \, dx$

**301.** $\int \dfrac{dx}{a + b \cos x} = \dfrac{1}{c(b-a)} \left[ \int \dfrac{dz}{z+c} - \int \dfrac{dz}{z-c} \right]$,

where $z = \tan \tfrac{1}{2} x$, and $c^2 = (b+a)/(b-a)$

**302.** $\int \dfrac{dx}{a \pm b \sin x} = \int \dfrac{2\,dz}{a \pm 2\,bz + az^2}$, where $z = \tan \frac{1}{2} x$

**303.** $\int \dfrac{dx}{1 + \sin x} = -\tan\left(\frac{1}{4}\pi - \frac{1}{2}x\right)$

**304.** $\int \dfrac{dx}{1 - \sin x} = \operatorname{ctn}\left(\frac{1}{4}\pi - \frac{1}{2}x\right) = \tan\left(\frac{1}{4}\pi + \frac{1}{2}x\right)$

**305.** $\int \dfrac{dx}{1 + \cos x} = \tan \frac{1}{2}x = \csc x - \operatorname{ctn} x$

**306.** $\int \dfrac{dx}{1 - \cos x} = -\operatorname{ctn} \frac{1}{2}x = -\operatorname{ctn} x - \csc x$

**307.** $\int \dfrac{dx}{a + b \sin x} = \dfrac{2}{\sqrt{a^2 - b^2}} \tan^{-1} \dfrac{a \tan \frac{1}{2}x + b}{\sqrt{a^2 - b^2}}$,

$\qquad$ or $\dfrac{1}{\sqrt{b^2 - a^2}} \log \dfrac{a \tan \frac{1}{2}x + b - \sqrt{b^2 - a^2}}{a \tan \frac{1}{2}x + b + \sqrt{b^2 - a^2}}$,

$\qquad$ or $\dfrac{-2}{\sqrt{b^2 - a^2}} \tanh^{-1} \dfrac{a \tan \frac{1}{2}x + b}{\sqrt{b^2 - a^2}}$,

$\qquad$ or $\dfrac{-2}{\sqrt{b^2 - a^2}} \operatorname{ctnh}^{-1} \dfrac{a \tan \frac{1}{2}x + b}{\sqrt{b^2 - a^2}}$

$$-\pi < x < \pi$$

**308.** $\int \dfrac{dx}{a + b \sin x} = \dfrac{1}{b \cos \alpha} \log \dfrac{\sin \frac{1}{2}(x + \alpha)}{\cos \frac{1}{2}(x - \alpha)}$,

$\qquad a = b \sin \alpha, \quad \sqrt{b^2 - a^2} = b \cos \alpha, \quad -\pi < x < \pi$

**309.** $\int \dfrac{dx}{a + b \cos x} = \dfrac{2}{\sqrt{a^2 - b^2}} \tan^{-1} \dfrac{\sqrt{a^2 - b^2} \tan \frac{1}{2}x}{a + b}$,

$\qquad$ or $\dfrac{1}{\sqrt{b^2 - a^2}} \log \dfrac{\sqrt{b^2 - a^2} \tan \frac{1}{2}x + a + b}{\sqrt{b^2 - a^2} \tan \frac{1}{2}x - a - b}$,

$\qquad$ or $\dfrac{2}{\sqrt{b^2 - a^2}} \tanh^{-1} \dfrac{\sqrt{b^2 - a^2} \tan \frac{1}{2}x}{a + b}$,

$\qquad$ or $\dfrac{2}{\sqrt{b^2 - a^2}} \operatorname{ctnh}^{-1} \dfrac{\sqrt{b^2 - a^2} \tan \frac{1}{2}x}{a + b}$

$$-\pi < x < \pi$$

**310.** $\int \dfrac{dx}{a + b \tan x} = \dfrac{1}{a^2 + b^2} [b \log (a \cos x + b \sin x) + ax]$

**311.** $\int \dfrac{dx}{\sin x + \cos x} = \dfrac{1}{\sqrt{2}} \log \tan (\tfrac{1}{2} x + \tfrac{1}{8} \pi)$

**312.** $\int \dfrac{\sin x \, dx}{a + b \cos x} = -\dfrac{1}{b} \log (a + b \cos x)$

**313.** $\int \dfrac{(a' + b' \cos x)dx}{a + b \cos x} = \dfrac{b'x}{b} + \dfrac{a'b - ab'}{b} \int \dfrac{dx}{a + b \cos x}$

**314.** $\int \dfrac{(a' + b' \cos x)dx}{(a + b \cos x)^2} = \dfrac{ab' - a'b}{a^2 - b^2} \cdot \dfrac{\sin x}{a + b \cos x} + \dfrac{aa' - bb'}{a^2 - b^2} \int \dfrac{dx}{a + b \cos x}$

**315.** $\int \dfrac{(a' + b' \cos x)dx}{(a + b \cos x)^n}$

$= \dfrac{1}{(n-1)(a^2 - b^2)} \left[ \dfrac{(ab' - a'b) \sin x}{(a + b \cos x)^{n-1}} + \int \dfrac{[(aa' - bb')(n-1) + (n-2)(ab' - a'b) \cos x]dx}{(a + b \cos x)^{n-1}} \right]$

**316.** $\int \dfrac{(a' + b' \cos x)dx}{(1 + \cos x)^n} = \dfrac{(a' - b')\tan \tfrac{1}{2} x}{(2n-1)(1 + \cos x)^{n-1}} + \dfrac{n(a' + b')}{2n-1} \int \dfrac{dx}{(1 + \cos x)^{n-1}} - a' \int \dfrac{dx}{(1 + \cos x)^{n-1}}$

**317.** $\int \dfrac{dx}{(a + b \cos x)^n}$

$= \dfrac{1}{(n-1)(a^2 - b^2)} \left[ \dfrac{-b \sin x}{(a + b \cos x)^{n-1}} + (2n-3)a \int \dfrac{dx}{(a + b \cos x)^{n-1}} - (n-2) \int \dfrac{dx}{(a + b \cos x)^{n-2}} \right]$

**318.** $\displaystyle\int \frac{dx}{(1+\cos x)^n}$

$$= \frac{\tan \frac{1}{2}x}{(2n-1)(1+\cos x)^{n-1}} + \frac{n-1}{2n-1}\int \frac{dx}{(1+\cos x)^{n-1}}$$

**319.** $\displaystyle\int \frac{(a'+b'\cos x)dx}{\sin x(a+b\cos x)} = \frac{a'b-ab'}{a^2-b^2}\log(a+b\cos x)$

$$+ \frac{a'+b'}{a+b}\log\sin\frac{1}{2}x - \frac{a'-b'}{a-b}\log\cos\frac{1}{2}x$$

**320.** $\displaystyle\int \frac{(a'+b'\cos x)dx}{\cos x(a+b\cos x)}$

$$= \frac{a'}{a}\log\tan\frac{1}{2}(\tfrac{1}{2}\pi+x) + \frac{(ab'-a'b)}{a}\int \frac{dx}{a+b\cos x}$$

**321.** $\displaystyle\int \frac{(a'+b'\cos x)dx}{\sin x(1\pm\cos x)} = \pm\frac{\frac{1}{2}(a'\mp b')}{1\pm\cos x} + \frac{1}{2}(a'\pm b')\log\tan\frac{1}{2}x$

**322.** $\displaystyle\int \frac{dx}{(1-\cos x)^n}$

$$= \frac{-\operatorname{ctn}\frac{1}{2}x}{(2n-1)(1-\cos x)^{n-1}} + \frac{n-1}{2n-1}\int \frac{dx}{(1-\cos x)^{n-1}}$$

**323.** $\displaystyle\int \frac{dx}{a+b\sin^2 x} = \frac{1}{\sqrt{a^2+ab}}\tan^{-1}\frac{\sqrt{a^2+ab}\tan x}{a},$

$$\text{or } \frac{1}{2\sqrt{-a^2-ab}}\log\frac{\sqrt{-a^2-ab}\tan x+a}{\sqrt{-a^2-ab}\tan x-a},$$

$$\text{or } \frac{1}{\sqrt{-a^2-ab}}\tanh^{-1}\frac{\sqrt{-a^2-ab}\tan x}{a},$$

$$\text{or } \frac{1}{\sqrt{-a^2-ab}}\operatorname{ctnh}^{-1}\frac{\sqrt{-a^2-ab}\tan x}{a}$$

$$-\frac{\pi}{2} < x < \frac{\pi}{2}$$

**324.** $\int \dfrac{dx}{a + b \cos^2 x} = \dfrac{1}{\sqrt{a^2 + ab}} \tan^{-1} \dfrac{\sqrt{a^2 + ab}\, \tan x}{a + b},$

or $\dfrac{1}{2\sqrt{-a^2 - ab}} \log \dfrac{\sqrt{-a^2 - ab}\, \tan x + a + b}{\sqrt{-a^2 - ab}\, \tan x - a - b},$

or $\dfrac{1}{\sqrt{-a^2 - ab}} \tanh^{-1} \dfrac{\sqrt{-a^2 - ab}\, \tan x}{a + b},$

or $\dfrac{1}{\sqrt{-a^2 - ab}} \operatorname{ctnh}^{-1} \dfrac{\sqrt{-a^2 - ab}\, \tan x}{a + b}$

$$-\frac{\pi}{2} < x < \frac{\pi}{2}$$

**325.** $\int \dfrac{dx}{a \cos^2 x + b \sin^2 x} = \dfrac{1}{\sqrt{ab}} \tan^{-1} \dfrac{\sqrt{ab}\, \tan x}{a},$

or $\dfrac{1}{2\sqrt{-ab}} \log \dfrac{\sqrt{-ab}\, \tan x + a}{\sqrt{-ab}\, \tan x - a},$

or $\dfrac{1}{\sqrt{-ab}} \tanh^{-1} \dfrac{\sqrt{-ab}\, \tan x}{a},$

or $\dfrac{1}{\sqrt{-ab}} \operatorname{ctnh}^{-1} \dfrac{\sqrt{-ab}\, \tan x}{a}$

$$-\tfrac{1}{2}\pi < x < \tfrac{1}{2}\pi$$

**326.** $\int \dfrac{\sin x \cos x\, dx}{a \cos^2 x + b \sin^2 x} = \dfrac{1}{2(b - a)} \log (a \cos^2 x + b \sin^2 x)$

**327.** $\int \dfrac{dx}{(a + b \cos x + c \sin x)^n} = \int \dfrac{d(x - \alpha)}{[a + r \cos(x - \alpha)]^n},$

where $b = r \cos \alpha$ and $c = r \sin \alpha$

**328.** $\displaystyle\int \frac{dx}{a + b \cos x + c \sin x}$

$$= \frac{2}{\sqrt{a^2 - b^2 - c^2}} \tan^{-1} \frac{(a-b)\tan \frac{1}{2} x + c}{\sqrt{a^2 - b^2 - c^2}},$$

$$\text{or } \frac{1}{\sqrt{b^2 + c^2 - a^2}} \log \frac{(a-b)\tan \frac{1}{2} x + c - \sqrt{b^2 + c^2 - a^2}}{(a-b)\tan \frac{1}{2} x + c + \sqrt{b^2 + c^2 - a^2}},$$

$$\text{or } \frac{-2}{\sqrt{b^2 + c^2 - a^2}} \tanh^{-1} \frac{(a-b)\tan \frac{1}{2} x + c}{\sqrt{b^2 + c^2 - a^2}},$$

$$\text{or } \frac{-2}{\sqrt{b^2 + c^2 - a^2}} \operatorname{ctnh}^{-1} \frac{(a-b)\tan \frac{1}{2} x + c}{\sqrt{b^2 + c^2 - a^2}}$$

$$-\pi < x < \pi$$

**329.** $\displaystyle\int \frac{dx}{a(1 + \cos x) + c \sin x} = \frac{1}{c} \log \left( a + c \tan \frac{1}{2} x \right)$

**330.** $\displaystyle\int \frac{dx}{(a[1 + \cos x] + c \sin x)^2}$

$$= \frac{1}{c^3} \left[ \frac{c(a \sin x - c \cos x)}{a(1 + \cos x) + c \sin x} - a \log \left( a + c \tan \frac{1}{2} x \right) \right]$$

**331.** $\displaystyle\int \frac{(x + \sin x) dx}{1 + \cos x} = x \tan \frac{1}{2} x$

**332.** $\displaystyle\int \cos x \sqrt{1 - k^2 \sin^2 x}\, dx$

$$= \tfrac{1}{2} \sin x \sqrt{1 - k^2 \sin^2 x} + \frac{1}{2k} \sin^{-1}(k \sin x)$$

**333.** $\displaystyle\int \sin x \sqrt{1 - k^2 \sin^2 x}\, dx$

$$= -\tfrac{1}{2} \cos x \sqrt{1 - k^2 \sin^2 x} - \frac{1 - k^2}{2k} \log \left( k \cos x + \sqrt{1 - k^2 \sin^2 x} \right)$$

**334.** $\displaystyle\int \sin x (1 - k^2 \sin^2 x)^{\frac{3}{2}} dx = -\tfrac{1}{4} \cos x (1 - k^2 \sin^2 x)^{\frac{3}{2}}$

$$+ \tfrac{3}{4}(1 - k^2) \int \sin x \sqrt{1 - k^2 \sin^2 x}\, dx$$

**335.** $\int \dfrac{\cos x\, dx}{\sqrt{1 - k^2 \sin^2 x}} = \dfrac{1}{k} \sin^{-1}(k \sin x),$

or $\dfrac{1}{b} \log (b \sin x + \sqrt{1 + b^2 \sin^2 x})$, where $b^2 = - k^2$

**336.** $\int \dfrac{\sin x\, dx}{\sqrt{1 - k^2 \sin^2 x}} = - \dfrac{1}{k} \log (k \cos x + \sqrt{1 - k^2 \sin^2 x}),$

or $-\dfrac{1}{b} \sin^{-1} \dfrac{b \cos x}{\sqrt{1 + b^2}}$, where $b^2 = - k^2$

**337.** $\int \dfrac{\tan x\, dx}{\sqrt{1 - k^2 \sin^2 x}}$

$$= \dfrac{1}{2\sqrt{1 - k^2}} \log \left( \dfrac{\sqrt{1 - k^2 \sin^2 x} + \sqrt{1 - k^2}}{\sqrt{1 - k^2 \sin^2 x} - \sqrt{1 - k^2}} \right)$$

**338.** $\int \dfrac{x\, dx}{1 + \sin x} = - x \tan \tfrac{1}{2}(\tfrac{1}{2}\pi - x) + 2 \log \cos \tfrac{1}{2}(\tfrac{1}{2}\pi - x)$

**339.** $\int \dfrac{x\, dx}{1 - \sin x} = x \operatorname{ctn} \tfrac{1}{2}(\tfrac{1}{2}\pi - x) + 2 \log \sin \tfrac{1}{2}(\tfrac{1}{2}\pi - x)$

**340.** $\int \dfrac{x\, dx}{1 + \cos x} = x \tan \tfrac{1}{2} x + 2 \log \cos \tfrac{1}{2} x$

**341.** $\int \dfrac{x\, dx}{1 - \cos x} = - x \operatorname{ctn} \tfrac{1}{2} x + 2 \log \sin \tfrac{1}{2} x$

**342.** $\int \dfrac{\tan x\, dx}{\sqrt{a + b \tan^2 x}} = \dfrac{1}{\sqrt{b - a}} \cos^{-1} \left( \dfrac{\sqrt{b - a}}{\sqrt{b}} \cdot \cos x \right)$

**343.** $\int \dfrac{dx}{a + b \tan^2 x} = \dfrac{1}{a - b} \left[ x - \sqrt{\dfrac{b}{a}} \cdot \tan^{-1} \left( \sqrt{\dfrac{b}{a}} \cdot \tan x \right) \right]$

**344.** $\int \dfrac{\tan x\, dx}{a + b \tan x}$

$$= \dfrac{1}{a^2 + b^2} \left[ bx - a \log (a + b \tan x) + a \log \sec x \right]$$

**345.** $\int x \sin x\, dx = \sin x - x \cos x$

**346.** $\int x^2 \sin x \, dx = 2\, x \sin x - (x^2 - 2) \cos x$

**347.** $\int x^3 \sin x \, dx = (3\, x^2 - 6) \sin x - (x^3 - 6\, x) \cos x$

**348.** $\int x^m \sin x \, dx = -\, x^m \cos x + m \int x^{m-1} \cos x \, dx$

**349.** $\int x \cos x \, dx = \cos x + x \sin x$

**350.** $\int x^2 \cos x \, dx = 2\, x \cos x + (x^2 - 2) \sin x$

**351.** $\int x^3 \cos x \, dx = (3\, x^2 - 6) \cos x + (x^3 - 6\, x) \sin x$

**352.** $\int x^m \cos x \, dx = x^m \sin x - m \int x^{m-1} \sin x \, dx$

**353.** $\int \dfrac{\sin x}{x^m} \, dx = -\, \dfrac{1}{m-1} \cdot \dfrac{\sin x}{x^{m-1}} + \dfrac{1}{m-1} \int \dfrac{\cos x}{x^{m-1}} \, dx$

**354.** $\int \dfrac{\cos x}{x^m} \, dx = -\, \dfrac{1}{m-1} \cdot \dfrac{\cos x}{x^{m-1}} - \dfrac{1}{m-1} \int \dfrac{\sin x}{x^{m-1}} \, dx$

**355.** $\int \dfrac{x \, dx}{\sin^2 x} = -\, x \operatorname{ctn} x + \log \sin x$

**356.** $\int \dfrac{x \, dx}{\cos^2 x} = x \tan x + \log \cos x$

**357.** $n^2 \int x^m \sin^n x \, dx$

$\quad = x^{m-1} \sin^{n-1} x (m \sin x - nx \cos x)$

$\qquad + n(n-1) \int x^m \sin^{n-2} x \, dx - m(m-1) \int x^{m-2} \sin^n x \, dx$

**358.** $n^2 \int x^m \cos^n x \, dx$

$\quad = x^{m-1} \cos^{n-1} x (m \cos x + nx \sin x)$

$\qquad + n(n-1) \int x^m \cos^{n-2} x \, dx - m(m-1) \int x^{m-2} \cos^n x \, dx$

**359.** $\displaystyle\int \frac{x^m dx}{\sin^n x}$

$$= \frac{1}{(n-1)(n-2)}\left[ -\frac{x^{m-1}(m\sin x + (n-2)x\cos x)}{\sin^{n-1}x} + (n-2)^2\int \frac{x^m dx}{\sin^{n-2}x} + m(m-1)\int \frac{x^{m-2}dx}{\sin^{n-2}x} \right]$$

**360.** $\displaystyle\int \frac{x^m dx}{\cos^n x}$

$$= \frac{1}{(n-1)(n-2)}\left[ -\frac{x^{m-1}(m\cos x - (n-2)x\sin x)}{\cos^{n-1}x} + (n-2)^2\int \frac{x^m dx}{\cos^{n-2}x} + m(m-1)\int \frac{x^{m-2}dx}{\cos^{n-2}x} \right]$$

**361.** $\displaystyle\int \frac{\sin^n x\, dx}{x^m}$

$$= \frac{1}{(m-1)(m-2)}\left[ -\frac{\sin^{n-1}x((m-2)\sin x + nx\cos x)}{x^{m-1}} - n^2\int \frac{\sin^n x\, dx}{x^{m-2}} + n(n-1)\int \frac{\sin^{n-2}x\, dx}{x^{m-2}} \right]$$

**362.** $\displaystyle\int \frac{\cos^n x\, dx}{x^m}$

$$= \frac{1}{(m-1)(m-2)}\left[ \frac{\cos^{n-1}x(nx\sin x - (m-2)\cos x)}{x^{m-1}} - n^2\int \frac{\cos^n x\, dx}{x^{m-2}} + n(n-1)\int \frac{\cos^{n-2}x\, dx}{x^{m-2}} \right]$$

**363.** $\int x^p \sin^m x \cos^n x\, dx$

$= \frac{1}{(m+n)^2}\Big[ x^{p-1}\sin^m x \cos^{n-1} x\,(p\cos x + (m+n)x\sin x) + (n-1)(m+n)\int x^p \sin^m x \cos^{n-2} x\, dx$

$- mp\int x^{p-1}\sin^{m-1} x \cos^{n-1} x\, dx - p(p-1)\int x^{p-2}\sin^m x \cos^n x\, dx\Big]$

$= \frac{1}{(m+n)^2}\Big[ x^{p-1}\sin^{m-1} x \cos^n x\,(p\sin x - (m+n)x\cos x) + (m-1)(m+n)\int x^p \sin^{m-2} x \cos^n x\, dx$

$+ np\int x^{p-1}\sin^{m-1} x \cos^{n-1} x\, dx - p(p-1)\int x^{p-2}\sin^{m-2} x \cos^n x\, dx\Big]$

**364.** $\int \sin mx \sin nx\, dx = \frac{\sin (m-n)x}{2(m-n)} - \frac{\sin (m+n)x}{2(m+n)}$

**365.** $\int \sin mx \cos nx\, dx = -\frac{\cos (m-n)x}{2(m-n)} - \frac{\cos (m+n)x}{2(m+n)}$

**366.** $\int \cos mx \cos nx\, dx = \frac{\sin (m-n)x}{2(m-n)} + \frac{\sin (m+n)x}{2(m+n)}$

**367.** $\int \frac{dx}{a \cos^2 x + c \sin x \cdot \cos x + b \sin^2 x} = \int \frac{d(\tan x)}{a + c \tan x + b \tan^2 x}$

**368.** $\int \dfrac{(l + m \cos x + n \sin x)dx}{a + b \cos x + c \sin x} = \int \dfrac{(m \cos \delta + n \sin \delta) \cos z \cdot dz}{Z}$

$$+ \int \frac{l \cdot dz}{Z} - \int \frac{(m \sin \delta - n \cos \delta) \sin z \cdot dz}{Z},$$

where $b = q \cdot \cos \delta$, $c = q \cdot \sin \delta$, $z = x - \delta$, $Z = a + q \cdot \cos z$

**369.** $\int \sin (mx + a) \cdot \sin (nx + b)dx$

$$= \frac{\sin [mx - nx + a - b]}{2(m - n)} - \frac{\sin [mx + nx + a + b]}{2(m + n)}$$

**370.** $\int \cos (mx + a) \cdot \cos (nx + b)dx$

$$= \frac{\sin [mx + nx + a + b]}{2(m + n)} + \frac{\sin [mx - nx + a - b]}{2(m - n)}$$

**371.** $\int \sin (mx + a) \cdot \cos (nx + b)dx$

$$= - \frac{\cos [mx + nx + a + b]}{2(m + n)} - \frac{\cos [mx - nx + a - b]}{2(m - n)}$$

**372.** $\int \sin^2 mx \, dx = \dfrac{1}{2\,m} (mx - \sin mx \cos mx)$

**373.** $\int \cos^2 mx \, dx = \dfrac{1}{2\,m} (mx + \sin mx \cos mx)$

**374.** $\int \sin mx \cos mx \, dx = - \dfrac{1}{4\,m} \cos 2\,mx$

**375.** $\int \sin nx \sin^m x \, dx$

$$= \frac{1}{m + n} \left[ - \cos nx \sin^m x + m \int \cos (n - 1)x \cdot \sin^{m-1} x \, dx \right]$$

**376.** $\int \sin nx \cos^m x \, dx = \frac{1}{m+n} \left[ -\cos nx \cos^m x + m \int \sin (n-1)x \cdot \cos^{m-1}x \, dx \right]$

**377.** $\int \cos nx \sin^m x \, dx = \frac{1}{m+n} \left[ \sin nx \sin^m x - m \int \sin (n-1)x \cdot \sin^{m-1}x \, dx \right]$

**378.** $\int \cos nx \cos^m x \, dx = \frac{1}{m+n} \left[ \sin nx \cos^m x + m \int \cos (n-1)x \cdot \cos^{m-1}x \, dx \right]$

**379.** $\int \frac{\cos nx \, dx}{\cos^m x} = 2 \int \frac{\cos (n-1)x \, dx}{\cos^{m-1}x} - \int \frac{\cos (n-2)x \, dx}{\cos^m x}$

**380.** $\int \frac{\cos nx \, dx}{\sin^m x} = -2 \int \frac{\sin (n-1)x \, dx}{\sin^{m-1}x} + \int \frac{\cos (n-2)x \, dx}{\sin^m x}$

**381.** $\int \frac{\sin nx \, dx}{\sin^m x} = 2 \int \frac{\cos (n-1)x \, dx}{\sin^{m-1}x} + \int \frac{\sin (n-2)x \, dx}{\sin^m x}$

**382.** $\int \frac{\sin nx \, dx}{\cos^m x} = 2 \int \frac{\sin (n-1)x \, dx}{\cos^{m-1}x} - \int \frac{\sin (n-2)x \, dx}{\cos^m x}$

**383.** $\int \frac{(\cos px + i \sin px)dx}{\cos nx} = -2\,i \int \frac{z^{p+n-1}dz}{1+z^{2n}}$, where $z = \cos x + i \sin x$.

This yields two real integrals.

**384.** $\int \frac{(\cos px + i \sin px)dx}{\sin nx} = -2 \int \frac{z^{p+n-1}dz}{1-z^{2n}}$, where $z = \cos x + i \sin x$.

This yields two real integrals.

**385.** $\int \dfrac{(i \cos x - \sin x)\,dx}{\sqrt[n]{\cos nx}} = \int \dfrac{dy}{2 - y^n}$, where $y = \dfrac{\cos x + i \sin x}{\sqrt[n]{\cos nx}}$. This yields two real integrals.

**386.** $\int \sin ax \sin bx \sin cx \, dx$

$$= -\frac{1}{4}\left[\frac{\cos(a-b+c)x}{a-b+c} + \frac{\cos(b+c-a)x}{b+c-a} + \frac{\cos(a+b-c)x}{a+b-c} - \frac{\cos(a+b+c)x}{a+b+c}\right]$$

**387.** $\int \cos ax \cos bx \cos cx \, dx$

$$= \frac{1}{4}\left[\frac{\sin(a+b+c)x}{a+b+c} + \frac{\sin(b+c-a)x}{b+c-a} + \frac{\sin(a-b+c)x}{a-b+c} + \frac{\sin(a+b-c)x}{a+b-c}\right]$$

**388.** $\int \sin ax \cos bx \cos cx \, dx$

$$= -\frac{1}{4}\left[\frac{\cos(a+b+c)x}{a+b+c} - \frac{\cos(b+c-a)x}{b+c-a} + \frac{\cos(a+b-c)x}{a+b-c} + \frac{\cos(a+c-b)x}{a+c-b}\right]$$

**389.** $\int \cos ax \sin bx \sin cx \, dx$

$$= \frac{1}{4}\left[\frac{\sin(a+b-c)x}{a+b-c} + \frac{\sin(a-b+c)x}{a-b+c} - \frac{\sin(a+b+c)x}{a+b+c} - \frac{\sin(b+c-a)x}{b+c-a}\right]$$

## *Expressions Involving Inverse Trigonometric Functions*

**390.** $\int \sin^{-1}x \, dx = x \sin^{-1}x + \sqrt{1-x^2}$

**391.** $\int \cos^{-1}x \, dx = x \cos^{-1}x - \sqrt{1-x^2}$

**392.** $\int \tan^{-1}x \, dx = x \tan^{-1}x - \frac{1}{2} \log (1+x^2)$

**393.** $\int \text{ctn}^{-1}x \, dx = x \, \text{ctn}^{-1}x + \frac{1}{2} \log (1+x^2)$

**394.** $\int \sec^{-1}x \, dx = x \sec^{-1}x - \log (x + \sqrt{x^2-1})$

**395.** $\int \csc^{-1} x \, dx = x \csc^{-1}x + \log (x + \sqrt{x^2-1})$

**396.** $\int \text{versin}^{-1}x \, dx = (x-1) \, \text{versin}^{-1}x + \sqrt{2\,x - x^2}$

**397.** $\int (\sin^{-1}x)^2 dx = x(\sin^{-1}x)^2 - 2\,x + 2\sqrt{1-x^2} \sin^{-1}x$

**398.** $\int (\cos^{-1}x)^2 dx = x(\cos^{-1}x)^2 - 2\,x - 2\sqrt{1-x^2} \cos^{-1}x$

**399.** $\int x \sin^{-1}x \, dx = \frac{1}{4}[(2\,x^2 - 1) \sin^{-1}x + x\sqrt{1-x^2}]$

**400.** $\int x \cos^{-1}x \, dx = \frac{1}{4}[(2\,x^2 - 1) \cos^{-1}x - x\sqrt{1-x^2}]$

**401.** $\int x \tan^{-1}x \, dx = \frac{1}{2}[(x^2 + 1) \tan^{-1}x - x]$

**402.** $\int x \, \text{ctn}^{-1}x \, dx = \frac{1}{2}[(x^2 + 1) \, \text{ctn}^{-1}x + x]$

**403.** $\int x \sec^{-1}x \, dx = \frac{1}{2}[x^2 \sec^{-1}x - \sqrt{x^2-1}]$

**404.** $\int x \csc^{-1}x \, dx = \frac{1}{2}[x^2 \csc^{-1}x + \sqrt{x^2 - 1}]$

**405.** $\int x^n \sin^{-1}x \, dx = \frac{1}{n+1}\left(x^{n+1}\sin^{-1}x - \int \frac{x^{n+1}dx}{\sqrt{1-x^2}}\right)$

**406.** $\int x^n \cos^{-1}x \, dx = \frac{1}{n+1}\left(x^{n+1}\cos^{-1}x + \int \frac{x^{n+1}dx}{\sqrt{1-x^2}}\right)$

**407.** $\int x^n \tan^{-1}x \, dx = \frac{1}{n+1}\left(x^{n+1}\tan^{-1}x - \int \frac{x^{n+1}dx}{1+x^2}\right)$

**408.** $\int x^n \operatorname{ctn}^{-1}x \, dx = \frac{1}{n+1}\left(x^{n+1}\operatorname{ctn}^{-1}x + \int \frac{x^{n+1}dx}{1+x^2}\right)$

**409.** $\int \frac{\sin^{-1}x \, dx}{x^2} = \log\left(\frac{1 - \sqrt{1-x^2}}{x}\right) - \frac{\sin^{-1}x}{x}$

**410.** $\int \frac{\tan^{-1}x \, dx}{x^2} = \log x - \frac{1}{2}\log(1+x^2) - \frac{\tan^{-1}x}{x}$

## Expressions Involving Exponential Functions*

**411.** $\int e^{ax}dx = \frac{e^{ax}}{a}$

**412.** $\int f(e^{ax})dx = \int \frac{f(y)dy}{ay}, \; y = e^{ax}$

**413.** $\int xe^{ax}dx = \frac{e^{ax}}{a^2}(ax - 1)$

**414.** $\int x^2 e^{ax}dx = \frac{e^{ax}}{a^3}(a^2x^2 - 2ax + 2)$

**415.** $\int x^3 e^{ax}dx = \frac{e^{ax}}{a^4}(a^3x^3 - 3a^2x^2 + 6ax - 6)$

**416.** $\int x^4 e^{ax}dx = \frac{e^{ax}}{a^5}(a^4x^4 - 4a^3x^3 + 12a^2x^2 - 24ax + 24)$

*See also the special list of integrals useful in the theory of alternating currents, on pages 121–124.

**417.** $\int x^m e^{ax} dx = \dfrac{x^m e^{ax}}{a} - \dfrac{m}{a} \int x^{m-1} e^{ax} dx$

**418.** $\int x^n e^{f(x)} dx = \dfrac{1}{n+1} \left[ x^{n+1} e^{f(x)} - \int x^{n+1} f'(x) e^{f(x)} dx \right]$

**419.** $\int \dfrac{e^{ax}}{x^m} dx = \dfrac{1}{m-1} \left[ -\dfrac{e^{ax}}{x^{m-1}} + a \int \dfrac{e^{ax} dx}{x^{m-1}} \right],\ m \neq 1$

**420.** $\int a^{bx} dx = \dfrac{a^{bx}}{b \log a}$

**421.** $\int f(a^{bx}) dx = \int \dfrac{f(y) dy}{b \cdot \log a \cdot y},\ y = a^{bx}$

**422.** $\int x^n a^x dx = \dfrac{a^x x^n}{\log a} - \dfrac{na^x x^{n-1}}{(\log a)^2} + \dfrac{n(n-1)a^x x^{n-2}}{(\log a)^3} - \cdots + (-1)^n \dfrac{n(n-1)(n-2)\cdots 2.1\, a^x}{(\log a)^{n+1}}$

**423.** $\int \dfrac{a^x dx}{x^n} = \dfrac{1}{n-1} \left[ -\dfrac{a^x}{x^{n-1}} - \dfrac{a^x \cdot \log a}{(n-2)x^{n-2}} - \dfrac{a^x \cdot (\log a)^2}{(n-2)(n-3)x^{n-3}} - \cdots - \dfrac{a^x \cdot (\log a)^{n-2}}{(n-2)(n-3)\cdots 2 \cdot 1 \cdot x} + \dfrac{(\log a)^{n-1}}{(n-2)(n-3)\cdots 2 \cdot 1} \int \dfrac{a^x dx}{x} \right]$

**424.** $\int \dfrac{dx}{1+e^x} = \log \dfrac{e^x}{1+e^x}$

**425.** $\displaystyle\int \frac{dx}{a + be^{mx}} = \frac{1}{am}\left[mx - \log\left(a + be^{mx}\right)\right]$

**426.** $\displaystyle\int \frac{dx}{ae^{mx} + be^{-mx}} = \frac{1}{m\sqrt{ab}}\,\tan^{-1}\left(e^{mx}\sqrt{\frac{a}{b}}\right)$

**427.** $\displaystyle\int \frac{dx}{\sqrt{a + be^{mx}}} = \frac{-2}{m\sqrt{-a}}\,\sin^{-1}\sqrt{\frac{-a}{b}}\,e^{-\frac{1}{2}mx},$

$\qquad$ or $\dfrac{-2}{m\sqrt{a}}\log\left(\sqrt{a} + \sqrt{a + be^{mx}}\right) + \dfrac{x}{\sqrt{a}}$

**428.** $\displaystyle\int \frac{xe^x\,dx}{(1 + x)^2} = \frac{e^x}{1 + x}$

**429.** $\displaystyle\int x^n \cdot e^{ax^{n+1}}\,dx = \frac{e^{ax^{n+1}}}{a(n + 1)}$

**430.** $\displaystyle\int e^{ax}\sin px\,dx = \frac{e^{ax}(a\sin px - p\cos px)}{a^2 + p^2}$

**431.** $\displaystyle\int e^{ax}\cos px\,dx = \frac{e^{ax}(a\cos px + p\sin px)}{a^2 + p^2}$

**432.** $\displaystyle\int e^{ax}\log x\,dx = \frac{e^{ax}\log x}{a} - \frac{1}{a}\int \frac{e^{ax}\,dx}{x}$

**433.** $\displaystyle\int e^{ax}\sin^2 x\,dx = \frac{e^{ax}}{4 + a^2}\left(\sin x(a\sin x - 2\cos x) + \frac{2}{a}\right)$

**434.** $\displaystyle\int e^{ax}\cos^2 x\,dx = \frac{e^{ax}}{4 + a^2}\left(\cos x(2\sin x + a\cos x) + \frac{2}{a}\right)$

**435.** $\int e^{ax} \sin^n bx \, dx = \frac{1}{a^2 + n^2 b^2} \left( (a \sin bx - nb \cos bx) e^{ax} \sin^{n-1} bx + n(n-1) b^2 \int e^{ax} \sin^{n-2} bx \cdot dx \right)$

**436.** $\int e^{ax} \cos^n bx \, dx = \frac{1}{a^2 + n^2 b^2} \left( (a \cos bx + nb \sin bx) e^{ax} \cos^{n-1} bx + n(n-1) b^2 \int e^{ax} \cos^{n-2} bx \, dx \right)$

**437.** $\int e^{ax} \tan^n x \, dx = \frac{e^{ax} \tan^{n-1} x}{n-1} - \frac{a}{n-1} \int e^{ax} \tan^{n-1} x \, dx - \int e^{ax} \tan^{n-2} x \, dx$

**438.** $\int e^{ax} \operatorname{ctn}^n x \, dx = -\frac{e^{ax} \operatorname{ctn}^{n-1} x}{n-1} + \frac{a}{n-1} \int e^{ax} \operatorname{ctn}^{n-1} x \, dx - \int e^{ax} \operatorname{ctn}^{n-2} x \, dx$

**439.** $\int \frac{e^{ax} dx}{\sin^n x} = -e^{ax} \frac{a \sin x + (n-2) \cos x}{(n-1)(n-2) \sin^{n-1} x} + \frac{a^2 + (n-2)^2}{(n-1)(n-2)} \int \frac{e^{ax} dx}{\sin^{n-2} x}$

**440.** $\int \frac{e^{ax} dx}{\cos^n x} = -e^{ax} \frac{a \cos x - (n-2) \sin x}{(n-1)(n-2) \cos^{n-1} x} + \frac{a^2 + (n-2)^2}{(n-1)(n-2)} \int \frac{e^{ax} dx}{\cos^{n-2} x}$

**441.** $\int e^{ax} \sin^m x \cos^n x \, dx$

$$= \frac{1}{(m+n)^2 + a^2} \left[ e^{ax} \sin^m x \cos^{n-1} x (a \cos x + (m+n) \sin x) \right.$$

$$- ma \int e^{ax} \sin^{m-1} x \cos^{n-1} x \, dx$$

$$\left. + (n-1)(m+n) \int e^{ax} \sin^m x \cos^{n-2} x \, dx \right]$$

$$= \frac{1}{(m+n)^2 + a^2} \left[ e^{ax} \sin^{m-1} x \cos^n x (a \sin x - (m+n) \cos x) \right.$$

$$+ na \int e^{ax} \sin^{m-1} x \cos^{n-1} x \, dx$$

$$\left. + (m-1)(m+n) \int e^{ax} \sin^{m-2} x \cos^n x \, dx \right]$$

$$= \frac{1}{(m+n)^2 + a^2} \left[ [e^{ax} \cos^{n-1} x \sin^{m-1} x (a \sin x \cos x + n \sin^2 x \right.$$

$$- m \cos^2 x)] + n(n-1) \int e^{ax} \sin^m x \cos^{n-2} x \, dx$$

$$\left. + m(m-1) \int e^{ax} \sin^{m-2} x \cos^n x \, dx \right]$$

$$= \frac{1}{(m+n)^2 + a^2} \left[ [e^{ax} \sin^{m-1} x \cos^{n-1} x (a \sin x \cos x + n \sin^2 x \right.$$

$$- m \cos^2 x)] + n(n-1) \int e^{ax} \sin^{m-2} x \cos^{n-2} x \, dx$$

$$\left. + (m-n)(m+n-1) \int e^{ax} \sin^{m-2} x \cos^n x \, dx \right]$$

$$= \frac{1}{(m+n)^2 + a^2} \left[ [e^{ax} \sin^{m-1} x \cos^{n-1} x (a \sin x \cos x + n \sin^2 x \right.$$

$$- m \cos^2 x)] + m(m-1) \int e^{ax} \sin^{m-2} x \cos^{n-2} x \, dx$$

$$\left. - (m-n)(m+n-1) \int e^{ax} \sin^m x \cos^{n-2} x \, dx \right]$$

## *Expressions Involving Logarithmic Functions*

**442.** $\int \log x \, dx = x \log x - x$

**443.** $\int x^m \log x \, dx = x^{m+1} \left[ \dfrac{\log x}{m+1} - \dfrac{1}{(m+1)^2} \right]$

**444.** $\int (\log x)^n dx = x(\log x)^n - n \int (\log x)^{n-1} dx$

**445.** $\int x^m (\log x)^n dx = \dfrac{x^{m+1}(\log x)^n}{m+1} - \dfrac{n}{m+1} \int x^m (\log x)^{n-1} \, dx$

**446.** $\int \dfrac{(\log x)^n dx}{x} = \dfrac{(\log x)^{n+1}}{n+1}, \; n \neq -1$

**447.** $\int \dfrac{dx}{(\log x)^n} = -\dfrac{x}{(n-1)(\log x)^{n-1}} + \dfrac{1}{n-1} \int \dfrac{dx}{(\log x)^{n-1}}$

**448.** $\int \dfrac{x^m dx}{(\log x)^n} = -\dfrac{x^{m+1}}{(n-1)(\log x)^{n-1}} + \dfrac{m+1}{n-1} \int \dfrac{x^m dx}{(\log x)^{n-1}}$

**449.** $\int \dfrac{x^m dx}{\log x} = \int \dfrac{e^{-y}}{y} \, dy$, where $y = -(m+1) \log x$.

**450.** $\int \dfrac{dx}{x \log x} = \log (\log x)$

**451.** $\int \dfrac{(n-1)dx}{x(\log x)^n} = \dfrac{-1}{(\log x)^{n-1}}$

**452.** $\int \log (a^2 + x^2) dx = x \cdot \log (a^2 + x^2) - 2x + 2a \cdot \tan^{-1}\left(\dfrac{x}{a}\right)$

**453.** $\int (a + bx)^m \log x \, dx$

$= \dfrac{1}{b(m+1)} \left[ (a+bx)^{m+1} \log x - \int \dfrac{(a+bx)^{m+1}dx}{x} \right]$

**454.** $\int x^m \log (a + bx) dx$

$= \dfrac{1}{m+1} \left[ x^{m+1} \log (a+bx) - b \int \dfrac{x^{m+1}dx}{a+bx} \right]$

**455.** $\displaystyle\int \frac{\log x \, dx}{(a+bx)^m}$

$$= \frac{1}{b(m-1)}\left[-\frac{\log x}{(a+bx)^{m-1}} + \int \frac{dx}{x(a+bx)^{m-1}}\right]$$

**456.** $\displaystyle\int \frac{\log x \, dx}{a+bx} = \frac{1}{b}\log x \cdot \log (a+bx) - \frac{1}{b}\int \frac{\log (a+bx)dx}{x}$

**457.** $\displaystyle\int (a+bx) \log x \, dx = \frac{(a+bx)^2}{2b}\log x - \frac{a^2 \log x}{2b} - ax - \frac{1}{4}bx^2$

**458.** $\displaystyle\int \frac{\log x \, dx}{\sqrt{a+bx}}$

$$= \frac{2}{b}\left[(\log x - 2)\sqrt{a+bx} + \sqrt{a}\log (\sqrt{a+bx} + \sqrt{a})\right.$$
$$\left. - \sqrt{a}\log (\sqrt{a+bx} - \sqrt{a})\right], \text{ if } a > 0$$

$$= \frac{2}{b}\left[(\log x - 2)\sqrt{a+bx} + 2\sqrt{-a}\tan^{-1}\sqrt{\frac{a+bx}{-a}}\right], \text{ if } a < 0$$

**459.** $\displaystyle\int \sin \log x \, dx = \frac{1}{2}x[\sin \log x - \cos \log x]$

**460.** $\displaystyle\int \cos \log x \, dx = \frac{1}{2}x[\sin \log x + \cos \log x]$

## Expressions Involving Hyperbolic Functions

**461.** $\displaystyle\int \sinh x \, dx = \cosh x$

**462.** $\displaystyle\int \cosh x \, dx = \sinh x$

**463.** $\displaystyle\int \tanh x \, dx = \log \cosh x$

**464.** $\displaystyle\int \operatorname{ctnh} x \, dx = \log \sinh x$

**465.** $\displaystyle\int \operatorname{sech} x \, dx = 2 \tan^{-1}e^x$

**466.** $\int \operatorname{csch} x \, dx = \log \tanh \dfrac{x}{2}$

**467.** $\int \sinh^n x \, dx = \dfrac{1}{n} \sinh^{n-1}x \cdot \cosh x - \dfrac{n-1}{n} \int \sinh^{n-2}x \, dx$

$$= \dfrac{1}{n+1} \sinh^{n+1}x \cosh x - \dfrac{n+2}{n+1} \int \sinh^{n+2}x \, dx$$

**468.** $\int \cosh^n x \, dx = \dfrac{1}{n} \sinh x \cdot \cosh^{n-1}x + \dfrac{n-1}{n} \int \cosh^{n-2}x \, dx$

$$= -\dfrac{1}{n+1} \sinh x \cosh^{n+1}x + \dfrac{n+2}{n+1} \int \cosh^{n+2}x \, dx$$

**469.** $\int x \sinh x \, dx = x \cosh x - \sinh x$

**470.** $\int x \cosh x \, dx = x \sinh x - \cosh x$

**471.** $\int x^2 \sinh x \, dx = (x^2 + 2) \cosh x - 2 \, x \sinh x$

**472.** $\int x^n \sinh x \, dx = x^n \cosh x - nx^{n-1} \sinh x$

$$+ \, n(n-1) \int x^{n-2} \sinh x \, dx$$

**473.** $\int \sinh^2 x \, dx = \frac{1}{2}(\sinh x \cosh x - x)$

**474.** $\int \sinh x \cdot \cosh x \, dx = \frac{1}{4} \cosh (2 \, x)$

**475.** $\int \cosh^2 x \, dx = \frac{1}{2}(\sinh x \cosh x + x)$

**476.** $\int \tanh^2 x \, dx = x - \tanh x$

**477.** $\int \operatorname{ctnh}^2 x \, dx = x - \operatorname{ctnh} x$

**478.** $\int \operatorname{sech}^2 x \, dx = \tanh x$

**479.** $\int \text{csch}^2x \, dx = - \text{ctnh } x$

**480.** $\int \sinh^{-1}x \, dx = x \sinh^{-1}x - \sqrt{1 + x^2}$

**481.** $\int \cosh^{-1}x \, dx = x \cosh^{-1}x - \sqrt{x^2 - 1}$

**482.** $\int \tanh^{-1}x \, dx = x \tanh^{-1}x + \frac{1}{2} \log (1 - x^2)$

**483.** $\int x \sinh^{-1}x \, dx = \frac{1}{4}[(2 \, x^2 + 1) \sinh^{-1}x - x\sqrt{1 + x^2}]$

**484.** $\int x \cosh^{-1}x \, dx = \frac{1}{4}[(2 \, x^2 - 1) \cosh^{-1}x - x\sqrt{x^2 - 1}]$

**485.** $\int \dfrac{dx}{\cosh a + \cosh x}$
$$= \text{csch } a[\log \cosh \tfrac{1}{2}(x + a) - \log \cosh \tfrac{1}{2}(x - a)]$$
$$= 2 \, \text{csch } a \cdot \tanh^{-1}(\tanh \tfrac{1}{2} x \cdot \tanh \tfrac{1}{2} a)$$

**486.** $\int \dfrac{dx}{\cos a + \cosh x} = 2 \csc a \cdot \tan^{-1}(\tanh \tfrac{1}{2} x \cdot \tan \tfrac{1}{2} a)$

**487.** $\int \dfrac{dx}{1 + \cos a \cdot \cosh x} = 2 \csc a \cdot \tanh^{-1}(\tanh \tfrac{1}{2} x \cdot \tan \tfrac{1}{2} a)$

**488.** $\int \sinh x \cdot \cos x \, dx = \frac{1}{2}(\cosh x \cdot \cos x + \sinh x \cdot \sin x)$

**489.** $\int \cosh x \cdot \cos x \, dx = \frac{1}{2}(\sinh x \cdot \cos x + \cosh x \cdot \sin x)$

**490.** $\int \sinh x \cdot \sin x \, dx = \frac{1}{2}(\cosh x \cdot \sin x - \sinh x \cdot \cos x)$

**491.** $\int \cosh x \cdot \sin x \, dx = \frac{1}{2}(\sinh x \cdot \sin x - \cosh x \cdot \cos x)$

**492.** $\int \sinh (mx) \sinh (nx) dx$
$$= \frac{1}{m^2 - n^2}\left[ m \sinh (nx) \cosh (mx) - n \cosh (nx) \sinh (mx) \right]$$

**493.** $\int \cosh{(mx)} \sinh{(nx)}dx$

$$= \frac{1}{m^2 - n^2}\Big[ m \sinh{(nx)} \sinh{(mx)} - n \cosh{(nx)} \cosh{(mx)} \Big]$$

**494.** $\int \cosh{(mx)} \cosh{(nx)}dx$

$$= \frac{1}{m^2 - n^2}\Big[ m \sinh{(mx)} \cosh{(nx)} - n \sinh{(nx)} \cosh{(mx)} \Big]$$

# PART II

# Definite
# Integrals*

## MISCELLANEOUS DEFINITE INTEGRALS

**495.** $\displaystyle\int_0^\infty \frac{a\,dx}{a^2+x^2} = \frac{\pi}{2}$, if $a > 0$; $0$, if $a = 0$; $-\frac{\pi}{2}$, if $a < 0$.

**496.** $\displaystyle\int_0^\infty x^{a-1}e^{-x}dx = \int_0^1 \left[\log\frac{1}{x}\right]^{a-1}dx = \Gamma(a)$ $\qquad a > 0$

[For a discussion of the gamma function, $\Gamma(x)$, see pages 94, 95. For tables of values, see pages 126, 127.]

**497.** $\displaystyle\int_0^1 x^{a-1}(1-x)^{b-1}dx = \int_0^\infty \frac{x^{a-1}dx}{(1+x)^{a+b}} = \frac{\Gamma(a)\Gamma(b)}{\Gamma(a+b)}$

$\qquad\qquad a > 0,\ b > 0$

**498.** $\displaystyle\int_0^{\frac{\pi}{2}}\sin^n x\,dx = \int_0^{\frac{\pi}{2}}\cos^n x\,dx$

$\qquad = \dfrac{1\cdot 3\cdot 5\cdots (n-1)}{2\cdot 4\cdot 6\cdots (n)}\cdot\dfrac{\pi}{2}$, if $n$ is an even integer,

$\qquad = \dfrac{2\cdot 4\cdot 6\cdots (n-1)}{1\cdot 3\cdot 5\cdot 7\cdots n}$, if $n$ is an odd integer,

$\qquad = \tfrac{1}{2}\sqrt{\pi}\ \dfrac{\Gamma\left(\dfrac{n+1}{2}\right)}{\Gamma\left(\dfrac{n}{2}+1\right)}$, for any value of $n$ greater than $-1$.

*For very complete lists of definite integrals, see D. Bierens de Haan, *Nouvelles tables d'intégrales définies*, Leyden, 1867; corrected edition, New York, 1939.

**499.** $\int_0^\infty \dfrac{\sin ax\, dx}{x} = \dfrac{\pi}{2}$, if $a > 0$; $0$, if $a = 0$; $-\dfrac{\pi}{2}$, if $a < 0$

**500.** $\int_0^\infty \dfrac{\sin x \cdot \cos ax\, dx}{x} = 0$, if $a < -1$ or $a > 1$;

$\qquad \cdot \quad \dfrac{\pi}{4}$, if $a = -1$ or $a = 1$; $\dfrac{\pi}{2}$, if $-1 < a < 1$

**501.** $\int_0^\infty \dfrac{\sin^2 x\, dx}{x^2} = \dfrac{\pi}{2}$

**502.** $\int_0^\infty \cos (x^2)dx = \int_0^\infty \sin (x^2)dx = \tfrac{1}{2}\sqrt{\dfrac{\pi}{2}}$

**503.** $\int_0^\pi \sin kx \cdot \sin mx\, dx = \int_0^\pi \cos kx \cdot \cos mx\, dx = 0$,

$\qquad$ if $k$ and $m$ are unequal positive integers

**504.** $\int_0^\pi \sin^2 mx\, dx = \int_0^\pi \cos^2 mx\, dx = \dfrac{\pi}{2}$, if $m$ is a positive integer

**505.** $\int_0^\infty \dfrac{\cos ax\, dx}{1 + x^2} = \dfrac{\pi}{2} \cdot e^{-a}$ $\qquad\qquad\qquad a > 0$

**506.** $\int_0^\infty \dfrac{\cos x\, dx}{\sqrt{x}} = \int_0^\infty \dfrac{\sin x\, dx}{\sqrt{x}} = \sqrt{\dfrac{\pi}{2}}$

**507.** $\int_0^\infty e^{-a^2 x^2}dx = \dfrac{1}{2a}\sqrt{\pi} = \dfrac{1}{2a}\Gamma(\tfrac{1}{2})$ $\qquad\qquad a > 0$

**508.** $\int_0^\infty x^n e^{-ax}dx = \dfrac{n!}{a^{n+1}}$,

$\qquad$ if $n$ is a positive integer or zero, and $a > 0$

$$= \dfrac{\Gamma(n+1)}{a^{n+1}},$$

$\qquad$ for any value of $n$ greater than $-1$, and $a > 0$

**509.** $\int_0^\infty x^{2n} e^{-ax^2}dx = \dfrac{1 \cdot 3 \cdot 5 \cdots (2n-1)}{2^{n+1}a^n}\sqrt{\dfrac{\pi}{a}}$ $\qquad a > 0$

**510.** $\int_0^\infty e^{-x^2 - \frac{a^2}{x^2}}dx = \dfrac{e^{-2a}\sqrt{\pi}}{2}$ $\qquad\qquad\qquad a \geqq 0$

**511.** $\int_0^\infty e^{-ax}\sqrt{x}\,dx = \frac{1}{2a}\sqrt{\frac{\pi}{a}}$          $a > 0$

**512.** $\int_0^\infty \frac{e^{-ax}}{\sqrt{x}}\,dx = \sqrt{\frac{\pi}{a}}$          $a > 0$

**513.** $\int_0^\infty \frac{dx}{e^{nx} + e^{-nx}} = \frac{\pi}{4\,n}$

**514.** $\int_0^\infty \frac{x\,dx}{e^{nx} - e^{-nx}} = \frac{\pi^2}{8\,n^2}$

In the next six formulas, $m$ and $n$ are positive integers.

**515.** $\int_0^{\pi i} \sinh(mx) \cdot \sinh(nx)dx = \int_0^{\pi i} \cosh(mx) \cdot \cosh(nx)dx$

$$= 0, \text{ if } m \text{ is different from } n.$$

**516.** $\int_0^{\pi i} \cosh^2(mx)dx = -\int_0^{\pi i} \sinh^2(mx)dx = \frac{\pi i}{2}$

**517.** $\int_{-\pi i}^{+\pi i} \sinh(mx)dx = 0$

**518.** $\int_0^{\pi i} \cosh(mx)dx = 0$

**519.** $\int_{-\pi e}^{\pi i} \sinh(mx)\cosh(nx)dx = 0$

**520.** $\int_0^{\pi i} \sinh(mx)\cosh(mx)dx = 0$

**521.** $\int_0^\infty e^{-ax}\cos bx\,dx = \frac{a}{a^2 + b^2}$          $a > 0$

**522.** $\int_0^\infty e^{-ax}\sin bx\,dx = \frac{b}{a^2 + b^2}$          $a > 0$

**523.** $\int_0^\infty e^{-a^2x^2}\cos bx\,dx = \frac{\sqrt{\pi}\cdot e^{-\frac{b^2}{4a^2}}}{2\,a}$          $a > 0$

**524.** $\int_0^\infty x^{a-1}\cos bx\,dx = \frac{\Gamma(a)}{b^a}\cos\frac{\pi a}{2}$          $0 < a < 1, b > 0$

**525.** $\displaystyle\int_0^\infty x^{a-1} \sin bx \, dx = \frac{\Gamma(a)}{b^a} \sin \frac{\pi a}{2} \qquad 0 < |a| < 1, b > 0$

**526.** $\displaystyle\int_0^1 \frac{\log x}{1-x} \, dx = -\frac{\pi^2}{6}$

**527.** $\displaystyle\int_0^1 \frac{\log x}{1+x} \, dx = -\frac{\pi^2}{12}$

**528.** $\displaystyle\int_0^1 \frac{\log x}{1-x^2} \, dx = -\frac{\pi^2}{8}$

**529.** $\displaystyle\int_0^1 \log\left(\frac{1+x}{1-x}\right) \cdot \frac{dx}{x} = \frac{\pi^2}{4}$

**530.** $\displaystyle\int_0^1 \frac{\log x \, dx}{\sqrt{1-x^2}} = -\frac{\pi}{2} \log 2$

**531.** $\displaystyle\int_0^1 \frac{(x^p - x^q) dx}{\log x} = \log \frac{p+1}{q+1}$, if $p+1 > 0, q+1 > 0$

**532.** $\displaystyle\int_0^1 (\log x)^n dx = (-1)^n \cdot n!$

**533.** $\displaystyle\int_0^1 \left(\log \frac{1}{x}\right)^{\frac{1}{2}} dx = \frac{\sqrt{\pi}}{2}$

**534.** $\displaystyle\int_0^1 \left(\log \frac{1}{x}\right)^n dx = n!$

**535.** $\displaystyle\int_0^1 \frac{dx}{\sqrt{\log\left(\frac{1}{x}\right)}} = \sqrt{\pi}$

**536.** $\displaystyle\int_0^1 x^m \left(\log \frac{1}{x}\right)^n dx = \frac{\Gamma(n+1)}{(m+1)^{n+1}}$, if $m+1 > 0, n+1 > 0$

**537.** $\displaystyle\int_0^\infty \log\left(\frac{e^x+1}{e^x-1}\right) dx = \frac{\pi^2}{4}$

**538.** $\displaystyle\int_0^{\frac{\pi}{2}} \log \sin x \, dx = \int_0^{\frac{\pi}{2}} \log \cos x \, dx = -\frac{\pi}{2} \cdot \log 2$

**539.** $\int_0^\pi x \cdot \log \sin x \, dx = -\dfrac{\pi^2}{2} \log 2$

**540.** $\int_0^\pi \log (a \pm b \cos x) dx = \pi \log \left(\dfrac{a + \sqrt{a^2 - b^2}}{2}\right) \qquad a \geqq b$

**541.** $\int_0^\infty \left[\dfrac{1}{1 + x} - e^{-x}\right] \dfrac{dx}{x} = \gamma$

**542.** $\int_0^1 [1 - e^{-x} - e^{-1/x}] \dfrac{dx}{x} = \gamma,$

where $\gamma$ is Euler's constant (see page 95)

## ELLIPTIC INTEGRALS*

$$F(\phi, k) \equiv \int_0^\phi \frac{d\theta}{\sqrt{1 - k^2 \sin^2\theta}} \equiv \int_0^x \frac{dz}{\sqrt{1 - z^2}\sqrt{1 - k^2 z^2}} \equiv u,$$

where $k^2 < 1$, $x = \sin \phi$

$$E(\phi, k) \equiv \int_0^\phi \sqrt{1 - k^2 \sin^2\theta} \cdot d\theta$$

$$\Pi(\phi, n, k) \equiv \int_0^\phi \frac{d\theta}{(1 + n \sin^2\theta)\sqrt{1 - k^2 \sin^2\theta}}$$

$\phi \equiv \operatorname{am} u, \sin \phi \equiv x \equiv \operatorname{sn} u, \cos \phi \equiv \sqrt{1 - x^2} \equiv \operatorname{cn} u, \tan\phi \equiv \operatorname{tn} u,$

$\Delta\phi \equiv \sqrt{1 - k^2 \sin^2\phi} \equiv \sqrt{1 - k^2 x^2} \equiv \operatorname{dn} u, \ k'^2 \equiv 1 - k^2$

$u \equiv \operatorname{am}^{-1}(\phi, k) \equiv \operatorname{sn}^{-1}(x, k) \equiv \operatorname{cn}^{-1}(\sqrt{1 - x^2}, k)$

$$\equiv \operatorname{dn}^{-1}(\sqrt{1 - k^2 x^2}, k)$$

$K \equiv F(\tfrac{1}{2} \pi, k), K' \equiv F(\tfrac{1}{2} \pi, k'), E \equiv E(\tfrac{1}{2} \pi, k), E' \equiv E(\tfrac{1}{2} \pi, k')$

If $k_0 = \dfrac{2 k^{\frac{1}{2}}}{1 + k}$ and $\tan \phi \equiv \dfrac{\sin 2 \omega}{k + \cos 2 \omega},$

$$F(\phi, k) \equiv \frac{2}{1 + k} F(\omega, k_0)$$

*See also the section on elliptic functions, pages 89–91, and tables of values on pages 133–135.

**543.** $\displaystyle\int_0^{\frac{\pi}{2}} \frac{d\theta}{\sqrt{1-k^2\sin^2\theta}} = \frac{\pi}{2}\left[1 + \left(\tfrac{1}{2}\right)^2 k^2 + \left(\frac{1\cdot3}{2\cdot4}\right)^2 k^4 + \left(\frac{1\cdot3\cdot5}{2\cdot4\cdot6}\right)^2 k^6 + \dots\right] = K$, if $k^2 < 1$

**544.** $\displaystyle\int_0^{\frac{\pi}{2}} \sqrt{1-k^2\sin^2\theta}\cdot d\theta = \frac{\pi}{2}\left[1 - \left(\tfrac{1}{2}\right)^2 k^2 - \left(\frac{1\cdot3}{2\cdot4}\right)^2 \frac{k^4}{3} - \left(\frac{1\cdot3\cdot5}{2\cdot4\cdot6}\right)^2 \frac{k^6}{5} - \dots\right] = E$, if $k^2 < 1$

**545.** $\displaystyle\int_0^{\phi} \frac{d\theta}{\sqrt{1-k^2\sin^2\theta}} = \frac{2}{\pi}\phi\cdot K - \sin\phi\cos\phi\left[\frac{1\cdot1}{2\cdot2}k^2 + \frac{1\cdot3}{2\cdot4}A_4 k^4 + \frac{1\cdot3\cdot5}{2\cdot4\cdot6}A_6 k^6 + \dots\right]$

$= F(\phi, k)$, where $A_4 \equiv \tfrac{1}{4}\sin^2\phi + \dfrac{3}{2\cdot4}$, $A_6 \equiv \tfrac{1}{6}\sin^4\phi + \dfrac{5}{6\cdot4}\sin^2\phi + \dfrac{5\cdot3}{6\cdot4\cdot2}$,

$A_8 \equiv \tfrac{1}{8}\sin^6\phi + \dfrac{7}{8\cdot6}\sin^4\phi + \dfrac{7\cdot5}{8\cdot6\cdot4}\sin^2\phi + \dfrac{7\cdot5\cdot3}{8\cdot6\cdot4\cdot2}$, etc.

**546.** $\displaystyle\int_0^{\phi} \sqrt{1-k^2\sin^2\theta}\cdot d\theta = \frac{2}{\pi}\phi\cdot E + \sin\phi\cos\phi\left[\frac{1\cdot1}{2\cdot2}k^2 + \frac{1}{2\cdot4}k^4 A_4 + \frac{1\cdot3}{2\cdot4\cdot6}k^6 A_6 + \dots\right]$

$= E(\phi, k)$

**547.** Since $\sin^2\theta \equiv \dfrac{1}{k^2} - \dfrac{1}{k^2}(1 - k^2\cdot\sin^2\theta)$,

$\displaystyle\int_0^{\frac{\pi}{2}} \frac{\sin^2\theta\cdot d\theta}{\sqrt{1-k^2\sin^2\theta}} = \frac{1}{k^2}\int_0^{\frac{\pi}{2}}\frac{d\theta}{\sqrt{1-k^2\sin^2\theta}} - \frac{1}{k^2}\int_0^{\frac{\pi}{2}}\sqrt{1-k^2\sin^2\theta}\cdot d\theta$

**548.** $\displaystyle\int_0^{x} \frac{dx}{\sqrt{(1-x^2)(1-k^2x^2)}} = \mathrm{sn}^{-1}(x, k) = F(\sin^{-1}x, k)$      $0 < x < 1$

**549.** $\int_x^1 \dfrac{dx}{\sqrt{(1-x^2)(k'^2+k^2x^2)}} = \text{cn}^{-1}(x, k)$

$\qquad = F(\cos^{-1}x, k) = \text{sn}^{-1}(\sqrt{1-x^2}, k) \qquad 0 < x < 1$

**550.** $\int_x^1 \dfrac{dx}{\sqrt{(1-x^2)(x^2-k'^2)}} = \text{dn}^{-1}(x, k)$

$\qquad = F(\Delta^{-1}x, k) = \text{sn}^{-1}\left(\dfrac{1}{k}\sqrt{1-x^2}, k\right) \qquad 0 < x < 1$

**551.** $\int_0^x \dfrac{dx}{\sqrt{(1+x^2)(1+k'^2x^2)}} = \text{tn}^{-1}(x, k)$

$\qquad = F(\tan^{-1}x, k) = \text{sn}^{-1}\left(\dfrac{x}{\sqrt{1+x^2}}, k\right) \qquad 0 < x < 1$

**552.** $\int_0^x \dfrac{dx}{\sqrt{x(1-x)(1-k^2x)}} = 2\,\text{sn}^{-1}(\sqrt{x}, k)$

$\qquad = 2\,F(\sin^{-1}\sqrt{x}, k) \qquad 0 < x < 1$

**553.** $\int_x^1 \dfrac{dx}{\sqrt{x(1-x)(k'^2+k^2x)}} = 2\,\text{cn}^{-1}(\sqrt{x}, k)$

$\qquad = 2\,F(\cos^{-1}\sqrt{x}, k) = 2\,\text{sn}^{-1}(\sqrt{1-x}, k) \qquad 0 < x < 1$

**554.** $\int_x^1 \dfrac{dx}{\sqrt{x(1-x)(x-k'^2)}} = 2\,\text{dn}^{-1}(\sqrt{x}, k)$

$\qquad = 2\,F(\Delta^{-1}\sqrt{x}, k) = 2\,\text{sn}^{-1}\left(\dfrac{1}{k}\sqrt{1-x}, k\right), \quad 0 < x < 1$

**555.** $\int_0^x \dfrac{dx}{\sqrt{x(1+x)(1+k'^2x)}} = 2\,\text{tn}^{-1}(\sqrt{x}, k)$

$\qquad = 2\,F(\tan^{-1}\sqrt{x}, k) = 2\,\text{sn}^{-1}\left(\sqrt{\dfrac{x}{1+x}}, k\right), \quad 0 < x < 1$

**556.** $\int_0^x \dfrac{dx}{\sqrt{(a^2-x^2)(b^2-x^2)}} = \dfrac{1}{a}\,\text{sn}^{-1}\left(\dfrac{x}{b}, \dfrac{b}{a}\right), \quad a > b > x > 0$

**557.** $\int_x^\infty \dfrac{dx}{\sqrt{(x^2-a^2)(x^2-b^2)}} = \dfrac{1}{a}\,\text{sn}^{-1}\left(\dfrac{a}{x}, \dfrac{b}{a}\right) \qquad x > a > b$

**558.** $\int_x^b \dfrac{dx}{\sqrt{(a^2+x^2)(b^2-x^2)}}$

$$= \frac{1}{\sqrt{a^2+b^2}} \, \mathrm{cn}^{-1}\left(\frac{x}{b}, \frac{b}{\sqrt{a^2+b^2}}\right) \qquad\qquad b > x > 0$$

**559.** $\int_b^x \dfrac{dx}{\sqrt{(a^2+x^2)(x^2-b^2)}}$

$$= \frac{1}{\sqrt{a^2+b^2}} \, \mathrm{cn}^{-1}\left(\frac{b}{x}, \frac{a}{\sqrt{a^2+b^2}}\right) \qquad\qquad x > b > 0$$

**560.** $\int_x^a \dfrac{dx}{\sqrt{(a^2-x^2)(x^2-b^2)}}$

$$= \frac{1}{a} \, \mathrm{sn}^{-1}\left(\sqrt{\frac{a^2-x^2}{a^2-b^2}}, \sqrt{\frac{a^2-b^2}{a^2}}\right) \qquad\qquad a > x > b$$

**561.** $\int_0^x \dfrac{dx}{\sqrt{(x^2+a^2)(x^2+b^2)}}$

$$= \frac{1}{a} \, \mathrm{tn}^{-1}\left(\frac{x}{b}, \sqrt{\frac{a^2-b^2}{a^2}}\right) \qquad\qquad x > 0$$

In Formulas 562–569, $a > \beta > \gamma$

**562.** $\int_x^\infty \dfrac{dx}{\sqrt{(x-a)(x-\beta)(x-\gamma)}}$

$$= \frac{2}{\sqrt{a-\gamma}} \, \mathrm{sn}^{-1}\left(\sqrt{\frac{a-\gamma}{x-\gamma}}, \sqrt{\frac{\beta-\gamma}{a-\gamma}}\right) \qquad\qquad x > a$$

**563.** $\int_a^x \dfrac{dx}{\sqrt{(x-a)(x-\beta)(x-\gamma)}}$

$$= \frac{2}{\sqrt{a-\gamma}} \, \mathrm{sn}^{-1}\left(\sqrt{\frac{x-a}{x-\beta}}, \sqrt{\frac{\beta-\gamma}{a-\gamma}}\right) \qquad\qquad x > a$$

**564.** $\int_x^a \dfrac{dx}{\sqrt{(a-x)(x-\beta)(x-\gamma)}}$

$$= \frac{2}{\sqrt{a-\gamma}} \, \mathrm{sn}^{-1}\left(\sqrt{\frac{a-x}{a-\beta}}, \sqrt{\frac{a-\beta}{a-\gamma}}\right) \qquad\qquad a > x > \beta$$

**565.** $\int_\beta^x \dfrac{dx}{\sqrt{(a-x)(x-\beta)(x-\gamma)}}$

$$= \dfrac{2}{\sqrt{a-\gamma}} \operatorname{sn}^{-1}\left(\sqrt{\dfrac{a-\gamma}{a-\beta}\cdot\dfrac{x-\beta}{x-\gamma}}, \sqrt{\dfrac{a-\beta}{a-\gamma}}\right), \quad a > x > \beta$$

**566.** $\int_x^\beta \dfrac{dx}{\sqrt{(a-x)(\beta-x)(x-\gamma)}}$

$$= \dfrac{2}{\sqrt{a-\gamma}} \operatorname{sn}^{-1}\left(\sqrt{\dfrac{a-\gamma}{\beta-\gamma}\cdot\dfrac{\beta-x}{a-x}}, \sqrt{\dfrac{\beta-\gamma}{a-\gamma}}\right), \quad \beta > x > \gamma$$

**567.** $\int_\gamma^x \dfrac{dx}{\sqrt{(a-x)(\beta-x)(x-\gamma)}}$

$$= \dfrac{2}{\sqrt{a-\gamma}} \operatorname{sn}^{-1}\left(\sqrt{\dfrac{x-\gamma}{\beta-\gamma}}, \sqrt{\dfrac{\beta-\gamma}{a-\gamma}}\right) \qquad \beta > x > \gamma$$

**568.** $\int_x^\gamma \dfrac{dx}{\sqrt{(a-x)(\beta-x)(\gamma-x)}}$

$$= \dfrac{2}{\sqrt{a-\gamma}} \operatorname{sn}^{-1}\left(\sqrt{\dfrac{\gamma-x}{\beta-x}}, \sqrt{\dfrac{a-\beta}{a-\gamma}}\right) \qquad \gamma > x$$

**569.** $\int_{-\infty}^x \dfrac{dx}{\sqrt{(a-x)(\beta-x)(\gamma-x)}}$

$$= \dfrac{2}{\sqrt{a-\gamma}} \operatorname{sn}^{-1}\left(\sqrt{\dfrac{a-\gamma}{a-x}}, \sqrt{\dfrac{a-\beta}{a-\gamma}}\right) \qquad \gamma > x$$

In Formulas 570–576, $a > \beta > \gamma > \delta$

**570.** $\int_a^x \dfrac{dx}{\sqrt{(x-a)(x-\beta)(x-\gamma)(x-\delta)}}$

$$= \dfrac{2}{\sqrt{(a-\gamma)(\beta-\delta)}} \operatorname{sn}^{-1}\left(\sqrt{\dfrac{\beta-\delta}{a-\delta}\cdot\dfrac{x-a}{x-\beta}}, \sqrt{\dfrac{\beta-\gamma}{a-\gamma}\cdot\dfrac{a-\delta}{\beta-\delta}}\right)$$
$$x > a$$

**571.** $\displaystyle\int_x^a \frac{dx}{\sqrt{(a-x)(x-\beta)(x-\gamma)(x-\delta)}}$

$$=\frac{2}{\sqrt{(a-\gamma)(\beta-\delta)}}\,\mathrm{sn}^{-1}\left(\sqrt{\frac{\beta-\delta}{a-\beta}\cdot\frac{a-x}{x-\delta}},\ \sqrt{\frac{a-\beta}{a-\gamma}\cdot\frac{\gamma-\delta}{\beta-\delta}}\right)$$

$$a>x>\beta$$

**572.** $\displaystyle\int_\beta^x \frac{dx}{\sqrt{(a-x)(x-\beta)(x-\gamma)(x-\delta)}}$

$$=\frac{2}{\sqrt{(a-\gamma)(\beta-\delta)}}\,\mathrm{sn}^{-1}\left(\sqrt{\frac{a-\gamma}{a-\beta}\cdot\frac{x-\beta}{x-\gamma}},\ \sqrt{\frac{a-\beta}{a-\gamma}\cdot\frac{\gamma-\delta}{\beta-\delta}}\right)$$

$$a>x>\beta$$

**573.** $\displaystyle\int_x^\beta \frac{dx}{\sqrt{(a-x)(\beta-x)(x-\gamma)(x-\delta)}}$

$$=\frac{2}{\sqrt{(a-\gamma)(\beta-\delta)}}\,\mathrm{sn}^{-1}\left(\sqrt{\frac{a-\gamma}{\beta-\gamma}\cdot\frac{\beta-x}{a-x}},\ \sqrt{\frac{\beta-\gamma}{a-\gamma}\cdot\frac{a-\delta}{\beta-\delta}}\right)$$

$$\beta>x>\gamma$$

**574.** $\displaystyle\int_\gamma^x \frac{dx}{\sqrt{(a-x)(\beta-x)(x-\gamma)(x-\delta)}}$

$$=\frac{2}{\sqrt{(a-\gamma)(\beta-\delta)}}\,\mathrm{sn}^{-1}\left(\sqrt{\frac{\beta-\delta}{\beta-\gamma}\cdot\frac{x-\gamma}{x-\delta}},\ \sqrt{\frac{\beta-\gamma}{a-\gamma}\cdot\frac{a-\delta}{\beta-\delta}}\right)$$

$$\beta>x>\gamma$$

**575.** $\displaystyle\int_x^\gamma \frac{dx}{\sqrt{(a-x)(\beta-x)(\gamma-x)(x-\delta)}}$

$$=\frac{2}{\sqrt{(a-\gamma)(\beta-\delta)}}\,\mathrm{sn}^{-1}\left(\sqrt{\frac{\beta-\delta}{\gamma-\delta}\cdot\frac{\gamma-x}{\beta-x}},\ \sqrt{\frac{a-\beta}{a-\gamma}\cdot\frac{\gamma-\delta}{\beta-\delta}}\right)$$

$$\gamma>x>\delta$$

**576.** $\displaystyle\int_\delta^x \frac{dx}{\sqrt{(a-x)(\beta-x)(\gamma-x)(x-\delta)}}$

$$=\frac{2}{\sqrt{(a-\gamma)(\beta-\delta)}}\,\mathrm{sn}^{-1}\left(\sqrt{\frac{a-\gamma}{\gamma-\delta}\cdot\frac{x-\delta}{a-x}},\ \sqrt{\frac{a-\beta}{a-\gamma}\cdot\frac{\gamma-\delta}{\beta-\delta}}\right)$$

$$\gamma>x>\delta$$

**577.** $\displaystyle\int_x^\delta \frac{dx}{\sqrt{(a-x)(\beta-x)(\gamma-x)(\delta-x)}}$

$$= \frac{2}{\sqrt{(a-\gamma)(\beta-\delta)}}\ \mathrm{sn}^{-1}\left(\sqrt{\frac{a-\gamma}{a-\delta}\cdot\frac{\delta-x}{\gamma-x}},\ \sqrt{\frac{\beta-\gamma}{a-\gamma}\cdot\frac{a-\delta}{\beta-\delta}}\right)$$

$$\delta > x$$

**578.** $\displaystyle\int \mathrm{sn}\,x\,dx = -\frac{1}{k}\cosh^{-1}\left(\frac{\mathrm{dn}\,x}{k'}\right)$

**579.** $\displaystyle\int \mathrm{cn}\,x\,dx = \frac{1}{k}\cos^{-1}(\mathrm{dn}\,x)$

**580.** $\displaystyle\int \mathrm{dn}\,x\,dx = \sin^{-1}(\mathrm{sn}\,x) = \mathrm{am}\,x$

**581.** $\displaystyle\int \frac{dx}{\mathrm{sn}\,x} = \log\left[\frac{\mathrm{sn}\,x}{\mathrm{cn}\,x + \mathrm{dn}\,x}\right]$

**582.** $\displaystyle\int \frac{dx}{\mathrm{cn}\,x} = \frac{1}{k'}\log\left[\frac{k'\,\mathrm{sn}\,x + \mathrm{dn}\,x}{\mathrm{cn}\,x}\right]$

**583.** $\displaystyle\int \frac{dx}{\mathrm{dn}\,x} = \frac{1}{k'}\tan^{-1}\left[\frac{k'\,\mathrm{sn}\,x - \mathrm{cn}\,x}{k'\,\mathrm{sn}\,x + \mathrm{cn}\,x}\right]$

**584.** $\displaystyle\int_0^x \mathrm{sn}^2 x\,dx = \frac{1}{k^2}\left[x - E(\mathrm{am}\,x,\,k)\right]$

**585.** $\displaystyle\int_0^x \mathrm{cn}^2 x\,dx = \frac{1}{k^2}\left[E(\mathrm{am}\,x,\,k) - k'^2 x\right]$

**586.** $\displaystyle\int_0^x \mathrm{dn}^2 x\,dx = E(\mathrm{am}\,x,\,k)$

**587.** $\displaystyle(m+1)\int \mathrm{sn}^m x\,dx = (m+2)(1+k^2)\int \mathrm{sn}^{m+2} x\,dx$

$$- (m+3)k^2\int \mathrm{sn}^{m+4} x\,dx + \mathrm{sn}^{m+1} x\,\mathrm{cn}\,x\,\mathrm{dn}\,x$$

**588.** $\displaystyle(m+1)k'^2\int \mathrm{cn}^m x\,dx = (m+2)(1-2\,k^2)\int \mathrm{cn}^{m+2} x\,dx$

$$+ (m+3)k^2\int \mathrm{cn}^{m+4} x\,dx - \mathrm{cn}^{m+1} x\,\mathrm{sn}\,x\,\mathrm{dn}\,x$$

**589.** $\displaystyle(m+1)k'^2\int \mathrm{dn}^m x\,dx = (m+2)(2-k^2)\int \mathrm{dn}^{m+2} x\,dx$

$$- (m+3)\int \mathrm{dn}^{m+4} x\,dx + k^2\,\mathrm{dn}^{m+1} x\,\mathrm{sn}\,x\,\mathrm{cn}\,x$$

# PART III

# Auxiliary
# Formulas

## TRIGONOMETRIC FUNCTIONS

**590.** $\tan a \cdot \operatorname{ctn} a = \sin a \cdot \csc a = \cos a \cdot \sec a = 1,$

$\tan a = \sin a \div \cos a, \quad \sec^2 a = 1 + \tan^2 a,$

$\csc^2 a = 1 + \operatorname{ctn}^2 a, \qquad \sin^2 a + \cos^2 a = 1$

**591.*** $\sin a = \sqrt{1 - \cos^2 a} = 2 \sin \tfrac{1}{2} a \cdot \cos \tfrac{1}{2} a = \cos a \cdot \tan a$

$$= \frac{1}{\sqrt{1 + \operatorname{ctn}^2 a}} = \frac{\tan a}{\sqrt{1 + \tan^2 a}} = \sqrt{\frac{1 - \cos 2a}{2}} = \frac{2 \tan \tfrac{1}{2} a}{1 + \tan^2 \tfrac{1}{2} a}$$

$$= \sqrt{\frac{\sec^2 a - 1}{\sec^2 a}} = \operatorname{ctn} \tfrac{1}{2} a \cdot (1 - \cos a) = \tan \tfrac{1}{2} a \cdot (1 + \cos a)$$

**592.*** $\cos a = \sqrt{1 - \sin^2 a} = \dfrac{1}{\sqrt{1 + \tan^2 a}} = \dfrac{\operatorname{ctn} a}{\sqrt{1 + \operatorname{ctn}^2 a}}$

$$= \sqrt{\frac{1 + \cos 2a}{2}} = \frac{1 - \tan^2 \tfrac{1}{2} a}{1 + \tan^2 \tfrac{1}{2} a} = \cos^2 \tfrac{1}{2} a - \sin^2 \tfrac{1}{2} a$$

$$= 1 - 2 \sin^2 \tfrac{1}{2} a = 2 \cos^2 \tfrac{1}{2} a - 1 = \sin a \cdot \operatorname{ctn} a$$

$$= \frac{\sin 2a}{2 \sin a} = \sqrt{\frac{\csc^2 a - 1}{\csc^2 a}} = \frac{\operatorname{ctn} \tfrac{1}{2} a - \tan \tfrac{1}{2} a}{\operatorname{ctn} \tfrac{1}{2} a + \tan \tfrac{1}{2} a}$$

*To be strictly correct, a ± sign should be inserted before each
radical, the choice of sign depending upon the quadrant.

**593.**\* $\tan a = \dfrac{\sin a}{\sqrt{1 - \sin^2 a}} = \dfrac{\sqrt{1 - \cos^2 a}}{\cos a} = \dfrac{\sin 2a}{1 + \cos 2a}$

$\qquad = \dfrac{1 - \cos 2a}{\sin 2a} = \sqrt{\dfrac{1 - \cos 2a}{1 + \cos 2a}} = \dfrac{2 \tan \frac{1}{2} a}{1 - \tan^2 \frac{1}{2} a}$

$\qquad = \dfrac{\sec a}{\csc a} = \dfrac{2}{\operatorname{ctn} \frac{1}{2} a - \tan \frac{1}{2} a} = \dfrac{2 \operatorname{ctn} \frac{1}{2} a}{\operatorname{ctn}^2 \frac{1}{2} a - 1}$

**594.**

|  | $-\alpha$ | $90° \pm \alpha$ | $180° \pm \alpha$ | $270° \pm \alpha$ | $360° \pm \alpha$ |
|---|---|---|---|---|---|
| sin | $- \sin \alpha$ | $+ \cos \alpha$ | $\mp \sin \alpha$ | $- \cos \alpha$ | $\pm \sin \alpha$ |
| cos | $+ \cos \alpha$ | $\mp \sin \alpha$ | $- \cos \alpha$ | $\pm \sin \alpha$ | $+ \cos \alpha$ |
| tan | $- \tan \alpha$ | $\mp \operatorname{ctn} \alpha$ | $\pm \tan \alpha$ | $\mp \operatorname{ctn} \alpha$ | $\pm \tan \alpha$ |
| ctn | $- \operatorname{ctn} \alpha$ | $\mp \tan \alpha$ | $\pm \operatorname{ctn} \alpha$ | $\mp \tan \alpha$ | $\pm \operatorname{ctn} \alpha$ |
| sec | $+ \sec \alpha$ | $\mp \csc \alpha$ | $- \sec \alpha$ | $\pm \csc \alpha$ | $+ \sec \alpha$ |
| csc | $- \csc \alpha$ | $+ \sec \alpha$ | $\mp \csc \alpha$ | $- \sec \alpha$ | $\pm \csc \alpha$ |

**595.**

|  | $0°$ | $30°$ | $45°$ | $60°$ | $90°$ | $120°$ | $135°$ | $150°$ | $180°$ |
|---|---|---|---|---|---|---|---|---|---|
| sin | $0$ | $\frac{1}{2}$ | $\frac{1}{2}\sqrt{2}$ | $\frac{1}{2}\sqrt{3}$ | $1$ | $\frac{1}{2}\sqrt{3}$ | $\frac{1}{2}\sqrt{2}$ | $\frac{1}{2}$ | $0$ |
| cos | $1$ | $\frac{1}{2}\sqrt{3}$ | $\frac{1}{2}\sqrt{2}$ | $\frac{1}{2}$ | $0$ | $-\frac{1}{2}$ | $-\frac{1}{2}\sqrt{2}$ | $-\frac{1}{2}\sqrt{3}$ | $-1$ |
| tan | $0$ | $\frac{1}{\sqrt{3}}$ | $1$ | $\sqrt{3}$ | $\infty$ | $-\sqrt{3}$ | $-1$ | $-\frac{1}{\sqrt{3}}$ | $0$ |
| ctn | $\infty$ | $\sqrt{3}$ | $1$ | $\frac{1}{\sqrt{3}}$ | $0$ | $-\frac{1}{\sqrt{3}}$ | $-1$ | $-\sqrt{3}$ | $\infty$ |
| sec | $1$ | $\frac{2}{\sqrt{3}}$ | $\sqrt{2}$ | $2$ | $\infty$ | $-2$ | $-\sqrt{2}$ | $-\frac{2}{\sqrt{3}}$ | $-1$ |
| csc | $\infty$ | $2$ | $\sqrt{2}$ | $\frac{2}{\sqrt{3}}$ | $1$ | $\frac{2}{\sqrt{3}}$ | $\sqrt{2}$ | $2$ | $\infty$ |

\*To be strictly correct, a $\pm$ sign should be inserted before each radical, the choice of sign depending upon the quadrant.

**596.*** $\sin \frac{1}{2} a = \sqrt{\frac{1}{2}(1 - \cos a)}$

**597.*** $\cos \frac{1}{2} a = \sqrt{\frac{1}{2}(1 + \cos a)}$

**598.*** $\tan \frac{1}{2} a = \sqrt{\dfrac{1 - \cos a}{1 + \cos a}} = \dfrac{1 - \cos a}{\sin a} = \dfrac{\sin a}{1 + \cos a}$

**599.** $\sin 2\, a = 2 \sin a \cos a$

**600.** $\sin 3\, a = 3 \sin a - 4 \sin^3 a$

**601.** $\sin 4\, a = 8 \cos^3 a \cdot \sin a - 4 \cos a \sin a$

**602.** $\sin 5\, a = 5 \sin a - 20 \sin^3 a + 16 \sin^5 a$

**603.** $\sin 6\, a = 32 \cos^5 a \sin a - 32 \cos^3 a \sin a + 6 \cos a \sin a$

**604.** $\cos 2\, a = \cos^2 a - \sin^2 a = 1 - 2 \sin^2 a = 2 \cos^2 a - 1$

**605.** $\cos 3\, a = 4 \cos^3 a - 3 \cos a$

**606.** $\cos 4\, a = 8 \cos^4 a - 8 \cos^2 a + 1$

**607.** $\cos 5\, a = 16 \cos^5 a - 20 \cos^3 a + 5 \cos a$

**608.** $\cos 6\, a = 32 \cos^6 a - 48 \cos^4 a + 18 \cos^2 a - 1$

**609.** $\tan 2\, a = \dfrac{2 \tan a}{1 - \tan^2 a}$

**610.** $\operatorname{ctn} 2\, a = \dfrac{\operatorname{ctn}^2 a - 1}{2 \operatorname{ctn} a}$

**611.** $\sin (a \pm \beta) = \sin a \cdot \cos \beta \pm \cos a \cdot \sin \beta$

**612.** $\cos (a \pm \beta) = \cos a \cdot \cos \beta \mp \sin a \cdot \sin \beta$

**613.** $\tan (a \pm \beta) = \dfrac{\tan a \pm \tan \beta}{1 \mp \tan a \cdot \tan \beta}$

**614.** $\operatorname{ctn} (a \pm \beta) = \dfrac{\operatorname{ctn} a \cdot \operatorname{ctn} \beta \mp 1}{\operatorname{ctn} \beta \pm \operatorname{ctn} a}$

*To be strictly correct, a $\pm$ sign should be inserted before each radical, the choice of sign depending upon the quadrant.

**615.** $\sin a \pm \sin \beta = 2 \sin \frac{1}{2}(a \pm \beta) \cdot \cos \frac{1}{2}(a \mp \beta)$

**616.** $\cos a + \cos \beta = 2 \cos \frac{1}{2}(a + \beta) \cdot \cos \frac{1}{2}(a - \beta)$

**617.** $\cos a - \cos \beta = -2 \sin \frac{1}{2}(a + \beta) \cdot \sin \frac{1}{2}(a - \beta)$

**618.** $\tan a \pm \tan \beta = \dfrac{\sin(a \pm \beta)}{\cos a \cdot \cos \beta}$

**619.** $\operatorname{ctn} a \pm \operatorname{ctn} \beta = \pm \dfrac{\sin(a \pm \beta)}{\sin a \cdot \sin \beta}$

**620.** $\dfrac{\sin a \pm \sin \beta}{\cos a + \cos \beta} = \tan \frac{1}{2}(a \pm \beta)$

**621.** $\dfrac{\sin a \pm \sin \beta}{\cos a - \cos \beta} = -\operatorname{ctn} \frac{1}{2}(a \mp \beta)$

**622.** $\dfrac{\sin a + \sin \beta}{\sin a - \sin \beta} = \dfrac{\tan \frac{1}{2}(a + \beta)}{\tan \frac{1}{2}(a - \beta)}$

**623.** $\sin^2 a - \sin^2 \beta = \sin(a + \beta) \cdot \sin(a - \beta)$

**624.** $\cos^2 a - \cos^2 \beta = -\sin(a + \beta) \cdot \sin(a - \beta)$

**625.** $\cos^2 a - \sin^2 \beta = \cos(a + \beta) \cdot \cos(a - \beta)$

**626.** $\sin xi = \frac{1}{2} i(e^x - e^{-x}) = i \sinh x$

**627.** $\cos xi = \frac{1}{2}(e^x + e^{-x}) = \cosh x$

**628.** $\tan xi = \dfrac{i(e^x - e^{-x})}{e^x + e^{-x}} = i \tanh x$

**629.** $e^{x+yi} = e^x \cos y + i e^x \sin y$

**630.** $a^{x+yi} = a^x \cos(y \cdot \log a) + i a^x \sin(y \cdot \log a)$

**631.** $(\cos \theta \pm i \cdot \sin \theta)^n = \cos n\theta \pm i \cdot \sin n\theta$

**632.** $\sin x = -\frac{1}{2} i(e^{xi} - e^{-xi})$

**633.** $\cos x = \frac{1}{2}(e^{xi} + e^{-xi})$

**634.** $\tan x = -i \dfrac{e^{2xi} - 1}{e^{2xi} + 1}$

**635.** $\sin (x \pm yi) = \sin x \cos yi \pm \cos x \sin yi$
$$= \sin x \cosh y \pm i \cos x \sinh y$$

**636.** $\cos (x \pm yi) = \cos x \cos yi \mp \sin x \sin yi$
$$= \cos x \cosh y \mp i \sin x \sinh y$$

**637.** $\sin x + \sin (x + y) + \sin (x + 2\,y) + \cdots + \sin [x + (n-1)y]$
$$= \frac{\sin [x + \frac{1}{2}(n - 1)y] \sin \frac{1}{2} ny}{\sin \frac{1}{2} y}$$

**638.** $\cos x + \cos (x + y) + \cos (x + 2\,y) + \cdots + \cos [x + (n-1)y]$
$$= \frac{\cos [x + \frac{1}{2}(n - 1)y] \sin \frac{1}{2} ny}{\sin \frac{1}{2} y}$$

**639.** $\dfrac{1}{2} + \cos x + \cos 2\,x + \cdots + \cos nx = \dfrac{\sin (n + \frac{1}{2})x}{2 \sin \frac{1}{2} x}$

**640.** $\dfrac{n}{2} + (n - 1) \cos x + (n - 2) \cos 2\,x + \cdots + \cos (n - 1)x$
$$= \frac{\sin^2 \frac{1}{2} nx}{2 \sin^2 \frac{1}{2} x}$$

## TRIGONOMETRY

In any plane triangle,

**641.** $\dfrac{a}{\sin A} = \dfrac{b}{\sin B} = \dfrac{c}{\sin C}$

**642.** $a^2 = b^2 + c^2 - 2\,bc \cos A$

**643.** $\dfrac{a + b}{a - b} = \dfrac{\sin A + \sin B}{\sin A - \sin B} = \dfrac{\tan \frac{1}{2}(A + B)}{\tan \frac{1}{2}(A - B)} = \dfrac{\operatorname{ctn} \frac{1}{2} C}{\tan \frac{1}{2}(A - B)}$

**644.** $\sin \frac{1}{2} A = \sqrt{\dfrac{(s - b)(s - c)}{bc}}$, where $2\,s = a + b + c$

**645.** $\cos \frac{1}{2} A = \sqrt{\dfrac{s(s - a)}{bc}}$

**646.** $\tan \frac{1}{2} A = \sqrt{\dfrac{(s-b)(s-c)}{s(s-a)}} = \dfrac{1}{s-a} \sqrt{\dfrac{(s-a)(s-b)(s-c)}{s}}$

**647.** Area $= \frac{1}{2} bc \sin A = \sqrt{s(s-a)(s-b)(s-c)}$

In any spherical triangle,

**648.** $\dfrac{\sin A}{\sin a} = \dfrac{\sin B}{\sin b} = \dfrac{\sin C}{\sin c}$

**649.** $\cos a = \cos b \cos c + \sin b \sin c \cos A$

**650.** $- \cos A = \cos B \cos C - \sin B \sin C \cos a$

**651.** $\sin a \operatorname{ctn} b = \sin C \operatorname{ctn} B + \cos a \cos C$

**652.** $\cos \frac{1}{2} A = \sqrt{\dfrac{\sin s \cdot \sin (s-a)}{\sin b \cdot \sin c}}$

**653.** $\sin \frac{1}{2} A = \sqrt{\dfrac{\sin (s-b) \cdot \sin (s-c)}{\sin b \cdot \sin c}}$

**654.** $\tan \frac{1}{2} A = \sqrt{\dfrac{\sin (s-b) \cdot \sin (s-c)}{\sin s \cdot \sin (s-a)}}$

**655.** $\cos \frac{1}{2} a = \sqrt{\dfrac{\cos (S-B) \cdot \cos (S-C)}{\sin B \cdot \sin C}}$

**656.** $\sin \frac{1}{2} a = \sqrt{\dfrac{- \cos S \cdot \cos (S-A)}{\sin B \sin C}}$

**657.** $\tan \frac{1}{2} a = \sqrt{\dfrac{- \cos S \cdot \cos (S-A)}{\cos (S-B) \cdot \cos (S-C)}}$

$$2s = a+b+c \qquad 2S = A+B+C$$

**658.** $\cos \frac{1}{2}(A+B) = \dfrac{\cos \frac{1}{2}(a+b)}{\cos \frac{1}{2} c} \sin \frac{1}{2} C$

**659.** $\cos \frac{1}{2}(A-B) = \dfrac{\sin \frac{1}{2}(a+b)}{\sin \frac{1}{2} c} \sin \frac{1}{2} C$

**660.** $\sin \frac{1}{2}(A+B) = \dfrac{\cos \frac{1}{2}(a-b)}{\cos \frac{1}{2} c} \cos \frac{1}{2} C$

**661.** $\sin \frac{1}{2}(A - B) = \dfrac{\sin \frac{1}{2}(a - b)}{\sin \frac{1}{2} c} \cos \frac{1}{2} C$

**662.** $\tan \frac{1}{2}(A + B) = \dfrac{\cos \frac{1}{2}(a - b)}{\cos \frac{1}{2}(a + b)} \operatorname{ctn} \frac{1}{2} C$

**663.** $\tan \frac{1}{2}(A - B) = \dfrac{\sin \frac{1}{2}(a - b)}{\sin \frac{1}{2}(a + b)} \operatorname{ctn} \frac{1}{2} C$

**664.** $\tan \frac{1}{2}(a + b) = \dfrac{\cos \frac{1}{2}(A - B)}{\cos \frac{1}{2}(A + B)} \tan \frac{1}{2} c$

**665.** $\tan \frac{1}{2}(a - b) = \dfrac{\sin \frac{1}{2}(A - B)}{\sin \frac{1}{2}(A + B)} \tan \frac{1}{2} c$

**666.** $\dfrac{\cos \frac{1}{2}(a + b)}{\cos \frac{1}{2}(a - b)} = \dfrac{\operatorname{ctn} \frac{1}{2} C}{\tan \frac{1}{2}(A + B)}$

## INVERSE TRIGONOMETRIC FUNCTIONS

In interpreting equations which involve logarithmic and inverse trigonometric functions, it is necessary to remember that these functions are multiple-valued. To save space the formulas in this section are printed in contracted form.

**667.** $\sin^{-1}x = \cos^{-1}\sqrt{1 - x^2} = \tan^{-1}\dfrac{x}{\sqrt{1 - x^2}} = \sec^{-1}\dfrac{1}{\sqrt{1 - x^2}}$

$\qquad = \csc^{-1}\dfrac{1}{x} = 2 \sin^{-1}[\frac{1}{2} - \frac{1}{2}\sqrt{1 - x^2}]^{\frac{1}{2}}$

$\qquad = \frac{1}{2} \sin^{-1}(2 x\sqrt{1 - x^2}) = 2 \tan^{-1}\left[\dfrac{1 - \sqrt{1 - x^2}}{x}\right]$

$\qquad = \frac{1}{2} \tan^{-1}\left[\dfrac{2 x\sqrt{1 - x^2}}{1 - 2 x^2}\right] = \frac{1}{2} \pi - \cos^{-1}x$

$\qquad = \frac{1}{2} \pi - \sin^{-1}\sqrt{1 - x^2} = - \sin^{-1}(- x)$

$\qquad = \operatorname{ctn}^{-1}\dfrac{\sqrt{1 - x^2}}{x} = (2 n + \frac{1}{2})\pi - i \log (x + \sqrt{x^2 - 1})$

$\qquad = \frac{1}{4} \pi + \frac{1}{2} \sin^{-1}(2 x^2 - 1) = \frac{1}{2} \cos^{-1}(1 - 2 x^2)$

**668.** $\cos^{-1}x = \sin^{-1}\sqrt{1-x^2} = \tan^{-1}\dfrac{\sqrt{1-x^2}}{x} = \sec^{-1}\dfrac{1}{x}$

$\qquad = \tfrac{1}{2}\pi - \sin^{-1}x = 2\cos^{-1}\sqrt{\dfrac{1+x}{2}}$

$\qquad = \tfrac{1}{2}\cos^{-1}(2x^2 - 1)$

$\qquad = 2\tan^{-1}\sqrt{\dfrac{1-x}{1+x}} = \tfrac{1}{2}\tan^{-1}\left[\dfrac{2x\sqrt{1-x^2}}{2x^2-1}\right]$

$\qquad = \csc^{-1}\dfrac{1}{\sqrt{1-x^2}} = \pi - \cos^{-1}(-x)$

$\qquad = \mathrm{ctn}^{-1}\dfrac{x}{\sqrt{1-x^2}}$

$\qquad = i\log(x + \sqrt{x^2-1}) = \pi - i\log(\sqrt{x^2-1} - x)$

**669.** $\tan^{-1}x = \sin^{-1}\dfrac{x}{\sqrt{1+x^2}} = \cos^{-1}\dfrac{1}{\sqrt{1+x^2}} = \tfrac{1}{2}\sin^{-1}\dfrac{2x}{1+x^2}$

$\qquad = \mathrm{ctn}^{-1}\dfrac{1}{x} = \tfrac{1}{2}\pi - \mathrm{ctn}^{-1}x = \sec^{-1}\sqrt{1+x^2}$

$\qquad = \tfrac{1}{2}\pi - \tan^{-1}\dfrac{1}{x}$

$\qquad = \csc^{-1}\dfrac{\sqrt{1+x^2}}{x} = \tfrac{1}{2}\cos^{-1}\left[\dfrac{1-x^2}{1+x^2}\right]$

$\qquad = 2\cos^{-1}\left[\dfrac{1+\sqrt{1+x^2}}{2\sqrt{1+x^2}}\right]^{\frac{1}{2}} = 2\sin^{-1}\left[\dfrac{\sqrt{1+x^2}-1}{2\sqrt{1+x^2}}\right]^{\frac{1}{2}}$

$\qquad = \tfrac{1}{2}\tan^{-1}\dfrac{2x}{1-x^2} = 2\tan^{-1}\left[\dfrac{\sqrt{1+x^2}-1}{x}\right]$

$\qquad = -\tan^{-1}c + \tan^{-1}\left[\dfrac{x+c}{1-cx}\right] = -\tan^{-1}(-x)$

$\qquad = \tfrac{1}{2}i\log\dfrac{1-xi}{1+xi} = \tfrac{1}{2}i\log\dfrac{i+x}{i-x}$

$\qquad = -\tfrac{1}{2}i\log\dfrac{1+xi}{1-xi}$

**670.** $\sin^{-1}x \pm \sin^{-1}y = \sin^{-1}[x\sqrt{1-y^2} \pm y\sqrt{1-x^2}]$

**671.** $\cos^{-1}x \pm \cos^{-1}y = \cos^{-1}[xy \mp \sqrt{(1-x^2)(1-y^2)}]$

**672.** $\tan^{-1}x \pm \tan^{-1}y = \tan^{-1}\left[\dfrac{x \pm y}{1 \mp xy}\right]$

**673.** $\sin^{-1}x \pm \cos^{-1}y = \sin^{-1}[xy \pm \sqrt{(1-x^2)(1-y^2)}]$
$$= \cos^{-1}[y\sqrt{1-x^2} \mp x\sqrt{1-y^2}]$$

**674.** $\tan^{-1}x \pm \mathrm{ctn}^{-1}y = \tan^{-1}\left[\dfrac{xy \pm 1}{y \mp x}\right] = \mathrm{ctn}^{-1}\left[\dfrac{y \mp x}{xy \pm 1}\right]$

**675.*** $\log(x + yi) = \frac{1}{2}\log(x^2 + y^2) + i\tan^{-1}(y/x)$

## HYPERBOLIC FUNCTIONS

**676.** $\sinh x = \frac{1}{2}(e^x - e^{-x}) = -\sinh(-x) = -i\sin(ix)$
$$= (\mathrm{csch}\ x)^{-1} = 2\tanh\tfrac{1}{2}x \div (1 - \tanh^2\tfrac{1}{2}x)$$

**677.** $\cosh x = \frac{1}{2}(e^x + e^{-x}) = \cosh(-x) = \cos(ix) = (\mathrm{sech}\ x)^{-1}$
$$= (1 + \tanh^2\tfrac{1}{2}x) \div (1 - \tanh^2\tfrac{1}{2}x)$$

**678.** $\tanh x = (e^x - e^{-x}) \div (e^x + e^{-x}) = -\tanh(-x)$
$$= -i\tan(ix) = (\mathrm{ctnh}\ x)^{-1} = \sinh x \div \cosh x$$

**679.** $\cosh xi = \cos x$

**680.** $\sinh xi = i\sin x$

**681.** $\cosh^2 x - \sinh^2 x = 1$

**682.** $1 - \tanh^2 x = \mathrm{sech}^2 x$

**683.** $1 - \mathrm{ctnh}^2 x = -\mathrm{csch}^2 x$

**684.** $\sinh(x \pm y) = \sinh x \cdot \cosh y \pm \cosh x \cdot \sinh y$

**685.** $\cosh(x \pm y) = \cosh x \cdot \cosh y \pm \sinh x \cdot \sinh y$

**686.** $\tanh(x \pm y) = (\tanh x \pm \tanh y) \div (1 \pm \tanh x \cdot \tanh y)$

**687.** $\sinh(2x) = 2\sinh x \cosh x$

*See explanation on page 3.

**688.** $\cosh{(2\,x)} = \cosh^2 x + \sinh^2 x = 2\cosh^2 x - 1 = 1 + 2\sinh^2 x$

**689.** $\tanh{(2\,x)} = 2\tanh x \div (1 + \tanh^2 x)$

**690.** $\sinh{(\tfrac{1}{2}\,x)} = \pm\sqrt{\tfrac{1}{2}(\cosh x - 1)}$

**691.** $\cosh{(\tfrac{1}{2}\,x)} = \sqrt{\tfrac{1}{2}(\cosh x + 1)}$

**692.** $\tanh{(\tfrac{1}{2}\,x)} = (\cosh x - 1) \div \sinh x = \sinh x \div (\cosh x + 1)$

**693.** $\sinh x + \sinh y = 2\sinh\tfrac{1}{2}(x + y) \cdot \cosh\tfrac{1}{2}(x - y)$

**694.** $\sinh x - \sinh y = 2\cosh\tfrac{1}{2}(x + y) \cdot \sinh\tfrac{1}{2}(x - y)$

**695.** $\cosh x + \cosh y = 2\cosh\tfrac{1}{2}(x + y) \cdot \cosh\tfrac{1}{2}(x - y)$

**696.** $\cosh x - \cosh y = 2\sinh\tfrac{1}{2}(x + y) \cdot \sinh\tfrac{1}{2}(x - y)$

**697.** $d\sinh x = \cosh x \cdot dx$

**698.** $d\cosh x = \sinh x \cdot dx$

**699.** $d\tanh x = \operatorname{sech}^2 x \cdot dx$

**700.** $d\operatorname{ctnh} x = -\operatorname{csch}^2 x \cdot dx$

**701.** $d\operatorname{sech} x = -\operatorname{sech} x \cdot \tanh x \cdot dx$

**702.** $d\operatorname{csch} x = -\operatorname{csch} x \cdot \operatorname{ctnh} x \cdot dx$

**703.** $\sinh^{-1} x = \log{(x + \sqrt{x^2 + 1})} = \displaystyle\int \frac{dx}{\sqrt{x^2 + 1}}$
$$= \cosh^{-1}\sqrt{x^2 + 1}$$

**704.** $\cosh^{-1} x = \log{(x + \sqrt{x^2 - 1})} = \displaystyle\int \frac{dx}{\sqrt{x^2 - 1}}$
$$= \sinh^{-1}\sqrt{x^2 - 1}$$

**705.** $\tanh^{-1} x = \tfrac{1}{2}\log{(1 + x)} - \tfrac{1}{2}\log{(1 - x)} = \displaystyle\int \frac{dx}{1 - x^2}$

**706.** $\operatorname{ctnh}^{-1} x = \tfrac{1}{2}\log{(1 + x)} - \tfrac{1}{2}\log{(x - 1)} = \displaystyle\int \frac{dx}{1 - x^2}$

**707.** $\operatorname{sech}^{-1} x = \log\left(\dfrac{1}{x} + \sqrt{\dfrac{1}{x^2} - 1}\right) = -\displaystyle\int \frac{dx}{x\sqrt{1 - x^2}}$

**708.** $\operatorname{csch}^{-1} x = \log\left(\dfrac{1}{x} + \sqrt{\dfrac{1}{x^2} + 1}\right) = -\displaystyle\int \frac{dx}{x\sqrt{x^2 + 1}}$

**709.** $d \sinh^{-1} x = \dfrac{dx}{\sqrt{1 + x^2}}$

**710.** $d \cosh^{-1} x = \dfrac{dx}{\sqrt{x^2 - 1}}$

**711.** $d \tanh^{-1} x = \dfrac{dx}{1 - x^2}$

**712.** $d \operatorname{ctnh}^{-1} x = -\dfrac{dx}{x^2 - 1}$

**713.** $d \operatorname{sech}^{-1} x = -\dfrac{dx}{x\sqrt{1 - x^2}}$

**714.** $d \operatorname{csch}^{-1} x = -\dfrac{dx}{x\sqrt{x^2 + 1}}$

If $m$ is an integer,

**715.** $\sinh (m\pi i) = 0$

**716.** $\cosh (m\pi i) = \cos m\pi = (-1)^m$

**717.** $\tanh (m\pi i) = 0$

**718.** $\sinh (x + m\pi i) = (-1)^m \sinh x$

**719.** $\cosh (x + m\pi i) = (-1)^m \cosh (x)$

**720.** $\sinh (2m + 1) \tfrac{1}{2} \pi i = i \sin (2m + 1) \tfrac{1}{2} \pi = \pm i$

**721.** $\cosh (2m + 1) \tfrac{1}{2} \pi i = 0$

**722.** $\sinh \left( \dfrac{\pi i}{2} \pm x \right) = i \cosh x$

**723.** $\cosh \left( \dfrac{\pi i}{2} \pm x \right) = \pm i \sinh x$

**724.** $\sinh u = \tan \operatorname{gd} u$

**725.** $\cosh u = \sec \operatorname{gd} u$

**726.** $\tanh u = \sin \operatorname{gd} u$

**727.** $\tanh \tfrac{1}{2} u = \tan \tfrac{1}{2} \operatorname{gd} u$

**728.** $u = \log \tan \left( \tfrac{1}{4} \pi + \tfrac{1}{2} \text{ gd } u \right)$

**729.** $\displaystyle\int \sec x \, dx = \text{gd}^{-1} x$

## ELLIPTIC FUNCTIONS

If $u \equiv F(\phi, k) \equiv \displaystyle\int_0^x \frac{dz}{\sqrt{(1-z^2)(1-k^2 z^2)}} \equiv \int_0^\phi \frac{d\theta}{\sqrt{1 - k^2 \sin^2\theta}}$,

where $k < 1$, and $x \equiv \sin \phi$, $\phi$ is called the *amplitude* of $u$ and is written am $(u, \text{mod } k)$, or, more simply, am $u$; $x \equiv \sin \phi \equiv$ sn $u$, $\sqrt{1-x^2} \equiv \cos \phi \equiv$ cn $u$, $\quad \sqrt{1-k^2 x^2} \equiv \Delta\phi \equiv \Delta n \, u \equiv$ dn $u$,

$$K \equiv F(\tfrac{1}{2} \pi, k), \qquad K' \equiv F(\tfrac{1}{2} \pi, k')$$

Hence, am $(0) = 0$, sn $(0) = 0$, cn $(0) = 1$, dn $(0) = 1$,

$$\text{am } (- u) = - \text{ am } u, \qquad \text{sn } (- u) = - \text{ sn } u,$$
$$\text{cn } (- u) = \text{cn } u, \qquad \text{dn } (- u) = \text{dn } u$$

**730.** $\text{sn}^2 u + \text{cn}^2 u = 1$

**731.** $\text{dn}^2 u + k^2 \text{ sn}^2 u = 1$

**732.** $\text{dn}^2 u - k^2 \text{ cn}^2 u = 1 - k^2 = k'^2$

**733.** $\text{sn } 2 \, u = \dfrac{2 \text{ sn } u \cdot \text{cn } u \cdot \text{dn } u}{1 - k^2 \text{ sn}^4 \, u}$

**734.** $\text{cn } 2 \, u = \dfrac{\text{cn}^2 u - \text{sn}^2 u \cdot \text{dn}^2 u}{1 - k^2 \text{ sn}^4 u} = \dfrac{1 - 2 \text{ sn}^2 u + k^2 \text{ sn}^4 \, u}{1 - k^2 \text{ sn}^4 u}$

$\qquad = 1 - \dfrac{2 \text{ sn}^2 u \cdot \text{dn}^2 u}{1 - k^2 \text{ sn}^4 u} = \dfrac{2 \text{ cn}^2 u}{1 - k^2 \text{ sn}^4 u} - 1$

**735.** $\text{dn } 2 \, u = \dfrac{\text{dn}^2 u - k^2 \text{ sn}^2 u \cdot \text{cn}^2 u}{1 - k^2 \text{ sn}^4 u} = \dfrac{1 - 2 \, k^2 \text{ sn}^2 u + k^2 \text{ sn}^4 u}{1 - k^2 \text{ sn}^4 u}$

$\qquad = 1 - \dfrac{2 \, k^2 \text{ sn}^2 u \cdot \text{cn}^2 u}{1 - k^2 \text{ sn}^4 u} = \dfrac{2 \text{ dn}^2 u}{1 - k^2 \text{ sn}^4 u} - 1$

**736.** $\text{sn}^2 \left( \dfrac{u}{2} \right) = \dfrac{1 - \text{cn } u}{1 + \text{dn } u} = \dfrac{1 - \text{dn } u}{k^2 (1 + \text{cn } u)} = \dfrac{\text{dn } u - \text{cn } u}{k'^2 + \text{dn } u - k^2 \text{ cn } u}$

**737.** $\mathrm{cn}^2\left(\dfrac{u}{2}\right) = \dfrac{\mathrm{dn}\ u + \mathrm{cn}\ u}{1 + \mathrm{dn}\ u} = \dfrac{k^2\,\mathrm{cn}\ u - k'^2 + \mathrm{dn}\ u}{k^2(1 + \mathrm{cn}\ u)}$

$$= \dfrac{k'^2(1 + \mathrm{cn}\ u)}{k'^2 + \mathrm{dn}\ u - k^2\,\mathrm{cn}\ u}$$

**738.** $\mathrm{dn}^2\left(\dfrac{u}{2}\right) = \dfrac{k'^2 + \mathrm{dn}\ u + k^2\,\mathrm{cn}\ u}{1 + \mathrm{dn}\ u} = \dfrac{k^2(\mathrm{cn}\ u + \mathrm{dn}\ u)}{k^2(1 + \mathrm{cn}\ u)}$

$$= \dfrac{k'^2(1 + \mathrm{dn}\ u)}{k'^2 + \mathrm{dn}\ u - k^2\,\mathrm{cn}\ u}$$

If, moreover, $v = \displaystyle\int_0^y \dfrac{dz}{\sqrt{(1 - z^2)(1 - k^2 z^2)}}$,

**739.** $\mathrm{sn}^2 u - \mathrm{sn}^2 v = \mathrm{cn}^2 v - \mathrm{cn}^2 u$

**740.** $\mathrm{sn}\ (u \pm v) = \dfrac{\mathrm{sn}\ u \cdot \mathrm{cn}\ v \cdot \mathrm{dn}\ v \pm \mathrm{cn}\ u \cdot \mathrm{sn}\ v \cdot \mathrm{dn}\ u}{1 - k^2\,\mathrm{sn}^2 u \cdot \mathrm{sn}^2 v}$

**741.** $\mathrm{cn}\ (u \pm v) = \dfrac{\mathrm{cn}\ u \cdot \mathrm{cn}\ v \mp \mathrm{sn}\ u \cdot \mathrm{sn}\ v \cdot \mathrm{dn}\ u \cdot \mathrm{dn}\ v}{1 - k^2\,\mathrm{sn}^2 u \cdot \mathrm{sn}^2 v}$

$$= \mathrm{cn}\ u \cdot \mathrm{cn}\ v \mp \mathrm{sn}\ u \cdot \mathrm{sn}\ v \cdot \mathrm{dn}\ (u \pm v)$$

**742.** $\mathrm{dn}\ (u \pm v) = \dfrac{\mathrm{dn}\ u \cdot \mathrm{dn}\ v \mp k^2\,\mathrm{sn}\ u \cdot \mathrm{sn}\ v \cdot \mathrm{cn}\ u \cdot \mathrm{cn}\ v}{1 - k^2\,\mathrm{sn}^2 u \cdot \mathrm{sn}^2 v}$

$$= \mathrm{dn}\ u \cdot \mathrm{dn}\ v \mp k^2\,\mathrm{sn}\ u \cdot \mathrm{sn}\ v \cdot \mathrm{cn}\ (u \pm v)$$

**743.** $\mathrm{tn}\ (u \pm v) = \dfrac{\mathrm{tn}\ u \cdot \mathrm{dn}\ v \pm \mathrm{tn}\ v \cdot \mathrm{dn}\ u}{1 \mp \mathrm{tn}\ u \cdot \mathrm{tn}\ v \cdot \mathrm{dn}\ u \cdot \mathrm{dn}\ v}$

**744.** $\mathrm{sn}\ (u + v) + \mathrm{sn}\ (u - v) = \dfrac{2\,\mathrm{sn}\ u \cdot \mathrm{cn}\ v \cdot \mathrm{dn}\ v}{1 - k^2\,\mathrm{sn}^2 u \cdot \mathrm{sn}^2 v}$

**745.** $\mathrm{sn}\ (u + v) - \mathrm{sn}\ (u - v) = \dfrac{2\,\mathrm{sn}\ v \cdot \mathrm{cn}\ u \cdot \mathrm{dn}\ u}{1 - k^2\,\mathrm{sn}^2 u \cdot \mathrm{sn}^2 v}$

**746.** $\mathrm{cn}\ (u + v) + \mathrm{cn}\ (u - v) = \dfrac{2\,\mathrm{cn}\ u \cdot \mathrm{cn}\ v}{1 - k^2\,\mathrm{sn}^2 u \cdot \mathrm{sn}^2 v}$

**747.** $\mathrm{cn}\ (u + v) - \mathrm{cn}\ (u - v) = -\dfrac{2\,\mathrm{sn}\ u \cdot \mathrm{sn}\ v \cdot \mathrm{dn}\ u \cdot \mathrm{dn}\ v}{1 - k^2\,\mathrm{sn}^2 u \cdot \mathrm{sn}^2 v}$

**748.** $\mathrm{dn}\ (u + v) + \mathrm{dn}\ (u - v) = \dfrac{2\,\mathrm{dn}\ u \cdot \mathrm{dn}\ v}{1 - k^2\,\mathrm{sn}^2 u \cdot \mathrm{sn}^2 v}$

**749.** $\mathrm{dn}\,(u+v) - \mathrm{dn}\,(u-v) = -\dfrac{2\,k^2\,\mathrm{sn}\,u \cdot \mathrm{sn}\,v \cdot \mathrm{cn}\,u \cdot \mathrm{cn}\,v}{1 - k^2\,\mathrm{sn}^2 u \cdot \mathrm{sn}^2 v}$

**750.** $\mathrm{sn}\,(u+v) \cdot \mathrm{sn}\,(u-v) = \dfrac{\mathrm{sn}^2 u - \mathrm{sn}^2 v}{1 - k^2\,\mathrm{sn}^2 u \cdot \mathrm{sn}^2 v}$

$\qquad = \dfrac{\mathrm{cn}^2 v + \mathrm{sn}^2 u \cdot \mathrm{dn}^2 v}{1 - k^2\,\mathrm{sn}^2 u \cdot \mathrm{sn}^2 v} - 1 = \dfrac{1}{k^2}\left[\dfrac{\mathrm{dn}^2 v + k^2\,\mathrm{sn}^2 u \cdot \mathrm{cn}^2 v}{1 - k^2\,\mathrm{sn}^2 u \cdot \mathrm{sn}^2 v} - 1\right]$

**751.** $\mathrm{cn}\,(u+v) \cdot \mathrm{cn}\,(u-v) = \dfrac{\mathrm{cn}^2 u - \mathrm{sn}^2 v + k^2\,\mathrm{sn}^2 u \cdot \mathrm{sn}^2 v}{1 - k^2\,\mathrm{sn}^2 u \cdot \mathrm{sn}^2 v}$

$\qquad = \dfrac{\mathrm{cn}^2 u + \mathrm{cn}^2 v}{1 - k^2\,\mathrm{sn}^2 u \cdot \mathrm{sn}^2 v} - 1 = 1 - \dfrac{\mathrm{sn}^2 u \cdot \mathrm{dn}^2 v + \mathrm{sn}^2 v \cdot \mathrm{dn}^2 u}{1 - k^2\,\mathrm{sn}^2 u \cdot \mathrm{sn}^2 v}$

**752.** $\mathrm{dn}\,(u+v) \cdot \mathrm{dn}\,(u-v)$

$\qquad = \dfrac{1 - k^2\,\mathrm{sn}^2 u - k^2\,\mathrm{sn}^2 v + k^2\,\mathrm{sn}^2 u \cdot \mathrm{sn}^2 v}{1 - k^2\,\mathrm{sn}^2 u \cdot \mathrm{sn}^2 v}$

$\qquad = \dfrac{\mathrm{dn}^2 u + \mathrm{dn}^2 v}{1 - k^2\,\mathrm{sn}^2 u \cdot \mathrm{sn}^2 v} - 1$

**753.** $\mathrm{sn}\,(u \pm v)\,\mathrm{cn}\,(u \mp v) = \dfrac{\mathrm{sn}\,u \cdot \mathrm{cn}\,u \cdot \mathrm{dn}\,v \pm \mathrm{sn}\,v \cdot \mathrm{cn}\,v \cdot \mathrm{dn}\,u}{1 - k^2\,\mathrm{sn}^2 u \cdot \mathrm{sn}^2 v}$

**754.** $\mathrm{sn}\,(u \pm v)\,\mathrm{dn}\,(u \mp v) = \dfrac{\mathrm{sn}\,u \cdot \mathrm{dn}\,u \cdot \mathrm{cn}\,v \pm \mathrm{sn}\,v \cdot \mathrm{dn}\,v \cdot \mathrm{cn}\,u}{1 - k^2\,\mathrm{sn}^2 u \cdot \mathrm{sn}^2 v}$

**755.** $\mathrm{cn}\,(u \pm v)\,\mathrm{dn}\,(u \mp v) = \dfrac{\mathrm{cn}\,u \cdot \mathrm{dn}\,u \cdot \mathrm{cn}\,v \cdot \mathrm{dn}\,v \mp k'^2\,\mathrm{sn}\,u \cdot \mathrm{sn}\,v}{1 - k^2\,\mathrm{sn}^2 u \cdot \mathrm{sn}^2 v}$

**756.** $[1 \pm \mathrm{sn}\,(u+v)][1 \pm \mathrm{sn}\,(u-v)] = \dfrac{(\mathrm{cn}\,v \pm \mathrm{sn}\,u \cdot \mathrm{dn}\,v)^2}{1 - k^2\,\mathrm{sn}^2 u \cdot \mathrm{sn}^2 v}$

**757.** $\mathrm{sn}\,(ui,\,k) = i\,\mathrm{sn}\,(u,\,k')/\mathrm{cn}\,(u,\,k')$

**758.** $\mathrm{cn}\,(ui,\,k) = 1/\mathrm{cn}\,(u,\,k')$

**759.** $\mathrm{dn}\,(ui,\,k) = \mathrm{dn}\,(u,\,k')/\mathrm{cn}\,(u,\,k')$

## BESSEL FUNCTIONS

**760.** $J_n(x) = \sum\limits_{k=0}^{\infty} \dfrac{(-1)^k x^{n+2k}}{2^{n+2k} \cdot k! \, \Gamma(n+k+1)}$

**761.** $J_n(x) = \dfrac{x^n}{2^n n!} \left[ 1 - \dfrac{x^2}{2(2n+2)} + \dfrac{x^4}{2 \cdot 4(2n+2)(2n+4)} \right.$

$$\left. - \dfrac{x^6}{2 \cdot 4 \cdot 6(2n+2)(2n+4)(2n+6)} + \cdots \right]$$

[If $n$ is an integer.]

**762.** $J_0(x) = 1 - \dfrac{x^2}{2^2} + \dfrac{x^4}{2^2 \cdot 4^2} - \dfrac{x^6}{2^2 \cdot 4^2 \cdot 6^2} + \cdots$

**763.** $Y_n(x) = \operatorname{ctn} n\pi \, J_n(x) - \csc n\pi \, J_{-n}(x)$

[Provided $n$ is not an integer.]

The Bessel function of the second kind, here denoted by $Y_n(x)$, is often denoted by $N_n(x)$.

**764.** $Y_n(x) = \dfrac{2}{\pi} J_n(x) \cdot \left( \log \dfrac{x}{2} + \gamma \right) - \dfrac{1}{\pi} \sum\limits_{0}^{n-1} \dfrac{(n-k-1)!}{k!} \left( \dfrac{x}{2} \right)^{-n+2k}$

$$- \dfrac{1}{\pi} \sum\limits_{0}^{\infty} \dfrac{(-1)^k}{(n+k)!k!} \left[ \left( \Omega_k + \Omega_{k+n} \right) \left( \dfrac{x}{2} \right)^{n+2k} \right]$$

[If $n$ is an integer. $\Omega_k = 1 + \tfrac{1}{2} + \tfrac{1}{3} + \cdots + 1/k. \quad \Omega_0 = 0.$]

**765.** $Y_0(x) = \dfrac{2}{\pi} \left[ J_0(x) \cdot \left( \log \dfrac{x}{2} + \gamma \right) + \dfrac{x^2}{2^2} \right.$

$$\left. - \dfrac{x^4 \cdot \Omega_2}{2^2 \cdot 4^2} + \dfrac{x^6 \cdot \Omega_3}{2^2 \cdot 4^2 \cdot 6^2} - \cdots \right]$$

**766.** According as $n$ is or is not an integer, $A \cdot J_n(x) + B \cdot Y_n(x)$, or $A \cdot J_n(x) + B \cdot J_{-n}(x)$ is a particular solution of Bessel's equation,

$$\frac{d^2 y}{dx^2} + \frac{1}{x} \cdot \frac{dy}{dx} + \left( 1 - \frac{n^2}{x^2} \right) y = 0$$

**767.** $dJ_0(x)/dx = -J_1(x); \quad d[x^n \cdot J_n(x)]/dx = x^n \cdot J_{n-1}(x);$

$d[x^{-n} \cdot J_n(x)]/dx = -x^{-n} \cdot J_{n+1}(x).$

**768.** $J_{n-1}(x) - J_{n+1}(x) = 2 \cdot dJ_n(x)/dx;$
    $2 n \cdot J_n(x) = x \cdot J_{n-1}(x) + x \cdot J_{n+1}(x)$

**769.** $J_{-n}(x) = (-1)^n J_n(x),$ if $n$ is an integer.

The relations 767, 768, 769 are also satisfied by $Y_n(x)$.

**770.** $J_{\frac{1}{2}}(x) = \sqrt{\dfrac{2}{\pi x}} \cdot \sin x; \; J_{-\frac{1}{2}}(x) = \sqrt{\dfrac{2}{\pi x}} \cdot \cos x$

**771.** $Y_{\frac{1}{2}}(x) = -\sqrt{\dfrac{2}{\pi x}} \cdot \cos x; \; Y_{-\frac{1}{2}}(x) = \sqrt{\dfrac{2}{\pi x}} \cdot \sin x$

**772.** $H_n^{(1)}(x) = J_n(x) + iY_n(x); \; H_n^{(2)}(x) = J_n(x) - iY(x)$

These functions, the Bessel functions of the third kind, are sometimes called Hankel functions.

**773.** $I_n(x) = i^{-n} J_n(ix) = i^n J_n(-ix)$

This is the modified Bessel function of the first kind.

**774.** $K_n(x) = \frac{1}{2} \pi i^{n+1} H_n^{(1)}(ix) = \frac{1}{2} \pi i^{-n-1} H_n^{(2)}(-ix)$

This is the modified Bessel function of the second kind.

**775.** $K_n(x) = \frac{1}{2} \pi \csc n\pi [I_{-n}(x) - I_n(x)]$

[Provided $n$ is not an integer.]

**776.** $I_{-n}(x) = I_n(x),$ if $n$ is an integer;
    $K_{-n}(x) = K_n(x),$ for all values of $n$

**777.** $I_{\frac{1}{2}}(x) = \sqrt{\dfrac{2}{\pi x}} \cdot \sinh x; \; I_{-\frac{1}{2}}(x) = \sqrt{\dfrac{2}{\pi x}} \cdot \cosh x;$

$K_{\frac{1}{2}}(x) = \sqrt{\dfrac{\pi}{2 x}} \cdot e^{-x}$

When $x$ is large it is sometimes convenient to compute approximate numerical values of $J_n(x)$ by means of the asymptotic series,

**778.** $J_n(x) \sim \sqrt{\dfrac{2}{\pi x}} \, [P_n \cdot \cos \{x - \frac{1}{2} n\pi - \frac{1}{4} \pi\}$

$- Q_n \cdot \sin \{x - \frac{1}{2} n\pi - \frac{1}{4} \pi\} ]$

**779.** $Y_n(x) \sim \sqrt{\dfrac{2}{\pi x}} \, [P_n \cdot \sin \, (x - \tfrac{1}{2} \, n\pi - \tfrac{1}{4} \, \pi)$

$$+ \, Q_n \cdot \cos \, (x - \tfrac{1}{2} \, n\pi - \tfrac{1}{4} \, \pi)]$$

**780.** $P_n = 1 - \dfrac{(4 \, n^2 - 1)(4 \, n^2 - 9)}{2! \, (8 \, x)^2}$

$$+ \, \dfrac{(4 \, n^2 - 1)(4 \, n^2 - 9)(4 \, n^2 - 25)(4 \, n^2 - 49)}{4! \, (8 \, x)^4} - \cdots$$

**781.** $Q_n = \dfrac{4 \, n^2 - 1}{8 \, x} - \dfrac{(4 \, n^2 - 1)(4 \, n^2 - 9)(4 \, n^2 - 25)}{3! \, (8 \, x)^3} + \cdots$

**782.** $I_n(x) \sim \dfrac{e^x}{\sqrt{2 \, \pi x}} \, [R_n - S_n]$

**783.** $K_n(x) \sim \sqrt{\dfrac{\pi}{2 \, x}} \, e^{-x} [R_n + S_n]$

**784.** $R_n = 1 + \dfrac{(4 \, n^2 - 1)(4 \, n^2 - 9)}{2! \, (8 \, x)^2}$

$$+ \, \dfrac{(4 \, n^2 - 1)(4 \, n^2 - 9)(4 \, n^2 - 25)(4 \, n^2 - 49)}{4! \, (8 \, x)^4} + \cdots$$

**785.** $S_n = \dfrac{4 \, n^2 - 1}{8 \, x} + \dfrac{(4 \, n^2 - 1)(4 \, n^2 - 9)(4 \, n^2 - 25)}{3! \, (8 \, x)^3} + \cdots$

## OTHER SPECIAL FUNCTIONS

The gamma function may be defined as an infinite integral.

**786.** $\Gamma(x) = \displaystyle\int_0^\infty t^{x-1} e^{-t} dt$ $\qquad\qquad x > 0$

It is often more desirable, however, to define the reciprocal of the gamma function as an infinite product [see formula 897].

**787.** $\Gamma(x + 1) = x\Gamma(x)$

**788.** $\Gamma(1) = 1; \, \Gamma(n) = (n - 1)!$, if $n$ is an integer

**789.** $\Gamma(x)\Gamma(1-x) = \dfrac{\pi}{\sin \pi x}$

**790.** $\Gamma(\frac{1}{2}) = \sqrt{\pi}$

**791.** $2^{2x-1}\Gamma(x)\Gamma(x + \frac{1}{2}) = \sqrt{\pi} \cdot \Gamma(2x)$

**792.** $\psi(x) = \dfrac{d}{dx} \log \Gamma(x) = \dfrac{\Gamma'(x)}{\Gamma(x)}$

This is the logarithmic derivate of the gamma function.

**793.** $\psi(x+1) = \dfrac{1}{x} + \psi(x)$

**794.** $\gamma = \lim\limits_{n \to \infty} \left[ 1 + \dfrac{1}{2} + \dfrac{1}{3} + \cdots + \dfrac{1}{n} - \log n \right]$

This number is sometimes called Euler's or Mascheroni's constant. Its numerical value is 0.5772157, correct to seven significant figures.

**795.** $\psi(1) = -\gamma$

**796.** $\psi(n) = 1 + \dfrac{1}{2} + \dfrac{1}{3} + \cdots + \dfrac{1}{n-1} - \gamma$, if $n$ is an integer

greater than unity.

**797.** $B(x, y) = \dfrac{\Gamma(x)\Gamma(y)}{\Gamma(x+y)}$

This function, called the beta function, is often defined as a definite integral:

**798.** $B(x, y) = \displaystyle\int_0^1 t^{x-1}(1-t)^{y-1}dt$ $\qquad x > 0, y > 0$

The following three functions, the sine-integral, cosine-integral, and exponential-integral, are defined as definite integrals:

**799.** $\mathrm{Si}(x) = \displaystyle\int_0^x \dfrac{\sin t}{t}\, dt$

**800.** $\mathrm{Ci}(x) = \displaystyle\int_{\infty}^{x} \frac{\cos t}{t}\, dt$

**801.** $\mathrm{Ei}(x) = \displaystyle\int_{x}^{\infty} \frac{e^{-t}}{t}\, dt$

It should be noted, however, that the cosine-integral is sometimes defined as the negative of that given above, and that the exponential-integral is very often taken to be

$$\int_{-\infty}^{x} \frac{e^{t}}{t}\, dt$$

**802.** $\mathrm{Si}(x) = x - \dfrac{x^3}{3\cdot 3!} + \dfrac{x^5}{5\cdot 5!} - \dfrac{x^7}{7\cdot 7!} + \cdots$

**803.** $\mathrm{Ci}(x) = \log x + \gamma - \dfrac{x^2}{2\cdot 2!} + \dfrac{x^4}{4\cdot 4!} - \dfrac{x^6}{6\cdot 6!} + \cdots$

**804.** $\mathrm{Ei}(x) = -\log x - \gamma + x - \dfrac{x^2}{2\cdot 2!} + \dfrac{x^3}{3\cdot 3!} - \dfrac{x^4}{4\cdot 4!} + \cdots$

For large positive values of $x$, the following asymptotic series are useful:

**805.** $\mathrm{Si}(x) \sim \dfrac{\pi}{2} - \cos x \left[\dfrac{1}{x} - \dfrac{2!}{x^3} + \dfrac{4!}{x^5} - \dfrac{6!}{x^7} + \cdots \right]$

$\qquad\qquad - \sin x \left[\dfrac{1}{x^2} - \dfrac{3!}{x^4} + \dfrac{5!}{x^6} - \dfrac{7!}{x^8} + \cdots \right]$

**806.** $\mathrm{Ci}(x) \sim \sin x \left[\dfrac{1}{x} - \dfrac{2!}{x^3} + \dfrac{4!}{x^5} - \dfrac{6!}{x^7} + \cdots \right]$

$\qquad\qquad - \cos x \left[\dfrac{1}{x^2} - \dfrac{3!}{x^4} + \dfrac{5!}{x^6} - \dfrac{7!}{x^8} + \cdots \right]$

**807.** $\mathrm{Ei}(x) \sim e^{-x} \left[\dfrac{1}{x} - \dfrac{1}{x^2} + \dfrac{2!}{x^3} - \dfrac{3!}{x^4} + \cdots \right]$

The error function, or probability integral (see table on pages 128–132), is defined as follows:

**808.** $\mathrm{erf}\,(x) = \dfrac{2}{\sqrt{\pi}} \displaystyle\int_{0}^{x} \exp\,(-u^2)\, du$

and its complementary function which follows:

**809.** $\mathrm{erfc}\ (x) = \dfrac{2}{\sqrt{\pi}} \displaystyle\int_x^\infty \exp\ (-u^2)du$

**810.** $\mathrm{erf}\ (x) + \mathrm{erfc}\ (x) = 1$

**811.** $\mathrm{erf}\ (x) = \dfrac{2}{\sqrt{\pi}} \left[ x - \dfrac{x^3}{3} + \dfrac{x^5}{5 \cdot 2!} - \dfrac{x^7}{7 \cdot 3!} + \cdots \right]$

For large positive values of $x$, the following asymptotic series is convenient:

**812.** $\mathrm{erf}\ (x) \sim$
$$1 - \frac{\exp\ (-x^2)}{x\sqrt{\pi}} \left[ 1 - \frac{1}{2\,x^2} + \frac{1 \cdot 3}{(2\,x^2)^2} - \frac{1 \cdot 3 \cdot 5}{(2\,x^2)^3} + \cdots \right]$$

## SERIES AND PRODUCTS

The expression in brackets attached to an infinite series shows values of the variable which lie within the interval of convergence. If a series is convergent for all finite values of $x$, the expression $[x^2 < \infty]$ is used.

**813.** $(a + b)^n = a^n + na^{n-1}b + \dfrac{n(n-1)}{2!}\,a^{n-2}b^2$
$$+ \cdots + \frac{n!a^{n-k}b^k}{(n-k)!k!} + \cdots \qquad [b^2 < a^2]$$

**814.** $(a - bx)^{-1} = \dfrac{1}{a}\left[ 1 + \dfrac{bx}{a} + \dfrac{b^2x^2}{a^2} + \dfrac{b^3x^3}{a^3} + \cdots \right] \quad [b^2x^2 < a^2]$

**815.** $(1 \pm x)^n = 1 \pm nx + \dfrac{n(n-1)}{2!}\,x^2 \pm \dfrac{n(n-1)(n-2)x^3}{3!}$
$$+ \cdots + \frac{(\pm 1)^k n! x^k}{(n-k)!k!} + \cdots \qquad [x^2 < 1]$$

**816.** $(1 \pm x)^{-n} = 1 \mp nx + \dfrac{n(n+1)}{2!}\,x^2 \mp \dfrac{n(n+1)(n+2)x^3}{3!}$
$$+ \cdots + (\mp 1)^k \frac{(n+k-1)!x^k}{(n-1)!k!} + \cdots \qquad [x^2 < 1]$$

**817.** $(1 \pm x)^{\frac{1}{2}} = 1 \pm \frac{1}{2}x - \dfrac{1 \cdot 1}{2 \cdot 4}x^2 \pm \dfrac{1 \cdot 1 \cdot 3}{2 \cdot 4 \cdot 6}x^3$

$$- \dfrac{1 \cdot 1 \cdot 3 \cdot 5}{2 \cdot 4 \cdot 6 \cdot 8}x^4 \pm \cdots \qquad [x^2 < 1]$$

**818.** $(1 \pm x)^{-\frac{1}{2}} = 1 \mp \frac{1}{2}x + \dfrac{1 \cdot 3}{2 \cdot 4}x^2 \mp \dfrac{1 \cdot 3 \cdot 5}{2 \cdot 4 \cdot 6}x^3$

$$+ \dfrac{1 \cdot 3 \cdot 5 \cdot 7}{2 \cdot 4 \cdot 6 \cdot 8}x^4 \mp \cdots \qquad [x^2 < 1]$$

**819.** $(1 \pm x)^{\frac{1}{3}} = 1 \pm \frac{1}{3}x - \dfrac{1 \cdot 2}{3 \cdot 6}x^2 \pm \dfrac{1 \cdot 2 \cdot 5}{3 \cdot 6 \cdot 9}x^3$

$$- \dfrac{1 \cdot 2 \cdot 5 \cdot 8}{3 \cdot 6 \cdot 9 \cdot 12}x^4 \pm \cdots \qquad [x^2 < 1]$$

**820.** $(1 \pm x)^{-\frac{1}{3}} = 1 \mp \frac{1}{3}x + \dfrac{1 \cdot 4}{3 \cdot 6}x^2 \mp \dfrac{1 \cdot 4 \cdot 7}{3 \cdot 6 \cdot 9}x^3$

$$+ \dfrac{1 \cdot 4 \cdot 7 \cdot 10}{3 \cdot 6 \cdot 9 \cdot 12}x^4 \mp \cdots \qquad [x^2 < 1]$$

**821.** $(1 \pm x^2)^{\frac{1}{2}} = 1 \pm \frac{1}{2}x^2 - \dfrac{x^4}{2 \cdot 4} \pm \dfrac{1 \cdot 3}{2 \cdot 4 \cdot 6}x^6 - \dfrac{1 \cdot 3 \cdot 5}{2 \cdot 4 \cdot 6 \cdot 8}x^8 \pm \cdots$

$$[x^2 < 1]$$

**822.** $(1 \pm x^2)^{-\frac{1}{2}} = 1 \mp \frac{1}{2}x^2 + \dfrac{1 \cdot 3}{2 \cdot 4}x^4 \mp \dfrac{1 \cdot 3 \cdot 5}{2 \cdot 4 \cdot 6}x^6 + \cdots$

$$[x^2 < 1]$$

**823.** $(1 \pm x)^{-1} = 1 \mp x + x^2 \mp x^3 + x^4 \mp x^5 + \cdots \qquad [x^2 < 1]$

**824.** $(1 \pm x)^{\frac{3}{2}} = 1 \pm \frac{3}{2}x + \dfrac{3 \cdot 1}{2 \cdot 4}x^2 \mp \dfrac{3 \cdot 1 \cdot 1}{2 \cdot 4 \cdot 6}x^3$

$$+ \dfrac{3 \cdot 1 \cdot 1 \cdot 3}{2 \cdot 4 \cdot 6 \cdot 8}x^4 \mp \dfrac{3 \cdot 1 \cdot 1 \cdot 3 \cdot 5}{2 \cdot 4 \cdot 6 \cdot 8 \cdot 10}x^5 + \cdots \qquad [x^2 < 1]$$

**825.** $(1 \pm x)^{-\frac{3}{2}} = 1 \mp \frac{3}{2}x + \dfrac{3 \cdot 5}{2 \cdot 4}x^2 \mp \dfrac{3 \cdot 5 \cdot 7}{2 \cdot 4 \cdot 6}x^3 + \cdots$

$$[x^2 < 1]$$

**826.** $(1 \pm x)^{-2} = 1 \mp 2x + 3x^2 \mp 4x^3 + 5x^4 \mp 6x^5 + \cdots$

$$[x^2 < 1]$$

**827.** $e^x = 1 + x + \dfrac{x^2}{2!} + \dfrac{x^3}{3!} + \cdots$ $\qquad\qquad [x^2 < \infty]$

**828.** $a^x = 1 + x \log a + \dfrac{(x \log a)^2}{2!} + \dfrac{(x \log a)^3}{3!} + \cdots \; [x^2 < \infty]$

**829.** $\frac{1}{2}(e^x + e^{-x}) = 1 + \dfrac{x^2}{2!} + \dfrac{x^4}{4!} + \dfrac{x^6}{6!} + \cdots$ $\qquad [x^2 < \infty]$

**830.** $\frac{1}{2}(e^x - e^{-x}) = x + \dfrac{x^3}{3!} + \dfrac{x^5}{5!} + \dfrac{x^7}{7!} + \cdots$ $\qquad [x^2 < \infty]$

**831.** $e^{-x^2} = 1 - x^2 + \dfrac{x^4}{2!} - \dfrac{x^6}{3!} + \dfrac{x^8}{4!} - \cdots$ $\qquad [x^2 < \infty]$

**832.** $1 + \dfrac{1}{2^2} + \dfrac{1}{3^2} + \dfrac{1}{4^2} + \cdots = \dfrac{\pi^2}{6}$

**833.** $1 - \dfrac{1}{2^2} + \dfrac{1}{3^2} - \dfrac{1}{4^2} + \cdots = \dfrac{\pi^2}{12}$

**834.** $1 + \dfrac{1}{3^2} + \dfrac{1}{5^2} + \dfrac{1}{7^2} + \cdots = \dfrac{\pi^2}{8}$

**835.** $\dfrac{1}{2^2} + \dfrac{1}{4^2} + \dfrac{1}{6^2} + \dfrac{1}{8^2} + \cdots = \dfrac{\pi^2}{24}$

A series of numbers, $B_1$, $B_2$, $B_3$, $\cdots$, of odd and even orders, which appear in the developments of many functions, may be computed by means of the equations,

$$B_{2n} - \frac{2\,n(2\,n-1)}{2!}\,B_{2n-2}$$

$$+ \frac{2\,n(2\,n-1)(2\,n-2)(2\,n-3)}{4!}\,B_{2n-4} - \cdots + (-1)^n = 0,$$

$$\frac{2^{2n}(2^{2n}-1)}{2\,n}\,B_{2n-1} = (2\,n-1)B_{2n-2}$$

$$- \frac{(2\,n-1)(2\,n-2)(2\,n-3)}{3!}\,B_{2n-4} + \cdots + (-1)^{n-1}$$

Whence $B_1 = \frac{1}{6}$, $B_2 = 1$, $B_3 = \frac{1}{30}$, $B_4 = 5$, $B_5 = \frac{1}{42}$, $B_6 = 61$,

$B_7 = \frac{1}{30}$, $B_8 = 1385$, $B_9 = \frac{5}{66}$, $B_{10} = 50521$, $B_{11} = \frac{691}{2730}$, $B_{12} = 2702765$, $B_{13} = \frac{7}{6}$, etc. The $B$'s of odd orders are called Bernoulli's Numbers; those of even orders, Euler's Numbers. What are here denoted by $B_{2n-1}$ and $B_{2n}$ are sometimes represented by $B_n$ and $E_n$, respectively,

**836.** $\dfrac{B_{2n-1}}{(2n)!} = \dfrac{2}{(2^{2n} - 1)\pi^{2n}} \left[1 + \dfrac{1}{3^{2n}} + \dfrac{1}{5^{2n}} + \dfrac{1}{7^{2n}} + \cdots \right]$

**837.** $\dfrac{B_{2n}}{(2n)!} = \dfrac{2^{2n+2}}{\pi^{2n+1}} \left[1 - \dfrac{1}{3^{2n+1}} + \dfrac{1}{5^{2n+1}} - \dfrac{1}{7^{2n+1}} + \cdots \right]$

**838.** $\dfrac{x}{e^x - 1} = 1 - \dfrac{x}{2} + \dfrac{B_1 x^2}{2!} - \dfrac{B_3 x^4}{4!} + \dfrac{B_5 x^6}{6!} - \dfrac{B_7 x^8}{8!} + \cdots$
$$[x < 2\pi]$$

**839.** $\log x = (x-1) - \frac{1}{2}(x-1)^2 + \frac{1}{3}(x-1)^3 - \cdots$
$$[2 > x > 0]$$

**840.** $\log x = \dfrac{x-1}{x} + \frac{1}{2}\left(\dfrac{x-1}{x}\right)^2 + \frac{1}{3}\left(\dfrac{x-1}{x}\right)^3 + \cdots \quad [x > \frac{1}{2}]$

**841.** $\log x = 2\left[\dfrac{x-1}{x+1} + \frac{1}{3}\left(\dfrac{x-1}{x+1}\right)^3 + \frac{1}{5}\left(\dfrac{x-1}{x+1}\right)^5 + \cdots\right]$
$$[x > 0]$$

**842.** $\log(1+x) = x - \frac{1}{2}x^2 + \frac{1}{3}x^3 - \frac{1}{4}x^4 + \cdots \qquad [x^2 < 1]$

**843.** $\log\left(\dfrac{1+x}{1-x}\right) = 2[x + \frac{1}{3}x^3 + \frac{1}{5}x^5 + \frac{1}{7}x^7 + \cdots] \qquad [x^2 < 1]$

**844.** $\log\left(\dfrac{x+1}{x-1}\right) = 2\left[\dfrac{1}{x} + \frac{1}{3}\left(\dfrac{1}{x}\right)^3 + \frac{1}{5}\left(\dfrac{1}{x}\right)^5 + \cdots\right] \qquad [x^2 > 1]$

**845.** $\log(x + \sqrt{1+x^2}) = x - \dfrac{1}{6}\dfrac{x^3}{1} + \dfrac{1 \cdot 3}{2 \cdot 4 \cdot 5}x^5 - \dfrac{1 \cdot 3 \cdot 5}{2 \cdot 4 \cdot 6 \cdot 7}x^7 + \cdots$
$$[x^2 < 1]$$

Series for denary and other logarithms can be obtained from the foregoing developments by aid of the equations,
$$\log_a x = \log_e x \cdot \log_a e, \quad \log_e x = \log_a x \cdot \log_e a,$$
$$\log_e(-z) = (2n+1)\pi i + \log_e z$$

**846.** $\sin x = x - \dfrac{x^3}{3!} + \dfrac{x^5}{5!} - \dfrac{x^7}{7!} + \cdots$ $\qquad$ $[x^2 < \infty]$

**847.** $\cos x = 1 - \dfrac{x^2}{2!} + \dfrac{x^4}{4!} - \dfrac{x^6}{6!} + \cdots = 1 - \text{versin } x.$ $\quad [x^2 < \infty]$

**848.** $\tan x = x + \dfrac{x^3}{3} + \dfrac{2\,x^5}{15} + \dfrac{17\,x^7}{315} + \dfrac{62\,x^9}{2835}$

$\qquad + \cdots + \dfrac{2^{2n}(2^{2n} - 1)B_{2n-1}x^{2n-1}}{(2\,n)!} + \cdots$ $\qquad [x^2 < \tfrac{1}{4}\,\pi^2]$

**849.** $\text{ctn } x = \dfrac{1}{x} - \dfrac{x}{3} - \dfrac{x^3}{45} - \dfrac{2\,x^5}{945} - \dfrac{x^7}{4725}$

$\qquad - \cdots - \dfrac{B_{2n-1}(2\,x)^{2n}}{x(2\,n)!} - \cdots$ $\qquad [x^2 < \pi^2]$

**850.** $\sec x = 1 + \dfrac{x^2}{2!} + \dfrac{5\,x^4}{4!} + \dfrac{61\,x^6}{6!} + \cdots + \dfrac{B_{2n}x^{2n}}{(2\,n)!} + \cdots$

$\qquad\qquad\qquad\qquad\qquad\qquad\qquad \left[x^2 < \dfrac{\pi^2}{4}\right]$

**851.** $\csc x = \dfrac{1}{x} + \dfrac{x}{3!} + \dfrac{7\,x^3}{3 \cdot 5!} + \dfrac{31\,x^5}{3 \cdot 7!}$

$\qquad + \cdots + \dfrac{2(2^{2n+1} - 1)}{(2\,n + 2)!}\,B_{2n+1}x^{2n+1} + \cdots$ $\qquad [x^2 < \pi^2]$

**852.** $\sin^{-1}x = x + \dfrac{x^3}{6} + \dfrac{1 \cdot 3}{2 \cdot 4} \cdot \dfrac{x^5}{5} + \dfrac{1 \cdot 3 \cdot 5}{2 \cdot 4 \cdot 6} \cdot \dfrac{x^7}{7} + \cdots$

$\qquad\qquad = \tfrac{1}{2}\,\pi - \cos^{-1}x$ $\qquad\qquad [x^2 < 1]$

**853.** $\tan^{-1}x = x - \tfrac{1}{3}\,x^3 + \tfrac{1}{5}\,x^5 - \tfrac{1}{7}\,x^7 + \cdots = \tfrac{1}{2}\,\pi - \text{ctn}^{-1}x$

$\qquad\qquad\qquad\qquad\qquad\qquad\qquad\qquad [x^2 < 1]$

**854.** $\tan^{-1}x = \dfrac{\pi}{2} - \dfrac{1}{x} + \dfrac{1}{3\,x^3} - \dfrac{1}{5\,x^5} + \cdots$ $\qquad [x^2 > 1]$

**855.** $\sec^{-1}x = \dfrac{\pi}{2} - \dfrac{1}{x} - \dfrac{1}{6\,x^3} - \dfrac{1 \cdot 3}{2 \cdot 4 \cdot 5\,x^5} - \dfrac{1 \cdot 3 \cdot 5}{2 \cdot 4 \cdot 6 \cdot 7\,x^7} - \cdots$

$\qquad\qquad = \tfrac{1}{2}\,\pi - \csc^{-1}x$ $\qquad\qquad [x^2 > 1]$

**856.** $\log \sin x = \log x - \frac{1}{6} x^2 - \frac{1}{180} x^4 - \frac{1}{2835} x^6$

$$- \cdots - \frac{2^{2n-1} B_{2n-1} x^{2n}}{n(2\,n)!} - \cdots \qquad [x^2 < \pi^2]$$

**857.** $\log \cos x = - \frac{1}{2} x^2 - \frac{1}{12} x^4 - \frac{1}{45} x^6 - \frac{17}{2520} x^8$

$$- \cdots - \frac{2^{2n-1}(2^{2n} - 1) B_{2n-1} x^{2n}}{n(2\,n)!} - \cdots \qquad [x^2 < \tfrac{1}{4} \pi^2]$$

**858.** $\log \tan x = \log x + \frac{1}{3} x^2 + \frac{7}{90} x^4 + \frac{62}{2835} x^6$

$$+ \cdots + \frac{(2^{2n-1} - 1) 2^{2n} B_{2n-1} x^{2n}}{n(2\,n)!} + \cdots \qquad [x^2 < \tfrac{1}{4} \pi^2]$$

**859.** $e^{\sin x} = 1 + x + \dfrac{x^2}{2!} - \dfrac{3\,x^4}{4!} - \dfrac{8\,x^5}{5!} - \dfrac{3\,x^6}{6!} + \dfrac{56\,x^7}{7!} + \cdots$

$$[x^2 < \infty]$$

**860.** $e^{\cos x} = e \left( 1 - \dfrac{x^2}{2!} + \dfrac{4\,x^4}{4!} - \dfrac{31\,x^6}{6!} + \cdots \right) \qquad [x^2 < \infty]$

**861.** $e^{\tan x} = 1 + x + \dfrac{x^2}{2!} + \dfrac{3\,x^3}{3!} + \dfrac{9\,x^4}{4!} + \dfrac{37\,x^5}{5!} + \cdots \quad [x^2 < \tfrac{1}{4} \pi^2]$

**862.** $e^{\sin^{-1} x} = 1 + x + \dfrac{x^2}{2!} + \dfrac{2\,x^3}{3!} + \dfrac{5\,x^4}{4!} + \cdots \qquad [x^2 < 1]$

**863.** $e^{\tan^{-1} x} = 1 + x + \dfrac{x^2}{2} - \dfrac{x^3}{6} - \dfrac{7\,x^4}{24} - \cdots \qquad [x^2 < 1]$

**864.** $\sinh x = x + \dfrac{x^3}{3!} + \dfrac{x^5}{5!} + \dfrac{x^7}{7!} + \cdots \qquad [x^2 < \infty]$

**865.** $\cosh x = 1 + \dfrac{x^2}{2!} + \dfrac{x^4}{4!} + \dfrac{x^6}{6!} + \dfrac{x^8}{8!} + \cdots \qquad [x^2 < \infty]$

**866.** $\tanh x = (2^2 - 1) 2^2 B_1 \dfrac{x}{2!} - (2^4 - 1) 2^4 B_3 \dfrac{x^3}{4!} + \cdots$

$$= \Sigma [(-1)^{n-1} 2^{2n} (2^{2n} - 1) B_{2n-1} x^{2n-1} / (2\,n)!]$$

$$[x^2 < \tfrac{1}{4} \pi^2]$$

**867.** $\operatorname{ctnh} x = \dfrac{1}{x} \left(1 + \Sigma[(-1)^{n-1} 2^{2n} B_{2n-1} x^{2n}/(2\,n)!]\right)$

$$[x^2 < \pi^2]$$

**868.** $\operatorname{sech} x = 1 + \Sigma[(-1)^n B_{2n} x^{2n}/(2\,n)!] \qquad [x^2 < \tfrac{1}{4}\,\pi^2]$

**869.** $\operatorname{csch} x = \dfrac{1}{x} - (2-1)2\,B_1 \dfrac{x}{2!} + (2^3-1)2\,B_3 \dfrac{x^3}{4!} - \cdots$

$$= \dfrac{1}{x}\left(1 + 2\,\Sigma[(-1)^n(2^{2n-1}-1)B_{2n-1}x^{2n}/(2\,n)!]\right)$$

$$[x^2 < \pi^2]$$

**870.** $\sinh^{-1}x = x - \tfrac{1}{6}\,x^3 + \dfrac{1 \cdot 3\,x^5}{2 \cdot 4 \cdot 5} - \dfrac{1 \cdot 3 \cdot 5 \cdot x^7}{2 \cdot 4 \cdot 6 \cdot 7} + \cdots$

$$[x^2 < 1]$$

**871.** $\tanh^{-1}x = x + \dfrac{x^3}{3} + \dfrac{x^5}{5} + \dfrac{x^7}{7} + \cdots \qquad [x^2 < 1]$

**872.** $\operatorname{ctnh}^{-1}x = \dfrac{1}{x} + \dfrac{1}{3\,x^3} + \dfrac{1}{5\,x^5} + \cdots \qquad [x^2 > 1]$

**873.** $\operatorname{csch}^{-1}x = \dfrac{1}{x} - \dfrac{1}{2 \cdot 3 \cdot x^3} + \dfrac{1 \cdot 3}{2 \cdot 4 \cdot 5 \cdot x^5} - \dfrac{1 \cdot 3 \cdot 5}{2 \cdot 4 \cdot 6 \cdot 7 \cdot x^7} + \cdots$

$$[x^2 > 1]$$

**874.** $\displaystyle\int_0^x e^{-x^2}dx = x - \tfrac{1}{3}\,x^3 + \dfrac{x^5}{5 \cdot 2!} - \dfrac{x^7}{7 \cdot 3!} + \cdots \qquad [x^2 < \infty]$

**875.** $\displaystyle\int_0^x \cos(x^2)dx = x - \dfrac{x^5}{5 \cdot 2!} + \dfrac{x^9}{9 \cdot 4!} - \dfrac{x^{13}}{13 \cdot 6!} + \cdots$

$$[x^2 < \infty]$$

**876.** $\displaystyle\int_0^x \dfrac{\sin x}{x}\,dx = x - \dfrac{x^3}{3 \cdot 3!} + \dfrac{x^5}{5 \cdot 5!} - \dfrac{x^7}{7 \cdot 7!} + \cdots \qquad [x^2 < \infty]$

**877.** $\displaystyle\int_0^1 \dfrac{x^{a-1}dx}{1+x^b} = \dfrac{1}{a} - \dfrac{1}{a+b} + \dfrac{1}{a+2\,b} - \dfrac{1}{a+3\,b} + \cdots$

878. $\sec x = 4\,\pi \left[ \dfrac{1}{\pi^2 - 4\,x^2} - \dfrac{3}{9\,\pi^2 - 4\,x^2} + \dfrac{5}{25\,\pi^2 - 4\,x^2} - \dfrac{7}{49\,\pi^2 - 4\,x^2} + \cdots \right]$

879. $\csc x = \dfrac{1}{x} + 2\,x \left[ \dfrac{1}{\pi^2 - x^2} - \dfrac{1}{4\,\pi^2 - x^2} + \dfrac{1}{9\,\pi^2 - x^2} - \dfrac{1}{16\,\pi^2 - x^2} + \cdots \right]$

880. $\tan x = 8\,x \left[ \dfrac{1}{\pi^2 - 4\,x^2} + \dfrac{1}{9\,\pi^2 - 4\,x^2} + \dfrac{1}{25\,\pi^2 - 4\,x^2} + \dfrac{1}{49\,\pi^2 - 4\,x^2} + \cdots \right]$

881. $\operatorname{ctn} x = \dfrac{1}{x} - 2\,x \left[ \dfrac{1}{\pi^2 - x^2} + \dfrac{1}{4\,\pi^2 - x^2} + \dfrac{1}{9\,\pi^2 - x^2} + \dfrac{1}{16\,\pi^2 - x^2} + \cdots \right]$

882. $f(x + h) = f(x) + h \cdot f'(x + \theta h)$

883. $f(x + h) = f(x) + h \cdot f'(x) + \dfrac{h^2}{2!} f''(x) + \cdots + \dfrac{h^n}{n!} \cdot f^n(x + \theta h)$

884. $f(x + h) = f(x) + h \cdot f'(x) + \dfrac{h^2}{2!} f''(x) + \cdots + \dfrac{h^n}{(n-1)!} \cdot (1 - \theta)^{n-1} \cdot f^n(x + \theta h)$

885. $f(x + h, y + k) = f(x, y) + h f'_x(x + \theta h, y + \theta k) + k f'_y(x + \theta h, y + \theta k)$

**886.** $f(x+h, y+k) = f(x, y) + \left( h\dfrac{\partial f(x, y)}{\partial x} + k\dfrac{\partial f(x, y)}{\partial y} \right)$

$+ \dfrac{1}{2!}\left( h^2 \dfrac{\partial^2 f(x, y)}{\partial x^2} + 2\,hk\dfrac{\partial^2 f(x, y)}{\partial x \cdot \partial y} + k^2 \dfrac{\partial^2 f(x, y)}{\partial y^2} \right)$

$+ \dfrac{1}{3!}\left( h^3 \dfrac{\partial^3 f(x, y)}{\partial x^3} + 3\,h^2k\dfrac{\partial^3 f(x, y)}{\partial y \cdot \partial x^2} + 3\,hk^2\dfrac{\partial^3 f(x, y)}{\partial x \cdot \partial y^2} + k^3 \dfrac{\partial^3 f(x, y)}{\partial y^3} \right) + \cdots + R_n$

$= f(x, y) + (hD_x + kD_y)f(x, y) + \dfrac{1}{2!}\,(hD_x + kD_y)^2 f(x, y)$

$+ \cdots + \dfrac{1}{(n-1)!}\,(hD_x + kD_y)^{n-1}f(x, y) + \dfrac{1}{n!}\,(hD_x + kD_y)^n f(x + \theta h, y + \theta k)$

**887.** $1 = \dfrac{4}{\pi}\left[ \sin\dfrac{\pi x}{c} + \dfrac{1}{3}\sin\dfrac{3\,\pi x}{c} + \dfrac{1}{5}\sin\dfrac{5\,\pi x}{c} + \cdots \right]$ $\qquad [0 < x < c]$

**888.** $x = \dfrac{2\,c}{\pi}\left[ \sin\dfrac{\pi x}{c} - \dfrac{1}{2}\sin\dfrac{2\,\pi x}{c} + \dfrac{1}{3}\sin\dfrac{3\,\pi x}{c} - \cdots \right]$ $\qquad [-c < x < c]$

**889.** $x = \dfrac{c}{2} - \dfrac{4\,c}{\pi^2}\left[ \cos\dfrac{\pi x}{c} + \dfrac{1}{3^2}\cos\dfrac{3\,\pi x}{c} + \dfrac{1}{5^2}\cos\dfrac{5\,\pi x}{c} + \cdots \right]$ $\qquad [0 < x < c]$

**890.** $x^2 = \dfrac{2\,c^2}{\pi^3} \left[ \left(\dfrac{\pi^2}{1} - \dfrac{4}{1}\right) \sin \dfrac{\pi x}{c} - \dfrac{\pi^2}{2} \sin \dfrac{2\,\pi x}{c} + \left(\dfrac{\pi^2}{3} - \dfrac{4}{3^3}\right) \sin \dfrac{3\,\pi x}{c} - \dfrac{\pi^2}{4} \sin \dfrac{4\,\pi x}{c} \right.$

$\left. + \left(\dfrac{\pi^2}{5} - \dfrac{4}{5^3}\right) \sin \dfrac{5\,\pi x}{c} + \cdots \right]$  $[0 < x < c]$

**891.** $x^2 = \dfrac{c^2}{3} - \dfrac{4\,c^2}{\pi^2} \left[ \cos \dfrac{\pi x}{c} - \dfrac{1}{2^2} \cos \dfrac{2\,\pi x}{c} + \dfrac{1}{3^2} \cos \dfrac{3\,\pi x}{c} - \dfrac{1}{4^2} \cos \dfrac{4\,\pi x}{c} + \cdots \right]$  $[-c < x < c]$

**892.** $\log \sin \tfrac{1}{2} x = -\log 2 - \cos x - \tfrac{1}{2} \cos 2\,x - \tfrac{1}{3} \cos 3\,x - \cdots$  $[0 < x < \tfrac{1}{2}\pi]$

**893.** $\log \cos \tfrac{1}{2} x = -\log 2 + \cos x - \tfrac{1}{2} \cos 2\,x + \tfrac{1}{3} \cos 3\,x - \cdots$  $[0 < x < \tfrac{1}{2}\pi]$

**894.** $f(x) = \tfrac{1}{2} a_0 + a_1 \cos \dfrac{\pi x}{c} + a_2 \cos \dfrac{2\,\pi x}{c} + \cdots + b_1 \sin \dfrac{\pi x}{c} + b_2 \sin \dfrac{2\,\pi x}{c} + \cdots,$  $[-c < x < c]$

where $a_m = \dfrac{1}{c} \displaystyle\int_{-c}^{+c} f(t) \cos \dfrac{m\pi t}{c}\, dt, \; b_m = \dfrac{1}{c} \displaystyle\int_{-c}^{+c} f(t) \sin \dfrac{m\pi t}{c}\, dt$

**896.** $\cos \theta = \left[ 1 - \left( \dfrac{2\,\theta}{\pi} \right)^2 \right] \left[ 1 - \left( \dfrac{2\,\theta}{3\,\pi} \right)^2 \right] \left[ 1 - \left( \dfrac{2\,\theta}{5\,\pi} \right)^2 \right] \cdots$

$$[\theta^2 < \infty]$$

**897.** $\dfrac{1}{\Gamma(x)} = x e^{\gamma x} \displaystyle\prod_{k=1}^{\infty} \left[ \left( 1 + \dfrac{x}{k} \right) e^{-\frac{x}{k}} \right]$

**898.** $\Gamma(x) = \dfrac{1}{x} \displaystyle\prod_{k=1}^{\infty} \dfrac{\left( 1 + \dfrac{1}{k} \right)^x}{1 + \dfrac{x}{k}}$

**899.** $\dfrac{2^2 \cdot 4^2 \cdot 6^2 \cdots (2\,m)^2 (2\,m + 2)}{1^2 \cdot 3^2 \cdot 5^2 \cdots (2\,m + 1)^2} > \dfrac{\pi}{2}$

$$> \dfrac{2^2 \cdot 4^2 \cdot 6^2 \cdots (2\,m)^2 (2\,m + 1)}{1^2 \cdot 3^2 \cdot 5^2 \cdots (2\,m + 1)^2}$$

## DERIVATIVES

**900.** $\dfrac{d(au)}{dx} = \dfrac{a\,du}{dx}$

**901.** $\dfrac{d(u + v)}{dx} = \dfrac{du}{dx} + \dfrac{dv}{dx}$

**902.** $\dfrac{d(uv)}{dx} = v\,\dfrac{du}{dx} + u\,\dfrac{dv}{dx}$

**903.** $\dfrac{d\left( \dfrac{u}{v} \right)}{dx} = \dfrac{v\,\dfrac{du}{dx} - u\,\dfrac{dv}{dx}}{v^2}$

**904.** $\dfrac{df(u)}{dx} = \dfrac{df(u)}{du} \cdot \dfrac{du}{dx}$

**905.** $\dfrac{d^2 f(u)}{dx^2} = \dfrac{df}{du} \cdot \dfrac{d^2 u}{dx^2} + \dfrac{d^2 f}{du^2} \cdot \dfrac{du^2}{dx^2}$

**906.** $\dfrac{dx^n}{dx} = n x^{n-1}$

**907.** $\dfrac{de^x}{dx} = e^x$

**908.** $\dfrac{da^u}{dx} = a^u \cdot \dfrac{du}{dx} \cdot \log a$

**909.** $\dfrac{dx^x}{dx} = x^x(1 + \log x)$

**910.** $\dfrac{du^v}{dx} = vu^{v-1}\dfrac{du}{dx} + u^v \log u \dfrac{dv}{dx}$

**911.** $\dfrac{d\,(\log_a x)}{dx} = \dfrac{1}{x \cdot \log a} = \dfrac{\log_a e}{x}$

**912.** $\dfrac{d\,\sin x}{dx} = \cos x$

**913.** $\dfrac{d\,\cos x}{dx} = -\sin x$

**914.** $\dfrac{d\,\tan x}{dx} = \sec^2 x$

**915.** $\dfrac{d\,\operatorname{ctn} x}{dx} = -\csc^2 x$

**916.** $\dfrac{d\,\sec x}{dx} = \tan x \cdot \sec x$

**917.** $\dfrac{d\,\csc x}{dx} = -\operatorname{ctn} x \cdot \csc x$

**918.** $\dfrac{d\,\sin^{-1}x}{dx} = \dfrac{1}{\sqrt{1 - x^2}}$

**919.** $\dfrac{d\,\cos^{-1}x}{dx} = \dfrac{-1}{\sqrt{1 - x^2}}$

**920.** $\dfrac{d\,\tan^{-1}x}{dx} = \dfrac{1}{1 + x^2}$

**921.** $\dfrac{d\,\operatorname{ctn}^{-1}x}{dx} = -\dfrac{1}{1 + x^2}$

**922.** $\dfrac{d\,\sec^{-1}x}{dx} = \dfrac{1}{x\sqrt{x^2 - 1}}$

**923.** $\dfrac{d \csc^{-1} x}{dx} = -\dfrac{1}{x\sqrt{x^2 - 1}}$

**924.** $\dfrac{d \sinh x}{dx} = \cosh x$

**925.** $\dfrac{d \cosh x}{dx} = \sinh x$

**926.** $\dfrac{d \tanh x}{dx} = \operatorname{sech}^2 x$

**927.** $\dfrac{d \operatorname{ctnh} x}{dx} = -\operatorname{csch}^2 x$

**928.** $\dfrac{d \operatorname{sech} x}{dx} = -\operatorname{sech} x \cdot \tanh x$

**929.** $\dfrac{d \operatorname{csch} x}{dx} = -\operatorname{csch} x \cdot \operatorname{ctnh} x$

**930.** $\dfrac{d \sinh^{-1} x}{dx} = \dfrac{1}{\sqrt{x^2 + 1}}$

**931.** $\dfrac{d \cosh^{-1} x}{dx} = \dfrac{1}{\sqrt{x^2 - 1}}$

**932.** $\dfrac{d \tanh^{-1} x}{dx} = \dfrac{1}{1 - x^2}$

**933.** $\dfrac{d \operatorname{ctnh}^{-1} x}{dx} = \dfrac{1}{1 - x^2}$

**934.** $\dfrac{d \operatorname{sech}^{-1} x}{dx} = \dfrac{-1}{x\sqrt{1 - x^2}}$

**935.** $\dfrac{d \operatorname{csch}^{-1} x}{dx} = \dfrac{-1}{x\sqrt{x^2 + 1}}$

**936.** $\dfrac{d}{db} \displaystyle\int_a^b f(x)\,dx = f(b)$

**937.** $\dfrac{d}{da} \displaystyle\int_a^b f(x)\,dx = -f(a)$

**938.** $\dfrac{d}{dc}\displaystyle\int_a^b f(x, c)dx = \int_a^b D_c f(x, c) \cdot dx + f(b, c)\dfrac{db}{dc} - f(a, c)\dfrac{da}{dc}$

**939.** $\dfrac{d^n(u \cdot v)}{dx^n} = v \cdot \dfrac{d^n u}{dx^n} + n \cdot \dfrac{dv}{dx} \cdot \dfrac{d^{n-1}u}{dx^{n-1}}$

$$+ \dfrac{n(n-1)}{2!} \cdot \dfrac{d^2 v}{dx^2} \cdot \dfrac{d^{n-2}u}{dx^{n-2}} + \cdots + u\dfrac{d^n v}{dx^n}$$

**940.** If $f(x, y, z, \cdots)$ is a homogeneous function of the $n$th order, so that $f(\lambda x, \lambda y, \lambda z, \cdots) \equiv \lambda^n f(x, y, z, \cdots)$,

$$x \cdot D_x f + y \cdot D_y f + z \cdot D_z f + \cdots \equiv nf$$

**941.** If $x = \phi(y)$,

$$\dfrac{dy}{dx} = \dfrac{1}{\phi'(y)}, \quad \dfrac{d^2 y}{dx^2} = -\dfrac{\phi''(y)}{[\phi'(y)]^3},$$

$$\dfrac{d^3 y}{dx^3} = \dfrac{3[\phi''(y)]^2 - \phi'(y) \cdot \phi'''(y)}{[\phi'(y)]^5}$$

**942.** If $x = f(t)$ and $y = \phi(t)$,

$$\dfrac{dy}{dx} = \dfrac{\phi'(t)}{f'(t)}, \quad \dfrac{d^2 y}{dx^2} = \dfrac{f'(t) \cdot \phi''(t) - f''(t) \cdot \phi'(t)}{[f'(t)]^3}$$

**943.** If $f(x, y) = 0$,

$$\dfrac{dy}{dx} = -\dfrac{\partial f}{\partial x} \bigg/ \dfrac{\partial f}{\partial y} \equiv -\dfrac{D_x f}{D_y f},$$

$$\dfrac{d^2 y}{dx^2} = -\dfrac{D_x^2 f \cdot (D_y f)^2 - 2 D_x D_y f \cdot D_x f \cdot D_y f + D_y^2 f \cdot (D_x f)^2}{(D_y f)^3}$$

**944.** If $y = f(u, v)$, $u = \phi(x)$, and $v = \psi(x)$,

$$\dfrac{df}{dx} = \dfrac{\partial f}{\partial u} \cdot \dfrac{du}{dx} + \dfrac{\partial f}{\partial v} \cdot \dfrac{dv}{dx} = u' \cdot D_u f + v' \cdot D_v f,$$

$$\dfrac{d^2 f}{dx^2} = \dfrac{\partial^2 f}{\partial u^2} \cdot \left(\dfrac{du}{dx}\right)^2 + 2\dfrac{\partial^2 f}{\partial u \cdot \partial v} \cdot \dfrac{du}{dx} \cdot \dfrac{dv}{dx} + \dfrac{\partial^2 f}{\partial^2 v} \cdot \left(\dfrac{dv}{dx}\right)^2$$

$$+ \dfrac{\partial f}{\partial u} \cdot \dfrac{d^2 u}{dx^2} + \dfrac{\partial f}{\partial v} \cdot \dfrac{d^2 v}{dx^2}$$

$$= u'^2 \cdot D_u^2 f + 2 u' \cdot v' \cdot D_u D_v f + v'^2 \cdot D_v^2 f$$

$$+ u'' \cdot D_u f + v'' \cdot D_v f$$

**945.** If $f(x, y, z) = 0$, $D_x z = - D_x f / D_z f$,

$$D_x^2 z = - [D_x^2 f \cdot (D_z f)^2$$
$$- 2 D_z f \cdot D_x f \cdot D_x D_z f + D_z^2 f \cdot (D_x f)^2] / (D_z f)^3,$$

$$D_x D_y z = - [D_x D_y f \cdot (D_z f)^2 - D_z f \cdot D_x f \cdot D_y D_z f$$
$$- D_z f \cdot D_y f \cdot D_x D_z f + D_x f \cdot D_y f \cdot D_z^2 f] / (D_z f)^3$$

**946.** If $V = \phi(u, v)$, $u = f_1(x, y)$, and $v = f_2(x, y)$,

$$D_x V = D_u \phi \cdot D_x u + D_v \phi \cdot D_x v,$$

$$D_x^2 V = D_u^2 \phi \cdot (D_x u)^2 + D_v^2 \phi \cdot (D_x v)^2 + 2 D_u D_v \phi \cdot D_x u \cdot D_x v$$
$$+ D_u \phi \cdot D_x^2 u + D_v \phi \cdot D_x^2 v,$$

$$D_y D_x V = D_u^2 \phi \cdot D_x u \cdot D_y u + D_v^2 \phi \cdot D_x v \cdot D_y v$$
$$+ D_u D_v \phi \cdot (D_x v \cdot D_y u + D_x u \cdot D_y v)$$
$$+ D_u \phi \cdot D_x D_y u + D_v \phi \cdot D_x D_y v,$$

$$D_x^2 V + D_y^2 V = D_u^2 \phi \cdot [(D_x u)^2 + (D_y u)^2]$$
$$+ D_v^2 \phi \cdot [(D_x v)^2 + (D_y v)^2]$$
$$+ 2 D_u D_v \phi \cdot [D_x u \cdot D_x v + D_y u \cdot D_y v]$$
$$+ D_u \phi \cdot [D_x^2 u + D_y^2 u]$$
$$+ D_v \phi \cdot [D_x^2 v + D_y^2 v]$$

**947.** In the special case, $u \equiv r \equiv \sqrt{x^2 + y^2}$, $v \equiv \theta \equiv \tan^{-1}(y/x)$,
we have $D_r x = \cos \theta = x / \sqrt{x^2 + y^2}$; $D_r y = \sin \theta = y / \sqrt{x^2 + y^2}$;

$$D_\theta x = - r \sin \theta = - y; \quad D_\theta y = r \cos \theta = x;$$
$$D_x r = x / \sqrt{x^2 + y^2} = \cos \theta; \quad D_y r = y / \sqrt{x^2 + y^2} = \sin \theta;$$
$$D_x \theta = - y / (x^2 + y^2) = - \sin \theta / r;$$
$$D_y \theta = x / (x^2 + y^2) = \cos \theta / r; \quad \text{and}$$

$$D_x^2 V + D_y^2 V = D_r^2 V + \frac{1}{r} \cdot D_r V + \frac{1}{r^2} \cdot D_\theta^2 V$$

**948.** If $V = \phi(u, v)$, $u = f_1(r, \theta)$, and $v = f_2(r, \theta)$,

$$D_r{}^2V + \frac{1}{r} \cdot D_rV + \frac{1}{r^2} \cdot D_\theta{}^2V = D_u{}^2V \cdot \left[ (D_ru)^2 + \frac{(D_\theta u)^2}{r^2} \right]$$

$$+ D_v{}^2V \cdot \left[ (D_rv)^2 + \frac{(D_\theta v)^2}{r^2} \right]$$

$$+ 2\,D_uD_vV \cdot \left[ D_ru \cdot D_rv + \frac{D_\theta u \cdot D_\theta v}{r^2} \right]$$

$$+ D_uV \cdot \left[ D_r{}^2u + \frac{1}{r} \cdot D_ru + \frac{1}{r^2} \cdot D_\theta{}^2u \right]$$

$$+ D_vV \cdot \left[ D_r{}^2v + \frac{1}{r} \cdot D_rv + \frac{1}{r^2} \cdot D_\theta{}^2v \right]$$

**949.** If $V = \phi(u, v, w)$,  $u = f_1(x, y, z)$,  $v = f_2(x, y, z)$,  and $w = f_3(x, y, z)$,

$$D_xV = D_uV \cdot D_xu + D_vV \cdot D_xv + D_wV \cdot D_xw,$$

$$D_x{}^2V = D_u{}^2V \cdot (D_xu)^2 + D_v{}^2V \cdot (D_xv)^2 + D_w{}^2V \cdot (D_xw)^2$$
$$+ D_uV \cdot D_x{}^2u + D_vV \cdot D_x{}^2v + D_wV \cdot D_x{}^2w$$
$$+ 2\,(D_uD_vV \cdot D_xu \cdot D_xv + D_uD_wV \cdot D_xu \cdot D_xw$$
$$+ D_vD_wV \cdot D_xv \cdot D_xw)$$

$$D_x{}^2V + D_y{}^2V + D_z{}^2V = D_u{}^2V \cdot [(D_xu)^2 + (D_yu)^2 + (D_zu)^2]$$
$$+ D_v{}^2V \cdot [(D_xv)^2 + (D_yv)^2 + (D_zv)^2]$$
$$+ D_w{}^2V \cdot [(D_xw)^2 + (D_yw)^2 + (D_zw)^2]$$
$$+ 2\,D_uD_vV \cdot [D_xu \cdot D_xv + D_yu \cdot D_yv + D_zu \cdot D_zv]$$
$$+ 2\,D_vD_wV \cdot [D_xv \cdot D_xw + D_yv \cdot D_yw + D_zv \cdot D_zw]$$
$$+ 2\,D_wD_uV \cdot [D_xw \cdot D_xu + D_yw \cdot D_yu + D_zw \cdot D_zu]$$
$$+ D_uV \cdot [D_x{}^2u + D_y{}^2u + D_z{}^2u]$$
$$+ D_vV \cdot [D_x{}^2v + D_y{}^2v + D_z{}^2v]$$
$$+ D_wV \cdot [D_x{}^2w + D_y{}^2w + D_z{}^2w]$$

**950.** In particular, if
$$x \equiv r \sin\theta \cos\phi,\ y \equiv r \sin\theta \sin\phi,\ z \equiv r\cos\theta,$$
so that $u \equiv r^2 \equiv x^2 + y^2 + z^2,\ v \equiv \theta \equiv \tan^{-1}(\sqrt{x^2+y^2}/z)$,
$w \equiv \phi \equiv \tan^{-1}(y/x)$, we have

$$D_r z = \cos\theta = z/\sqrt{x^2+y^2+z^2};$$
$$D_r x = \sin\theta \cos\phi = x/\sqrt{x^2+y^2+z^2};$$
$$D_r y = \sin\theta \sin\phi = y/\sqrt{x^2+y^2+z^2};$$
$$D_\theta z = -r\sin\theta = -\sqrt{x^2+y^2};$$
$$D_\theta x = r\cos\theta\cos\phi = zx/\sqrt{x^2+y^2};$$
$$D_\theta y = r\cos\theta\sin\phi = zy/\sqrt{x^2+y^2};$$
$$D_\phi z = 0;$$
$$D_\phi x = -r\sin\theta\sin\phi = -y;$$
$$D_\phi y = r\sin\theta\cos\phi = x;$$
$$D_z r = z/r = \cos\theta;$$
$$D_z \theta = -\sqrt{x^2+y^2}/r^2 = -\sin\theta/r;$$
$$D_z \phi = 0;$$
$$D_x r = x/r = \sin\theta\cos\phi;$$
$$D_x \theta = xz/r^2\sqrt{x^2+y^2} = \cos\theta\cos\phi/r;$$
$$D_x \phi = -y/(x^2+y^2) = -\sin\phi/r\sin\theta;$$
$$D_y r = y/r = \sin\theta\sin\phi;$$
$$D_y \theta = zy/r^2\sqrt{x^2+y^2} = \cos\theta\sin\phi/r;$$
$$D_y \phi = x/(x^2+y^2) = \cos\phi/r\sin\theta;$$
$$(D_x r)^2 + (D_y r)^2 + (D_z r)^2 = 1;$$
$$(D_x \theta)^2 + (D_y \theta)^2 + (D_z \theta)^2 = 1/r^2;$$
$$(D_x \phi)^2 + (D_y \phi)^2 + (D_z \phi)^2 = 1/r^2 \sin^2\theta;$$
$$(D_x V)^2 + (D_y V)^2 + (D_z V)^2$$
$$= (D_r V)^2 + \left(\frac{D_\theta V}{r}\right)^2 + \left(\frac{D_\phi V}{r\sin\theta}\right)^2;$$
$$D_x^2 V + D_y^2 V + D_z^2 V$$
$$= \frac{1}{r^2 \sin\theta}\left[D_r(r^2 \cdot D_r V)\cdot\sin\theta + \frac{D_\phi^2 V}{\sin\theta} + D_\theta(\sin\theta \cdot D_\theta V)\right]$$

**951.** If $x = f_1(u, v)$, $y = f_2(u, v)$, $z = f_3(u, v)$,

$$D_x z = \frac{D_u f_3 \cdot D_v f_2 - D_v f_3 \cdot D_u f_2}{D_u f_1 \cdot D_v f_2 - D_v f_1 \cdot D_u f_2},$$

$$D_y z = \frac{D_v f_3 \cdot D_u f_1 - D_u f_3 \cdot D_v f_1}{D_u f_1 \cdot D_v f_2 - D_v f_1 \cdot D_u f_2}$$

**952.** If $x = f(z, u)$, and $y = \phi(z, u)$,

$$D_x z = D_u \phi / (D_z f \cdot D_u \phi - D_z \phi \cdot D_u f),$$

$$D_y z = D_u f / (D_z \phi \cdot D_u f - D_z f \cdot D_u \phi)$$

**953.** If $F_1(x, y, z, u, v) = 0$,

$$F_2(x, y, z, u, v) = 0, \text{ and } F_3(x, y, z, u, v) = 0,$$

$$D_x z \cdot \begin{vmatrix} D_z F_1 & D_u F_1 & D_v F_1 \\ D_z F_2 & D_u F_2 & D_v F_2 \\ D_z F_3 & D_u F_3 & D_v F_3 \end{vmatrix} = - \begin{vmatrix} D_x F_1 & D_u F_1 & D_v F_1 \\ D_x F_2 & D_u F_2 & D_v F_2 \\ D_x F_3 & D_u F_3 & D_v F_3 \end{vmatrix}$$

**954.** If $F_1(x, y, z) = 0$, and $F_2(x, y, z) = 0$,

$$\frac{dy}{D_z F_1 \cdot D_x F_2 - D_z F_2 \cdot D_x F_1} = \frac{dz}{D_x F_1 \cdot D_y F_2 - D_x F_2 \cdot D_y F_1}$$

$$= \frac{dx}{D_y F_1 \cdot D_z F_2 - D_y F_2 \cdot D_z F_1}$$

---

If each of the quantities $y_1$, $y_2$, $y_3$, $\cdots y_n$ is a function of the $n$ variables $x_1$, $x_2$, $x_3$, $\cdots x_n$, the determinant,

$$\begin{vmatrix} D_{x_1} y_1 & D_{x_2} y_1 & \cdots D_{x_n} y_1 \\ D_{x_1} y_2 & D_{x_2} y_2 & \cdots D_{x_n} y_2 \\ \cdot & \cdot & \cdot \\ \cdot & \cdot & \cdot \\ D_{x_1} y_n & D_{x_2} y_n & \cdots D_{x_n} y_n \end{vmatrix}$$

is called the *functional determinant* or the *Jacobian* of the $y$'s with respect to the $x$'s and is denoted by the expression,

$$\frac{\partial(y_1, y_2, y_3, \cdots y_n)}{\partial(x_1, x_2, x_3, \cdots x_n)}, \text{ or by J } (y_1, y_2, \cdots y_n)$$

**955.** $\dfrac{\partial(y_1, y_2, y_3, \cdots y_n)}{\partial(x_1, x_2, x_3, \cdots x_n)} \cdot \dfrac{\partial(x_1, x_2, x_3, \cdots x_n)}{\partial(y_1, y_2, y_3, \cdots y_n)} \equiv 1$

**956.** $\dfrac{\partial(y_1, y_2, y_3, \cdots y_n)}{\partial(z_1, z_2, z_3, \cdots z_n)} \cdot \dfrac{\partial(z_1, z_2, z_3, \cdots z_n)}{\partial(x_1, x_2, x_3, \cdots x_n)}$

$$\equiv \dfrac{\partial(y_1, y_2, y_3, \cdots y_n)}{\partial(x_1, x_2, x_3, \cdots x_n)}$$

If the $y$'s are not all independent but are connected by an equation of the form $\phi(y_1, y_2, y_3, \cdots y_n) = 0$, the Jacobian of the $y$'s with respect to the $x$'s vanishes identically; and, conversely, if the Jacobian vanishes identically, the $y$'s are connected by one or more relations of the above-mentioned form.

---

The *directional derivative* of any scalar point function, $u$, at any point, $P$, in any fixed direction $PQ'$, is the limit, as $PQ$ approaches zero, of the ratio of $u_Q - u_P$ to $PQ$, where $Q$ is a point on the straight line $PQ'$ between $P$ and $Q'$. The *gradient*, $h_u$, of the function $u$ at $P$ is the directional derivative of $u$ at $P$ taken in the direction in which $u$ increases most rapidly. This direction is normal to the surface of constant $u$ which passes through $P$.

**957.** $h_u{}^2 \equiv (D_x u)^2 + (D_y u)^2 + (D_z u)^2$

The directional derivative of any scalar point function at any point in any given direction is evidently equal to the product of the gradient and the cosine of the angle between the given direction and that in which the function increases most rapidly.

The *normal derivative*, at any point, $P$, of a point function $u$, taken with respect to another point function $v$, is the limit as $PQ$ approaches zero of the ratio of $u_Q - u_P$ to $v_Q - v_P$, where $Q$ is a point so chosen on the normal at $P$ of the surface of constant $v$ which passes through $P$, that $v_Q - v_P$ is positive. If $(u, v)$ denotes the angle between the directions in which $u$ and $v$ increase most rapidly, the normal derivatives of $u$ with respect to $v$, and of $v$ with respect to $u$ may be written

$$h_u \cos (u, v) \div h_v, \quad \text{and} \quad h_v \cdot \cos (u, v) \div h_u$$

respectively. If $h_u = h_v$, these derivatives are equal.

## MISCELLANEOUS FORMULAS

If $s$ is a plane analytic closed curve, $n$ its normal drawn from within outwards, and $dA$ the element of plane area within $s$, the usual integral transformation formulas for the functions $u$ and $v$ which, with their derivatives of the first order, are continuous everywhere within $s$, may be written—

**958.** $\displaystyle\int u \cdot \cos (x, n) ds = \iint D_x u \cdot dA$

**959.** $\displaystyle\int [u \cdot \cos (x, n) + v \cdot \cos (y, n)] ds = \iint (D_x u + D_y v) dA$

**960.** $\displaystyle\int D_n u \cdot ds = \iint (D_x^2 u + D_y^2 u) dA$

**961.** $\displaystyle\iint (D_x u \cdot D_x v + D_y u \cdot D_y v) dA$

$$= \int u \cdot D_n v \cdot ds - \iint u(D_x^2 v + D_y^2 v) dA$$

$$= \int v \cdot D_n u \cdot ds - \iint v(D_x^2 u + D_y^2 v) dA$$

**962.** $\displaystyle\iint \lambda(D_x u \cdot D_x v + D_y u \cdot D_y v) dA = \int \lambda \cdot u \cdot D_n v \cdot ds$

$$- \iint u[D_x(\lambda \cdot D_x v) + D_y(\lambda \cdot D_y v)] dA$$

If $\xi$ and $\eta$ are two analytic functions which define a set of orthogonal curvilinear co-ordinates, and if $(\xi, n)$ and $(\eta, n)$ represent the angles between $n$ and the directions in which $\xi$ and $\eta$, respectively, increase most rapidly,

**963.** $\displaystyle\iint h_\xi \cdot h_\eta \cdot D_\eta \left(\frac{u}{h_\xi}\right) dA = \int u : \cos(\eta, n)ds$

**964.** $\displaystyle\iint h_\xi \cdot h_\eta \cdot D_\xi \left(\frac{u}{h_\eta}\right) dA = \int u \cdot \cos(\xi, n)ds$

**965.** If $r$ is the distance from a fixed point, $Q$, in the coordinate plane,

$$\int \frac{\cos(r, n)ds}{r} = 0, \pi, \text{ or } 2\pi, \text{ according as } Q \text{ is without,}$$

on, or within $s$.

---

If $S$ is an analytic closed surface, $n$ its normal drawn from within outwards, and $d\tau$ the element of volume shut in by $S$, the usual integral transformation formulas may be written—

**966.** $\displaystyle\iint u \cos(x, n)dS = \iiint D_x u \cdot d\tau$

**967.** $\displaystyle\iint [u \cos(x, n) + v \cos(y, n) + w \cos(z, n)]dS$
$$= \iiint (D_x u + D_y v + D_z w)d\tau$$

**968.** $\displaystyle\iint D_n u \cdot ds = \iiint (D_x^2 u + D_y^2 u + D_z^2 u)d\tau$

**969.** $\displaystyle\iiint (D_x u \cdot D_x v + D_y u \cdot D_y v + D_z u \cdot D_z v)d\tau$
$$= \iint u \cdot D_n v \cdot dS - \iiint u(D_x^2 v + D_y^2 v + D_z^2 v)d\tau$$
$$= \iint v \cdot D_n u \cdot dS - \iiint v(D_x^2 u + D_y^2 u + D_z^2 u)d\tau$$

**970.** $\displaystyle\int\!\!\int\!\!\int \lambda(D_x u \cdot D_x v + D_y u \cdot D_y v + D_z u \cdot D_z v)d\tau$

$\displaystyle = \int\!\!\int \lambda \cdot v \cdot D_n u \cdot dS$

$\displaystyle \qquad - \int\!\!\int\!\!\int v[D_x(\lambda\, D_x u) + D_y(\lambda\, D_y u) + D_z(\lambda\, D_z u)]d\tau$

If $\xi$, $\eta$, $\zeta$ are three analytic functions which define a system of orthogonal curvilinear co-ordinates,

**971.** $\displaystyle\int\!\!\int\!\!\int h_\xi \cdot h_\eta \cdot h_\zeta \cdot D_\xi\left(\frac{u}{h_\eta \cdot h_\zeta}\right)d\tau = \int\!\!\int u \cdot \cos\,(\xi,\, n)dS$

**972.** $\displaystyle\int\!\!\int\!\!\int h_\xi \cdot h_\eta \cdot h_\zeta \cdot D_\eta\left(\frac{u}{h_\xi \cdot h_\zeta}\right)d\tau = \int\!\!\int u \cdot \cos\,(\eta,\, n)dS$

**973.** $\displaystyle\int\!\!\int\!\!\int h_\xi \cdot h_\eta \cdot h_\zeta \cdot D_\zeta\left(\frac{u}{h_\xi \cdot h_\eta}\right)d\tau = \int\!\!\int u \cdot \cos\,(\zeta,\, n)dS$

**974.** If $r$ is the distance from a fixed point, $Q$,

$\displaystyle\int \frac{\cos\,(r,\, n)}{r^2}\,dS = 0,\ 2\,\pi,\ \text{or } 4\,\pi$ according as $Q$ is without, on, or within $S$.

———————

Stokes's Theorem. The line integral, taken around a closed curve, of the tangential component of a vector point function, is equal to the surface integral, taken over a surface bounded by the curve, of the normal component of the curl of the vector, the direction of integration around the curve forming a right-handed screw rotation about the normals.

If $X$, $Y$, $Z$ are the components of the vector,

**975.** $\displaystyle\int (X\,dx + Y\,dy + Z\,dz) = \int\!\!\int [(D_y Z - D_z Y)\,\cos\,(x,\, n)$

$\displaystyle \qquad\qquad\qquad + (D_z X - D_x Z)\,\cos\,(y,\, n)$

$\displaystyle \qquad\qquad\qquad + (D_x Y - D_y X)\,\cos\,(z,\, n)]dS$

Equations 976 to 980 give Poisson's Equation in orthogonal Cartesian, in cylindrical, in spherical, and in orthogonal curvilinear co-ordinates.

**976.** $\overline{\nabla}^2 V \equiv D_x^2 V + D_y^2 V + D_z^2 V = -4\pi\rho$

**977.** $\dfrac{1}{r} \cdot D_r(r \cdot D_r V) + \dfrac{1}{r^2} \cdot D_\theta^2 V + D_z^2 V = -4\pi\rho$

**978.** $\sin\theta \cdot D_r(r^2 \cdot D_r V) + \dfrac{D_\phi^2 V}{\sin\theta} + D_\theta(\sin\theta \cdot D_\theta V)$
$= -4\pi\rho r^2 \sin\theta$

**979.** $h_\xi^2 \cdot D_\xi^2 V + h_\eta^2 \cdot D_\eta^2 V + h_\zeta^2 \cdot D_\zeta^2 V$
$+ D_\xi V \cdot \overline{\nabla}^2\xi + D_\eta V \cdot \overline{\nabla}^2\eta + D_\zeta V \cdot \overline{\nabla}^2\zeta = -4\pi\rho$

**980.** $h_\xi \cdot h_\eta \cdot h_\zeta \left[ D_\xi\left(\dfrac{h_\xi}{h_\eta h_\zeta} \cdot D_\xi V\right) + D_\eta\left(\dfrac{h_\eta}{h_\xi h_\zeta} \cdot D_\eta V\right) \right.$
$\left. + D_\zeta\left(\dfrac{h_\zeta}{h_\xi h_\eta} \cdot D_\zeta V\right) \right] = -4\pi\rho$

## GENERAL FORMULAS OF INTEGRATION

$F$ and $f$ represent functions of $x$, and $F'$, $f'$, $F''$, $f''$, their first and second derivatives with respect to $x$.

**981.** $\displaystyle\int F' \cdot f \cdot dx = F \cdot f - \int F \cdot f' \cdot dx$

**982.** $\displaystyle\int (F)^n \cdot F' \cdot dx = (F)^{n+1}/(n+1)$

**983.** $\displaystyle\int (aF + b)^n \cdot F' \cdot dx = (aF + b)^{n+1}/a(n+1)$

**984.** $\displaystyle\int (F + f)^n \cdot dx = \int F(F + f)^{n-1}dx + \int f(F + f)^{n-1}dx$

**985.** $\displaystyle\int F'/(F)^n \cdot dx = -1/(n-1)(F)^{n-1}; \ \int F'/F \cdot dx = \log F$

**986.** $\int (F' \cdot f - F \cdot f')/(f)^2 \cdot dx = F/f$

**987.** $\int (F' \cdot f - F \cdot f')/Ff \cdot dx = \log (F/f)$

**988.** $\int \dfrac{dx}{F \cdot (x^2 - a^2)} = \dfrac{1}{2\,a} \int \dfrac{dx}{F \cdot (x - a)} - \dfrac{1}{2\,a} \int \dfrac{dx}{F \cdot (x + a)}$

**989.** $\int \dfrac{dx}{F(F \pm f)} = \pm \int \dfrac{dx}{F \cdot f} \mp \int \dfrac{dx}{f(F \pm f)}$

**990.** $\int \dfrac{F' \cdot dx}{\sqrt{aF + b}} = (2\sqrt{aF + b})/a$

**991.** $\int \dfrac{F' \cdot dx}{\sqrt{F^2 + a}} = \log (F + \sqrt{F^2 + a})$

**992.** $\int \dfrac{F \cdot dx}{(F + a)(F + b)} = \dfrac{a}{a - b} \int \dfrac{dx}{F + a} - \dfrac{b}{a - b} \int \dfrac{dx}{F + b}$

**993.** $\int \dfrac{F \cdot dx}{(F + f)^n} = \int \dfrac{dx}{(F + f)^{n-1}} - \int \dfrac{f\,dx}{(F + f)^n}$

**994.** $\int \dfrac{F' \cdot dx}{p^2 + q^2 F^2} = \dfrac{1}{pq} \cdot \tan^{-1} \dfrac{qF}{p}$; $\int \dfrac{F' \cdot dx}{q^2 F^2 - p^2} = \dfrac{1}{2\,pq} \log \dfrac{qF - p}{qF + p}$

**995.** $\int \dfrac{F^{2n} \cdot dx}{1 - F^{2n}} = -\,x + \int \dfrac{dx}{1 - F^{2n}}$

**996.** $\int \dfrac{F' \cdot dx}{F^2 + a^2} = \dfrac{1}{a} \tan^{-1} \left( \dfrac{F}{a} \right)$

**997.** $\int \dfrac{F' \cdot dx}{a^2 F^2 - b^2} = \dfrac{1}{2\,ab} \log \dfrac{aF - b}{aF + b}$

**998.** $\int \dfrac{F^{2n} \cdot dx}{F^{2n} - b^2} = \int \dfrac{F^n \cdot dx}{2(F^n - b)} + \int \dfrac{F^n \cdot dx}{2(F^n + b)}$

**999.** $\int \dfrac{F' \cdot dx}{\sqrt{b^2 - F^2}} = \sin^{-1} \left( \dfrac{F}{b} \right)$

**1000.** $\displaystyle\int \frac{F' \cdot dx}{aF^2 + bF} = \frac{1}{b} \log \frac{F}{aF + b}$

**1001.** $\displaystyle\int \frac{F' \cdot dx}{aF^2 - bF} = \frac{1}{b} \log \frac{aF - b}{F}$

**1002.** $\displaystyle\int \frac{F' \cdot dx}{F\sqrt{F^2 - b^2}} = \frac{1}{b} \sec^{-1}\left(\frac{F}{b}\right)$

**1003.** $\displaystyle\int \frac{(F' \cdot f - F \cdot f')dx}{F^2 + f^2} = \tan^{-1}\left(\frac{F}{f}\right)$

**1004.** $\displaystyle\int \frac{(F' \cdot f - F \cdot f')dx}{F^2 - f^2} = \frac{1}{2} \log\left(\frac{F - f}{F + f}\right)$

## INTEGRALS USEFUL IN THE THEORY OF ALTERNATING CURRENTS

**1005.** $\displaystyle\int \sin\,(\omega t + \phi)dt = -\frac{1}{\omega} \cdot \cos\,(\omega t + \phi)$

**1006.** $\displaystyle\int \cos\,(\omega t + \phi)dt = \frac{1}{\omega} \cdot \sin\,(\omega t + \phi)$

**1007.** $\displaystyle\int \sin^2(\omega t + \phi)dt = \frac{1}{2}\,t - \frac{1}{4\,\omega} \sin 2(\omega t + \phi)$

**1008.** $\displaystyle\int \sin\,(\omega t + \phi) \cdot \cos\,(\omega t + \phi)dt = \frac{1}{2\,\omega} \cdot \sin^2(\omega t + \phi)$

**1009.** $\displaystyle\int \cos^2\,(\omega t + \phi)dt = \frac{1}{2}\,t + \frac{1}{4\,\omega} \sin 2(\omega t + \phi)$

**1010.** $\displaystyle\int \sin\,(\omega t + \lambda) \cdot \sin\,(\omega t + \mu)dt$

$$= \frac{\cos\,(\mu - \lambda)}{2\,\omega}\,(\omega t) - \frac{\sin\,(\omega t + \lambda) \cdot \cos\,(\omega t + \mu)}{2\,\omega}$$

**1011.** $\displaystyle\int \sin\,(\omega t + \lambda) \cdot \cos\,(\omega t + \mu)dt$

$$= \frac{\sin\,(\omega t + \lambda) \cdot \sin\,(\omega t + \mu)}{2\,\omega} - \frac{\sin\,(\mu - \lambda)}{2\,\omega}\,(\omega t)$$

**1012.** $\int \cos{(\omega t + \lambda)} \cdot \cos{(\omega t + \mu)}dt$

$$= \frac{\cos{(\mu - \lambda)}}{2\,\omega}\,(\omega t) + \frac{\sin{(\omega t + \lambda)} \cdot \cos{(\omega t + \mu)}}{2\,\omega}$$

**1013.** $\int \sin{(mt + \lambda)} \cdot \sin{(nt + \mu)}dt$

$$= \frac{\sin{[mt - nt + \lambda - \mu]}}{2(m - n)} - \frac{\sin{[mt + nt + \lambda + \mu]}}{2(m + n)}$$

**1014.** $\int \cos{(mt + \lambda)} \cdot \cos{(nt + \mu)}dt$

$$= \frac{\sin{[mt + nt + \lambda + \mu]}}{2(m + n)} + \frac{\sin{[mt - nt + \lambda - \mu]}}{2(m - n)}$$

**1015.** $\int \sin{(mt + \lambda)} \cdot \cos{(nt + \mu)}dt$

$$= -\frac{\cos{[mt + nt + \lambda + \mu]}}{2(m + n)} - \frac{\cos{[mt - nt + \lambda - \mu]}}{2(m - n)}$$

**1016.** $\int \cos{(\omega t + \lambda + mx)} \cdot \cos{(\omega t + \lambda - mx)}dx$

$$= \cos^2{(\omega t + \lambda)}\left[\frac{mx + \sin{mx} \cdot \cos{mx}}{2\,m}\right]$$

$$- \sin^2{(\omega t + \lambda)}\left[\frac{mx - \sin{mx} \cdot \cos{mx}}{2\,m}\right]$$

**1017.** $\int e^{(-b \pm ci)t}dt$

$$= \frac{-b \mp ci}{b^2 + c^2}\,e^{(-b \pm ci)t}$$

$$= \frac{e^{-bt}}{b^2 + c^2}\,[(c \cdot \sin{ct} - b \cdot \cos{ct}) \mp i(b \cdot \sin{ct} + c \cdot \cos{ct})]$$

$$= \frac{e^{-bt}}{\sqrt{b^2 + c^2}}\,[\sin{(ct - \delta)} \mp i \cdot \cos{(ci - \delta)}],$$

$$\text{where} \quad \tan{\delta} = b/c$$

**1018.** $\int e^{\alpha t} \cdot \cos(\omega t + \phi) dt$

$$= \frac{e^{\alpha t}}{\alpha^2 + \omega^2} [\omega \sin(\omega t + \phi) + \alpha \cdot \cos(\omega t + \phi)]$$

$$= \frac{e^{\alpha t}}{\sqrt{\alpha^2 + \omega^2}} \cos[\omega t + \phi - \tan^{-1}(\omega/\alpha)]$$

**1019.** $\int e^{\alpha t} \cdot \sin(\omega t + \phi) dt$

$$= \frac{e^{\alpha t}}{\alpha^2 + \omega^2} [\alpha \cdot \sin(\omega t + \phi) - \omega \cdot \cos(\omega t + \phi)]$$

$$= \frac{e^{\alpha t}}{\sqrt{\alpha^2 + \omega^2}} \sin[\omega t + \phi - \tan^{-1}(\omega/\alpha)]$$

**1020.** $\int [e^{\alpha t} \cdot \sin(\omega t + \phi)]^2 dt$

$$= \frac{e^{2\alpha t}}{4} \left[ \frac{1}{\alpha} - \frac{\omega \cdot \sin 2(\omega t + \phi) + \alpha \cdot \cos 2(\omega t + \phi)}{\alpha^2 + \omega^2} \right]$$

$$= \frac{e^{2\alpha t}}{4} \left[ \frac{1}{\alpha} - \frac{\cos[2\omega t + 2\phi - \tan^{-1}(\omega/\alpha)]}{\sqrt{\alpha^2 + \omega^2}} \right]$$

**1021.** $\int [e^{\alpha t} \cdot \cos(\omega t + \phi)]^2 dt$

$$= \frac{e^{2\alpha t}}{4} \left[ \frac{1}{\alpha} + \frac{\omega \cdot \sin 2(\omega t + \phi) + \alpha \cdot \cos 2(\omega t + \phi)}{\alpha^2 + \omega^2} \right]$$

$$= \frac{e^{2\alpha t}}{4} \left[ \frac{1}{\alpha} + \frac{\cos[2\omega t + 2\phi - \tan^{-1}(\omega/\alpha)]}{\sqrt{\alpha^2 + \omega^2}} \right]$$

The following identities are sometimes convenient:

$$m \cdot \sin(\omega t + \phi) + n \cdot \cos(\omega t + \phi) \equiv \sqrt{m^2 + n^2} \cdot \sin(\omega t + \phi + \partial)$$

$$m \cdot \sin(\omega t + \phi) - n \cdot \cos(\omega t + \phi) \equiv \sqrt{m^2 + n^2} \cdot \sin(\omega t + \phi - \partial)$$

where $\tan \partial = n/m$

In the case of a direct trigonometric function of $(\omega t + \phi)$, $T = 2\pi/\omega$ is called the *period* or the *cycle*. The mean value for any whole number of periods, reckoned from any epoch, of $\sin(\omega t + \phi)$, $\cos(\omega t + \phi)$, or $\sin(\omega t + \phi) \cdot \cos(\omega t + \phi)$, is zero, whereas the mean value for any whole number of half periods, reckoned from any epoch, of either $\sin^2(\omega t + \phi)$ or $\cos^2(\omega t + \phi)$ is one half. The mean value of $\sin(\omega t)$ from $t = 0$ to $t = \frac{1}{2} T$, or of $\cos(\omega t)$ from $-\frac{1}{4} T$ to $+\frac{1}{4} T$, is $2/\pi$ or 0.6366.

The mean value, for any number of whole periods, of either $\sin(\omega t + \lambda) \cdot \sin(\omega t + \mu)$ or $\cos(\omega t + \lambda) \cdot \cos(\omega t + \mu)$ is $\frac{1}{2} \cdot \cos(\lambda - \mu)$, while the mean value of $\sin(\omega t + \lambda) \cdot \cos(\omega t + \mu)$ is $\frac{1}{2} \sin(\lambda - \mu)$.

_Numerical
Tables_

# PART IV

# Numerical
# Tables

## *Interpolation*

If values of an analytic function, $f(x)$, are given in a table for a number of values of the argument $x$, separated from one another consecutively by the constant small interval, $\delta$, the differences between successive tabular values of the function are called *first tabular differences*, the differences of these first differences, *second tabular differences*, and so on. The tabular differences of the first, second, third, and fourth orders corresponding to $x = a$ are

$$\Delta_1 \equiv f(a + \delta) - f(a),$$
$$\Delta_2 \equiv f(a + 2\,\delta) - 2 \cdot f(a + \delta) + f(a),$$
$$\Delta_3 \equiv f(a + 3\,\delta) - 3 \cdot f(a + 2\,\delta) + 3 \cdot f(a + \delta) - f(a),$$
$$\Delta_4 \equiv f(a + 4\,\delta) - 4 \cdot f(a + 3\,\delta) + 6 \cdot f(a + 2\,\delta)$$
$$- 4 \cdot f(a + \delta) + f(a),$$

where $f(a)$ is any tabulated value.

The value of the function for $x = (a + h)$, where $h = k\delta$, is

$$f(a + h) = f(a) + k \cdot \Delta_1 + \frac{k(k-1)}{2!} \cdot \Delta_2 + \frac{k(k-1)(k-2)}{3!} \cdot \Delta_3$$
$$+ \frac{k(k-1)(k-2)(k-3)}{4!} \cdot \Delta_4 + \cdots.$$

## 1. CERTAIN CONSTANTS

$$\pi = 3.14159\ 26535\ 89793$$
$$\log_{10} \pi = 0.49714\ 98726\ 94134$$
$$1/\pi = 0.31830\ 98861\ 83791$$
$$\pi^2 = 9.86960\ 44010\ 89359$$

$$1/\pi^2 = 0.10132\ 11836\ 42338$$
$$\sqrt{\pi} = 1.77245\ 38509\ 05516$$
$$1/\sqrt{\pi} = 0.56418\ 95835\ 47756$$
$$\log_{10} 2 = 0.30102\ 99956\ 63981$$

$$\log_{10} 3 = 0.47712\ 12547\ 19662$$
$$e = 2.71828\ 18284\ 59045$$
$$1/e = 0.36787\ 94411\ 71442$$
$$\log_{10} e = 0.43429\ 44819\ 03252$$

$$\log_{10} \log_{10} e = 9.63778\ 43113\ 00537$$
$$\log_e 10 = 2.30258\ 50929\ 94046$$
$$\log_e 2 = 0.69314\ 71805\ 59945$$
$$\log_e 3 = 1.09861\ 22886\ 68110$$

$$\log_e \pi = 1.14472\ 98858\ 49400$$
$$\gamma = 0.57721\ 56649\ 01533$$
$$\sqrt{2} = 1.41421\ 35623\ 73095$$
$$\sqrt{3} = 1.73205\ 08075\ 68877$$

$$\sqrt{5} = 2.23606\ 79774\ 99790$$
$$\sqrt{6} = 2.44948\ 97427\ 83178$$
$$\sqrt{10} = 3.16227\ 76601\ 68379$$
$$\sqrt[3]{2} = 1.25992\ 10372\ 95013$$

## 2. THE PROBABILITY INTEGRAL $\left(\dfrac{2}{\sqrt{\pi}}\displaystyle\int_0^x e^{-u^2}du\right)$

| x | 0 | 1 | 2 | 3 | 4 | 5 | 6 | 7 | 8 | 9 |
|---|---|---|---|---|---|---|---|---|---|---|
| **0.00** | 0.00 000 | 00 113 | 00 226 | 00 339 | 00 451 | 00 564 | 00 677 | 00 790 | 00 903 | 01 016 |
| 0.01 | 0.01 128 | 01 241 | 01 354 | 01 467 | 01 580 | 01 692 | 01 805 | 01 918 | 02 031 | 02 144 |
| 0.02 | 0.02 256 | 02 369 | 02 482 | 02 595 | 02 708 | 02 820 | 02 933 | 03 046 | 03 159 | 03 271 |
| 0.03 | 0.03 384 | 03 497 | 03 610 | 03 722 | 03 835 | 03 948 | 04 060 | 04 173 | 04 286 | 04 398 |
| 0.04 | 0.04 511 | 04 624 | 04 736 | 04 849 | 04 962 | 05 074 | 05 187 | 05 299 | 05 412 | 05 525 |
| 0.05 | 0.05 637 | 05 750 | 05 862 | 05 975 | 06 087 | 06 200 | 06 312 | 06 425 | 06 537 | 06 650 |
| 0.06 | 0.06 762 | 06 875 | 06 987 | 07 099 | 07 212 | 07 324 | 07 437 | 07 549 | 07 661 | 07 773 |
| 0.07 | 0.07 886 | 07 998 | 08 110 | 08 223 | 08 335 | 08 447 | 08 559 | 08 671 | 08 784 | 08 896 |
| 0.08 | 0.09 008 | 09 120 | 09 232 | 09 344 | 09 456 | 09 568 | 09 680 | 09 792 | 09 904 | 10 016 |
| 0.09 | 0.10 128 | 10 240 | 10 352 | 10 464 | 10 576 | 10 687 | 10 799 | 10 911 | 11 023 | 11 135 |
| **0.10** | 0.11 246 | 11 358 | 11 470 | 11 581 | 11 693 | 11 805 | 11 916 | 12 028 | 12 139 | 12 251 |
| 0.11 | 0.12 362 | 12 474 | 12 585 | 12 697 | 12 808 | 12 919 | 13 031 | 13 142 | 13 253 | 13 365 |
| 0.12 | 0.13 476 | 13 587 | 13 698 | 13 809 | 13 921 | 14 032 | 14 143 | 14 254 | 14 365 | 14 476 |
| 0.13 | 0.14 587 | 14 698 | 14 809 | 14 919 | 15 030 | 15 141 | 15 252 | 15 363 | 15 473 | 15 584 |
| 0.14 | 0.15 695 | 15 805 | 15 916 | 16 027 | 16 137 | 16 248 | 16 358 | 16 468 | 16 579 | 16 689 |
| 0.15 | 0.16 800 | 16 910 | 17 020 | 17 130 | 17 241 | 17 351 | 17 461 | 17 571 | 17 681 | 17 791 |
| 0.16 | 0.17 901 | 18 011 | 18 121 | 18 231 | 18 341 | 18 451 | 18 560 | 18 670 | 18 780 | 18 890 |
| 0.17 | 0.18 999 | 19 109 | 19 218 | 19 328 | 19 437 | 19 547 | 19 656 | 19 766 | 19 875 | 19 984 |
| 0.18 | 0.20 094 | 20 203 | 20 312 | 20 421 | 20 530 | 20 639 | 20 748 | 20 857 | 20 966 | 21 075 |
| 0.19 | 0.21 184 | 21 293 | 21 402 | 21 510 | 21 619 | 21 728 | 21 836 | 21 945 | 22 053 | 22 162 |
| **0.20** | 0.22 270 | 22 379 | 22 487 | 22 595 | 22 704 | 22 812 | 22 920 | 23 028 | 23 136 | 23 244 |
| 0.21 | 0.23 352 | 23 460 | 23 568 | 23 676 | 23 784 | 23 891 | 23 999 | 24 107 | 24 214 | 24 322 |
| 0.22 | 0.24 430 | 24 537 | 24 645 | 24 752 | 24 859 | 24 967 | 25 074 | 25 181 | 25 288 | 25 395 |
| 0.23 | 0.25 502 | 25 609 | 25 716 | 25 823 | 25 930 | 26 037 | 26 144 | 26 250 | 26 357 | 26 463 |
| 0.24 | 0.26 570 | 26 677 | 26 783 | 26 889 | 26 996 | 27 102 | 27 208 | 27 314 | 27 421 | 27 527 |
| 0.25 | 0.27 633 | 27 739 | 27 845 | 27 950 | 28 056 | 28 162 | 28 268 | 28 373 | 28 479 | 28 584 |
| 0.26 | 0.28 690 | 28 795 | 28 901 | 29 006 | 29 111 | 29 217 | 29 322 | 29 427 | 29 532 | 29 637 |
| 0.27 | 0.29 742 | 29 847 | 29 952 | 30 056 | 30 161 | 30 266 | 30 370 | 30 475 | 30 579 | 30 684 |
| 0.28 | 0.30 788 | 30 892 | 30 997 | 31 101 | 31 205 | 31 309 | 31 413 | 31 517 | 31 621 | 31 725 |
| 0.29 | 0.31 828 | 31 932 | 32 036 | 32 139 | 32 243 | 32 346 | 32 450 | 32 553 | 32 656 | 32 760 |
| **0.30** | 0.32 863 | 32 966 | 33 069 | 33 172 | 33 275 | 33 378 | 33 480 | 33 583 | 33 686 | 33 788 |
| 0.31 | 0.33 891 | 33 993 | 34 096 | 34 198 | 34 300 | 34 403 | 34 505 | 34 607 | 34 709 | 34 811 |
| 0.32 | 0.34 913 | 35 014 | 35 116 | 35 218 | 35 319 | 35 421 | 35 523 | 35 624 | 35 725 | 35 827 |
| 0.33 | 0.35 928 | 36 029 | 36 130 | 36 231 | 36 332 | 36 433 | 36 534 | 36 635 | 36 735 | 36 836 |
| 0.34 | 0.36 936 | 37 037 | 37 137 | 37 238 | 37 338 | 37 438 | 37 538 | 37 638 | 37 738 | 37 838 |
| 0.35 | 0.37 938 | 38 038 | 38 138 | 38 237 | 38 337 | 38 436 | 38 536 | 38 635 | 38 735 | 38 834 |
| 0.36 | 0.38 933 | 39 032 | 39 131 | 39 230 | 39 329 | 39 428 | 39 526 | 39 625 | 39 724 | 39 822 |
| 0.37 | 0.39 921 | 40 019 | 40 117 | 40 215 | 40 314 | 40 412 | 40 510 | 40 608 | 40 705 | 40 803 |
| 0.38 | 0.40 901 | 40 999 | 41 096 | 41 194 | 41 291 | 41 388 | 41 486 | 41 583 | 41 680 | 41 777 |
| 0.39 | 0.41 874 | 41 971 | 42 068 | 42 164 | 42 261 | 42 358 | 42 454 | 42 550 | 42 647 | 42 743 |
| **0.40** | 0.42 839 | 42 935 | 43 031 | 43 127 | 43 223 | 43 319 | 43 415 | 43 510 | 43 606 | 43 701 |
| 0.41 | 0.43 797 | 43 892 | 43 988 | 44 083 | 44 178 | 44 273 | 44 368 | 44 463 | 44 557 | 44 652 |
| 0.42 | 0.44 747 | 44 841 | 44 936 | 45 030 | 45 124 | 45 219 | 45 313 | 45 407 | 45 501 | 45 595 |
| 0.43 | 0.45 689 | 45 782 | 45 876 | 45 970 | 46 063 | 46 157 | 46 250 | 46 343 | 46 436 | 46 529 |
| 0.44 | 0.46 623 | 46 715 | 46 808 | 46 901 | 46 994 | 47 086 | 47 179 | 47 271 | 47 364 | 47 456 |
| 0.45 | 0.47 548 | 47 640 | 47 732 | 47 824 | 47 916 | 48 008 | 48 100 | 48 191 | 48 283 | 48 374 |
| 0.46 | 0.48 466 | 48 557 | 48 648 | 48 739 | 48 830 | 48 921 | 49 012 | 49 103 | 49 193 | 49 284 |
| 0.47 | 0.49 375 | 49 465 | 49 555 | 49 646 | 49 736 | 49 826 | 49 916 | 50 006 | 50 096 | 50 185 |
| 0.48 | 0.50 275 | 50 365 | 50 454 | 50 543 | 50 633 | 50 722 | 50 811 | 50 900 | 50 989 | 51 078 |
| 0.49 | 0.51 167 | 51 256 | 51 344 | 51 433 | 51 521 | 51 609 | 51 698 | 51 786 | 51 874 | 51 962 |

## 2. THE PROBABILITY INTEGRAL

| x | 0 | 1 | 2 | 3 | 4 | 5 | 6 | 7 | 8 | 9 |
|---|---|---|---|---|---|---|---|---|---|---|
| 0.50 | 0.52 050 | 52 138 | 52 226 | 52 313 | 52 401 | 52 488 | 52 576 | 52 663 | 52 750 | 52 837 |
| 0.51 | 0.52 924 | 53 011 | 53 098 | 53 185 | 53 272 | 53 358 | 53 445 | 53 531 | 53 617 | 53 704 |
| 0.52 | 0.53 790 | 53 876 | 53 962 | 54 048 | 54 134 | 54 219 | 54 305 | 54 390 | 54 476 | 54 561 |
| 0.53 | 0.54 646 | 54 732 | 54 817 | 54 902 | 54 987 | 55 071 | 55 156 | 55 241 | 55 325 | 55 410 |
| 0.54 | 0.55 494 | 55 578 | 55 662 | 55 746 | 55 830 | 55 914 | 55 998 | 56 082 | 56 165 | 56 249 |
| 0.55 | 0.56 332 | 56 416 | 56 499 | 56 582 | 56 665 | 56 748 | 56 831 | 56 914 | 56 996 | 57 079 |
| 0.56 | 0.57 162 | 57 244 | 57 326 | 57 409 | 57 491 | 57 573 | 57 655 | 57 737 | 57 818 | 57 900 |
| 0.57 | 0.57 982 | 58 063 | 58 144 | 58 226 | 58 307 | 58 388 | 58 469 | 58 550 | 58 631 | 58 712 |
| 0.58 | 0.58 792 | 58 873 | 58 953 | 59 034 | 59 114 | 59 194 | 59 274 | 59 354 | 59 434 | 59 514 |
| 0.59 | 0.59 594 | 59 673 | 59 753 | 59 832 | 59 912 | 59 991 | 60 070 | 60 149 | 60 228 | 60 307 |
| 0.60 | 0.60 386 | 60 464 | 60 543 | 60 621 | 60 700 | 60 778 | 60 856 | 60 934 | 61 012 | 61 090 |
| 0.61 | 0.61 168 | 61 246 | 61 323 | 61 401 | 61 478 | 61 556 | 61 633 | 61 710 | 61 787 | 61 864 |
| 0.62 | 0.61 941 | 62 018 | 62 095 | 62 171 | 62 248 | 62 324 | 62 400 | 62 477 | 62 553 | 62 629 |
| 0.63 | 0.62 705 | 62 780 | 62 856 | 62 932 | 63 007 | 63 083 | 63 158 | 63 233 | 63 309 | 63 384 |
| 0.64 | 0.63 459 | 63 533 | 63 608 | 63 683 | 63 757 | 63 832 | 63 906 | 63 981 | 64 055 | 64 129 |
| 0.65 | 0.64 203 | 64 277 | 64 351 | 64 424 | 64 498 | 64 572 | 64 645 | 64 718 | 64 791 | 64 865 |
| 0.66 | 0.64 938 | 65 011 | 65 083 | 65 156 | 65 229 | 65 301 | 65 374 | 65 446 | 65 519 | 65 591 |
| 0.67 | 0.65 663 | 65 735 | 65 807 | 65 878 | 65 950 | 66 022 | 66 093 | 66 165 | 66 236 | 66 307 |
| 0.68 | 0.66 378 | 66 449 | 66 520 | 66 591 | 66 662 | 66 732 | 66 803 | 66 873 | 66 944 | 67 014 |
| 0.69 | 0.67 084 | 67 154 | 67 224 | 67 294 | 67 364 | 67 433 | 67 503 | 67 572 | 67 642 | 67 711 |
| 0.70 | 0.67 780 | 67 849 | 67 918 | 67 987 | 68 056 | 68 125 | 68 193 | 68 262 | 68 330 | 68 398 |
| 0.71 | 0.68 467 | 68 535 | 68 603 | 68 671 | 68 738 | 68 806 | 68 874 | 68 941 | 69 009 | 69 076 |
| 0.72 | 0.69 143 | 69 210 | 69 278 | 69 344 | 69 411 | 69 478 | 69 545 | 69 611 | 69 678 | 69 744 |
| 0.73 | 0.69 810 | 69 877 | 69 943 | 70 009 | 70 075 | 70 140 | 70 206 | 70 272 | 70 337 | 70 403 |
| 0.74 | 0.70 468 | 70 533 | 70 598 | 70 663 | 70 728 | 70 793 | 70 858 | 70 922 | 70 987 | 71 051 |
| 0.75 | 0.71 116 | 71 180 | 71 244 | 71 308 | 71 372 | 71 436 | 71 500 | 71 563 | 71 627 | 71 690 |
| 0.76 | 0.71 754 | 71 817 | 71 880 | 71 943 | 72 006 | 72 069 | 72 132 | 72 195 | 72 257 | 72 320 |
| 0.77 | 0.72 382 | 72 444 | 72 507 | 72 569 | 72 631 | 72 693 | 72 755 | 72 816 | 72 878 | 72 940 |
| 0.78 | 0.73 001 | 73 062 | 73 124 | 73 185 | 73 246 | 73 307 | 73 368 | 73 429 | 73 489 | 73 550 |
| 0.79 | 0.73 610 | 73 671 | 73 731 | 73 791 | 73 851 | 73 911 | 73 971 | 74 031 | 74 091 | 74 151 |
| 0.80 | 0.74 210 | 74 270 | 74 329 | 74 388 | 74 447 | 74 506 | 74 565 | 74 624 | 74 683 | 74 742 |
| 0.81 | 0.74 800 | 74 859 | 74 917 | 74 976 | 75 034 | 75 092 | 75 150 | 75 208 | 75 266 | 75 323 |
| 0.82 | 0.75 381 | 75 439 | 75 496 | 75 553 | 75 611 | 75 668 | 75 725 | 75 782 | 75 839 | 75 896 |
| 0.83 | 0.75 952 | 76 009 | 76 066 | 76 122 | 76 178 | 76 234 | 76 291 | 76 347 | 76 403 | 76 459 |
| 0.84 | 0.76 514 | 76 570 | 76 626 | 76 681 | 76 736 | 76 792 | 76 847 | 76 902 | 76 957 | 77 012 |
| 0.85 | 0.77 067 | 77 122 | 77 176 | 77 231 | 77 285 | 77 340 | 77 394 | 77 448 | 77 502 | 77 556 |
| 0.86 | 0.77 610 | 77 664 | 77 718 | 77 771 | 77 825 | 77 878 | 77 932 | 77 985 | 78 038 | 78 091 |
| 0.87 | 0.78 144 | 78 197 | 78 250 | 78 302 | 78 355 | 78 408 | 78 460 | 78 512 | 78 565 | 78 617 |
| 0.88 | 0.78 669 | 78 721 | 78 773 | 78 824 | 78 876 | 78 928 | 78 979 | 79 031 | 79 082 | 79 133 |
| 0.89 | 0.79 184 | 79 235 | 79 286 | 79 337 | 79 388 | 79 439 | 79 489 | 79 540 | 79 590 | 79 641 |
| 0.90 | 0.79 691 | 79 741 | 79 791 | 79 841 | 79 891 | 79 941 | 79 990 | 80 040 | 80 090 | 80 139 |
| 0.91 | 0.80 188 | 80 238 | 80 287 | 80 336 | 80 385 | 80 434 | 80 482 | 80 531 | 80 580 | 80 628 |
| 0.92 | 0.80 677 | 80 725 | 80 773 | 80 822 | 80 870 | 80 918 | 80 966 | 81 013 | 81 061 | 81 109 |
| 0.93 | 0.81 156 | 81 204 | 81 251 | 81 299 | 81 346 | 81 393 | 81 440 | 81 487 | 81 534 | 81 580 |
| 0.94 | 0.81 627 | 81 674 | 81 720 | 81 767 | 81 813 | 81 859 | 81 905 | 81 951 | 81 997 | 82 043 |
| 0.95 | 0.82 089 | 82 135 | 82 180 | 82 226 | 82 271 | 82 317 | 82 362 | 82 407 | 82 452 | 82 497 |
| 0.96 | 0.82 542 | 82 587 | 82 632 | 82 677 | 82 721 | 82 766 | 82 810 | 82 855 | 82 899 | 82 943 |
| 0.97 | 0.82 987 | 83 031 | 83 075 | 83 119 | 83 162 | 83 206 | 83 250 | 83 293 | 83 337 | 83 380 |
| 0.98 | 0.83 423 | 83 466 | 83 509 | 83 552 | 83 595 | 83 638 | 83 681 | 83 723 | 83 766 | 83 808 |
| 0.99 | 0.83 851 | 83 893 | 83 935 | 83 977 | 84 020 | 84 061 | 84 103 | 84 145 | 84 187 | 84 229 |

## 2. THE PROBABILITY INTEGRAL

| x | 0 | 1 | 2 | 3 | 4 | 5 | 6 | 7 | 8 | 9 |
|---|---|---|---|---|---|---|---|---|---|---|
| **1.00** | 0.84 270 | 84 312 | 84 353 | 84 394 | 84 435 | 84 477 | 84 518 | 84 559 | 84 600 | 84 640 |
| 1.01 | 0.84 681 | 84 722 | 84 762 | 84 803 | 84 843 | 84 885 | 84 924 | 84 964 | 85 004 | 85 044 |
| 1.02 | 0.85 084 | 85 124 | 85 163 | 85 203 | 85 243 | 85 282 | 85 322 | 85 361 | 85 400 | 85 439 |
| 1.03 | 0.85 478 | 85 517 | 85 556 | 85 595 | 85 634 | 85 673 | 85 711 | 85 750 | 85 788 | 85 827 |
| 1.04 | 0.85 865 | 85 903 | 85 941 | 85 979 | 86 017 | 86 055 | 86 093 | 86 131 | 86 169 | 86 206 |
| 1.05 | 0.86 244 | 86 281 | 86 318 | 86 356 | 86 393 | 86 430 | 86 467 | 86 504 | 86 541 | 86 578 |
| 1.06 | 0.86 614 | 86 651 | 86 688 | 86 724 | 86 760 | 86 797 | 86 833 | 86 869 | 86 905 | 86 941 |
| 1.07 | 0.86 977 | 87 013 | 87 049 | 87 085 | 87 120 | 87 156 | 87 191 | 87 227 | 87 262 | 87 297 |
| 1.08 | 0.87 333 | 87 368 | 87 403 | 87 438 | 87 473 | 87 507 | 87 542 | 87 577 | 87 611 | 87 646 |
| 1.09 | 0.87 680 | 87 715 | 87 749 | 87 783 | 87 817 | 87 851 | 87 885 | 87 919 | 87 953 | 87 987 |
| **1.10** | 0.88 021 | 88 054 | 88 088 | 88 121 | 88 155 | 88 188 | 88 221 | 88 254 | 88 287 | 88 320 |
| 1.11 | 0.88 353 | 88 386 | 88 419 | 88 452 | 88 484 | 88 517 | 88 549 | 88 582 | 88 614 | 88 647 |
| 1.12 | 0.88 679 | 88 711 | 88 743 | 88 775 | 88 807 | 88 839 | 88 871 | 88 902 | 88 934 | 88 966 |
| 1.13 | 0.88 997 | 89 029 | 89 060 | 89 091 | 89 122 | 89 154 | 89 185 | 89 216 | 89 247 | 89 277 |
| 1.14 | 0.89 308 | 89 339 | 89 370 | 89 400 | 89 431 | 89 461 | 89 492 | 89 522 | 89 552 | 89 582 |
| 1.15 | 0.89 612 | 89 642 | 89 672 | 89 702 | 89 732 | 89 762 | 89 792 | 89 821 | 89 851 | 89.880 |
| 1.16 | 0.89 910 | 89 939 | 89 968 | 89 997 | 90 027 | 90 056 | 90 085 | 90 114 | 90 142 | 90 171 |
| 1.17 | 0.90 200 | 90 229 | 90 257 | 90 286 | 90 314 | 90 343 | 90 371 | 90 399 | 90 428 | 90 456 |
| 1.18 | 0.90 484 | 90 512 | 90 540 | 90 568 | 90 595 | 90 623 | 90 651 | 90 678 | 90 706 | 90 733 |
| 1.19 | 0.90 761 | 90 788 | 90 815 | 90 843 | 90 870 | 90 897 | 90 924 | 90 951 | 90 978 | 91 005 |
| **1.20** | 0.91 031 | 91 058 | 91 085 | 91 111 | 91 138 | 91 164 | 91 191 | 91 217 | 91 243 | 91 269 |
| 1.21 | 0.91 296 | 91 322 | 91 348 | 91 374 | 91 399 | 91 425 | 91 451 | 91 477 | 91 502 | 91 528 |
| 1.22 | 0.91 553 | 91 579 | 91 604 | 91 630 | 91 655 | 91 680 | 91 705 | 91 730 | 91 755 | 91 780 |
| 1.23 | 0.91 805 | 91 830 | 91 855 | 91 879 | 91 904 | 91 929 | 91 953 | 91 978 | 92 002 | 92 026 |
| 1.24 | 0.92 051 | 92 075 | 92 099 | 92 123 | 92 147 | 92 171 | 92 195 | 92 219 | 92 243 | 92 266 |
| 1.25 | 0.92 290 | 92 314 | 92 337 | 92 361 | 92 384 | 92 408 | 92 431 | 92 454 | 92 477 | 92 500 |
| 1.26 | 0.92 524 | 92 547 | 92 570 | 92 593 | 92 615 | 92 638 | 92 661 | 92 684 | 92 706 | 92 729 |
| 1.27 | 0.92 751 | 92 774 | 92 796 | 92 819 | 92 841 | 92 863 | 92 885 | 92 907 | 92 929 | 92 951 |
| 1.28 | 0.92 973 | 92 995 | 93 017 | 93 039 | 93 061 | 93 082 | 93 104 | 93 126 | 93 147 | 93 168 |
| 1.29 | 0.93 190 | 93 211 | 93 232 | 93 254 | 93 275 | 93 296 | 93 317 | 93 338 | 93 359 | 93 380 |
| **1.30** | 0.93 401 | 93 422 | 93 442 | 93 463 | 93 484 | 93 504 | 93 525 | 93 545 | 93 566 | 93 586 |
| 1.31 | 0.93 606 | 93 627 | 93 647 | 93 667 | 93 687 | 93 707 | 93 727 | 93 747 | 93 767 | 93 787 |
| 1.32 | 0.93 807 | 93 826 | 93 846 | 93 866 | 93 885 | 93 905 | 93 924 | 93 944 | 93 963 | 93 982 |
| 1.33 | 0.94 002 | 94 021 | 94 040 | 94 059 | 94 078 | 94 097 | 94 116 | 94 135 | 94 154 | 94 173 |
| 1.34 | 0.94 191 | 94 210 | 94 229 | 94 247 | 94 266 | 94 284 | 94 303 | 94 321 | 94 340 | 94 358 |
| 1.35 | 0.94 376 | 94 394 | 94 413 | 94 431 | 94 449 | 94 467 | 94 485 | 94 503 | 94 521 | 94 538 |
| 1.36 | 0.94 556 | 94 574 | 94 592 | 94 609 | 94 627 | 94 644 | 94 662 | 94 679 | 94 697 | 94 714 |
| 1.37 | 0.94 731 | 94 748 | 94 766 | 94 783 | 94 800 | 94 817 | 94 834 | 94 851 | 94 868 | 94 885 |
| 1.38 | 0.94 902 | 94 918 | 94 935 | 94 952 | 94 968 | 94 985 | 95 002 | 95 018 | 95 035 | 95 051 |
| 1.39 | 0.95 067 | 95 084 | 95 100 | 95 116 | 95 132 | 95 148 | 95 165 | 95 181 | 95 197 | 95 213 |
| **1.40** | 0.95 229 | 95 244 | 95 260 | 95 276 | 95 292 | 95 307 | 95 323 | 95 339 | 95 354 | 95 370 |
| 1.41 | 0.95 385 | 95 401 | 95 416 | 95 431 | 95 447 | 95 462 | 95 477 | 95 492 | 95 507 | 95 523 |
| 1.42 | 0.95 538 | 95 553 | 95 568 | 95 582 | 95 597 | 95 612 | 95 627 | 95 642 | 95 656 | 95 671 |
| 1.43 | 0.95 686 | 95 700 | 95 715 | 95 729 | 95 744 | 95 758 | 95 773 | 95 787 | 95 801 | 95 815 |
| 1.44 | 0.95 830 | 95 844 | 95 858 | 95 872 | 95 886 | 95 900 | 95 914 | 95 928 | 95 942 | 95 956 |
| 1.45 | 0.95 970 | 95 983 | 95 997 | 96 011 | 96 024 | 96 038 | 96 051 | 96 065 | 96 078 | 96 092 |
| 1.46 | 0.96 105 | 96 119 | 96 132 | 96 145 | 96 159 | 96 172 | 96 185 | 96 198 | 96 211 | 96 224 |
| 1.47 | 0.96 237 | 96 250 | 96 263 | 96 276 | 96 289 | 96 302 | 96 315 | 96 327 | 96 340 | 96 353 |
| 1.48 | 0.96 365 | 96 378 | 96 391 | 96 403 | 96 416 | 96 428 | 96 440 | 96 453 | 96 465 | 96 478 |
| 1.49 | 0.96 490 | 96 502 | 96 514 | 96 526 | 96 539 | 96 551 | 96 563 | 96 575 | 96 587 | 96 599 |

## 2. THE PROBABILITY INTEGRAL

| x | 0 | 2 | 4 | 6 | 8 | x | 0 | 2 | 4 | 6 | 8 |
|---|---|---|---|---|---|---|---|---|---|---|---|
| **1.50** | 0.96 611 | 96 634 | 96 658 | 96 681 | 96 705 | **2.00** | 0.99 532 | 99 536 | 99 540 | 99 544 | 99 548 |
| 1.51 | 0.96 728 | 96 751 | 96 774 | 96 796 | 96 819 | 2.01 | 0.99 552 | 99 556 | 99 560 | 99 564 | 99 568 |
| 1.52 | 0.96 841 | 96 864 | 96 886 | 96 908 | 96 930 | 2.02 | 0.99 572 | 99 576 | 99 580 | 99 583 | 99 587 |
| 1.53 | 0.96 952 | 96 973 | 96 995 | 97 016 | 97 037 | 2.03 | 0.99 591 | 99 594 | 99 598 | 99 601 | 99 605 |
| 1.54 | 0.97 059 | 97 080 | 97 100 | 97 121 | 97 142 | 2.04 | 0.99 609 | 99 612 | 99 616 | 99 619 | 99 622 |
| 1.55 | 0.97 162 | 97 183 | 97 203 | 97 223 | 97 243 | 2.05 | 0.99 626 | 99 629 | 99 633 | 99 636 | 99 639 |
| 1.56 | 0.97 263 | 97 283 | 97 302 | 97 322 | 97 341 | 2.06 | 0.99 642 | 99 646 | 99 649 | 99 652 | 99 655 |
| 1.57 | 0.97 360 | 97 379 | 97 398 | 97 417 | 97 436 | 2.07 | 0.99 658 | 99 661 | 99 664 | 99 667 | 99 670 |
| 1.58 | 0.97 455 | 97 473 | 97 492 | 97 510 | 97 528 | 2.08 | 0.99 673 | 99 676 | 99 679 | 99 682 | 99 685 |
| 1.59 | 0.97 546 | 97 564 | 97 582 | 97 600 | 97 617 | 2.09 | 0.99 688 | 99 691 | 99 694 | 99 697 | 99 699 |
| **1.60** | 0.97 635 | 97 652 | 97 670 | 97 687 | 97 704 | **2.10** | 0.99 702 | 99 705 | 99 707 | 99 710 | 99 713 |
| 1.61 | 0.97 721 | 97 738 | 97 754 | 97 771 | 97 787 | 2.11 | 0.99 715 | 99 718 | 99 721 | 99 723 | 99 726 |
| 1.62 | 0.97 804 | 97 820 | 97 836 | 97 852 | 97 868 | 2.12 | 0.99 728 | 99 731 | 99 733 | 99 736 | 99 738 |
| 1.63 | 0.97 884 | 97 900 | 97 916 | 97 931 | 97 947 | 2.13 | 0.99 741 | 99 743 | 99 745 | 99 748 | 99 750 |
| 1.64 | 0.97 962 | 97 977 | 97 993 | 98 008 | 98 023 | 2.14 | 0.99 753 | 99 755 | 99 757 | 99 759 | 99 762 |
| 1.65 | 0.98 038 | 98 052 | 98 067 | 98 082 | 98 096 | 2.15 | 0.99 764 | 99 766 | 99 768 | 99 770 | 99 773 |
| 1.66 | 0.98 110 | 98 125 | 98 139 | 98 153 | 98 167 | 2.16 | 0.99 775 | 99 777 | 99 779 | 99 781 | 99 783 |
| 1.67 | 0.98 181 | 98 195 | 98 209 | 98 222 | 98 236 | 2.17 | 0.99 785 | 99 787 | 99 789 | 99 791 | 99 793 |
| 1.68 | 0.98 249 | 98 263 | 98 276 | 98 289 | 98 302 | 2.18 | 0.99 799 | 99 797 | 99 799 | 99 801 | 99 803 |
| 1.69 | 0.98 315 | 98 328 | 98 341 | 98 354 | 98 366 | 2.19 | 0.99 805 | 99 806 | 99 808 | 99 810 | 99 812 |
| **1.70** | 0.98 379 | 98 392 | 98 404 | 98 416 | 98 429 | **2.20** | 0.99 814 | 99 815 | 99 817 | 99 819 | 99 821 |
| 1.71 | 0.98 441 | 98 453 | 98 465 | 98 477 | 98 489 | 2.21 | 0.99 822 | 99 824 | 99 826 | 99 827 | 99 829 |
| 1.72 | 0.98 500 | 98 512 | 98 524 | 98 535 | 98 546 | 2.22 | 0.99 831 | 99 832 | 99 834 | 99 836 | 99 837 |
| 1.73 | 0.98 558 | 98 569 | 98 580 | 98 591 | 98 602 | 2.23 | 0.99 839 | 99 840 | 99 842 | 99 843 | 99 845 |
| 1.74 | 0.98 613 | 98 624 | 98 635 | 98 646 | 98 657 | 2.24 | 0.99 846 | 99 848 | 99 849 | 99 851 | 99 852 |
| 1.75 | 0.98 667 | 98 678 | 98 688 | 98 699 | 98 709 | 2.25 | 0.99 854 | 99 855 | 99 857 | 99 858 | 99 859 |
| 1.76 | 0.98 719 | 98 729 | 98 739 | 98 749 | 98 759 | 2.26 | 0.99 861 | 99 862 | 99 863 | 99 865 | 99 866 |
| 1.77 | 0.98 769 | 98 779 | 98 789 | 98 798 | 98 808 | 2.27 | 0.99 867 | 99 869 | 99 870 | 99 871 | 99 873 |
| 1.78 | 0.98 817 | 98 827 | 98 836 | 98 846 | 98 855 | 2.28 | 0.99 874 | 99 875 | 99 876 | 99 877 | 99 879 |
| 1.79 | 0.98 864 | 98 873 | 98 882 | 98 891 | 98 900 | 2.29 | 0.99 880 | 99 881 | 99 882 | 99 883 | 99 885 |
| **1.80** | 0.98 909 | 98 918 | 98 927 | 98 935 | 98 944 | **2.30** | 0.99 886 | 99 887 | 99 888 | 99 889 | 99 890 |
| 1.81 | 0.98 952 | 98 961 | 98 969 | 98 978 | 98 986 | 2.31 | 0.99 891 | 99 892 | 99 893 | 99 894 | 99 896 |
| 1.82 | 0.98 994 | 99 003 | 99 011 | 99 019 | 99 027 | 2.32 | 0.99 897 | 99 898 | 99 899 | 99 900 | 99 901 |
| 1.83 | 0.99 035 | 99 043 | 99 050 | 99 058 | 99 066 | 2.33 | 0.99 902 | 99 903 | 99 904 | 99 905 | 99 906 |
| 1.84 | 0.99 074 | 99 081 | 99 089 | 99 096 | 99 104 | 2.34 | 0.99 906 | 99 907 | 99 908 | 99 909 | 99 910 |
| 1.85 | 0.99 111 | 99 118 | 99 126 | 99 133 | 99 140 | 2.35 | 0.99 911 | 99 912 | 99 913 | 99 914 | 99 915 |
| 1.86 | 0.99 147 | 99 154 | 99 161 | 99 168 | 99 175 | 2.36 | 0.99 915 | 99 916 | 99 917 | 99 918 | 99 919 |
| 1.87 | 0.99 182 | 99 189 | 99 196 | 99 202 | 99 209 | 2.37 | 0.99 920 | 99 920 | 99 921 | 99 922 | 99 923 |
| 1.88 | 0.99 216 | 99 222 | 99 229 | 99 235 | 99 242 | 2.38 | 0.99 924 | 99 924 | 99 925 | 99 926 | 99 927 |
| 1.89 | 0.99 248 | 99 254 | 99 261 | 99 267 | 99 273 | 2.39 | 0.99 928 | 99 928 | 99 929 | 99 930 | 99 930 |
| **1.90** | 0.99 279 | 99 285 | 99 291 | 99 297 | 99 303 | **2.40** | 0.99 931 | 99 932 | 99 933 | 99 933 | 99 934 |
| 1.91 | 0.99 309 | 99 315 | 99 321 | 99 326 | 99 332 | 2.41 | 0.99 935 | 99 935 | 99 936 | 99 937 | 99 937 |
| 1.92 | 0.99 338 | 99 343 | 99 349 | 99 355 | 99 360 | 2.42 | 0.99 938 | 99 939 | 99 939 | 99 940 | 99 940 |
| 1.93 | 0.99 366 | 99 371 | 99 376 | 99 382 | 99 387 | 2.43 | 0.99 941 | 99 942 | 99 942 | 99 943 | 99 943 |
| 1.94 | 0.99 392 | 99 397 | 99 403 | 99 408 | 99 413 | 2.44 | 0.99 944 | 99 945 | 99 945 | 99 946 | 99 946 |
| 1.95 | 0.99 418 | 99 423 | 99 428 | 99 433 | 99 438 | 2.45 | 9.99 947 | 99 947 | 99 948 | 99 949 | 99 949 |
| 1.96 | 0.99 443 | 99 447 | 99 452 | 99 457 | 99 462 | 2.46 | 0.99 950 | 99 950 | 99 951 | 99 951 | 99 952 |
| 1.97 | 0.99 466 | 99 471 | 99 476 | 99 480 | 99 485 | 2.47 | 0.99 952 | 99 953 | 99 953 | 99 954 | 99 954 |
| 1.98 | 0.99 489 | 99 494 | 99 498 | 99 502 | 99 507 | 2.48 | 6.99 955 | 99 955 | 99 956 | 99 956 | 99 957 |
| 1.99 | 0.99 511 | 99 515 | 99 520 | 99 524 | 99 528 | 2.49 | 0.99 957 | 99 958 | 99 958 | 99 958 | 99 959 |
| 2.00 | 0.99 532 | 99 536 | 99 540 | 99 544 | 99 548 | **2.50** | 0.99 959 | 99 960 | 99 960 | 99 961 | 99 961 |

## 2. THE PROBABILITY INTEGRAL

| x | 0 | 1 | 2 | 3 | 4 | 5 | 6 | 7 | 8 | 9 |
|---|---|---|---|---|---|---|---|---|---|---|
| **2.5** | 0.99 959 | 99 961 | 99 963 | 99 965 | 99 967 | 99 969 | 99 971 | 99 972 | 99 974 | 99 975 |
| **2.6** | 0.99 976 | 99 978 | 99 979 | 99 980 | 99 981 | 99 982 | 99 983 | 99 984 | 99 985 | 99 986 |
| **2.7** | 0.99 987 | 99 987 | 99 988 | 99 989 | 99 989 | 99 990 | 99 991 | 99 991 | 99 992 | 99 992 |
| **2.8** | 0.99 992 | 99 993 | 99 993 | 99 994 | 99 994 | 99 994 | 99 995 | 99 995 | 99 995 | 99 996 |
| **2.9** | 0.99 996 | 99 996 | 99 996 | 99 997 | 99 997 | 99 997 | 99 997 | 99 997 | 99 997 | 99 998 |
| **3.0** | 0.99 998 | 99 998 | 99 998 | 99 998 | 99 998 | 99 998 | 99 998 | 99 998 | 99 999 | 99 999 |

The value, $I$, of the Probability Integral may always be found from the convergent series

$$I = \frac{2}{\sqrt{\pi}}\left(x - \frac{x^3}{3 \cdot 1!} + \frac{x^5}{5 \cdot 2!} - \frac{x^7}{7 \cdot 3!} + \cdots\right),$$

but for large positive values of $x$, the asymptotic series

$$I \sim 1 - \frac{e^{-x^2}}{x\sqrt{\pi}}\left(1 - \frac{1}{2\,x^2} + \frac{1 \cdot 3}{(2\,x^2)^2} - \frac{1 \cdot 3 \cdot 5}{(2\,x^2)^3} + \cdots\right)$$

is convenient.

# 3. THE COMPLETE ELLIPTIC INTEGRALS, *K* AND *E*

$$K = \int_0^{\frac{\pi}{2}} \frac{dz}{\sqrt{1 - k^2 \sin^2 z}}; \quad E = \int_0^{\frac{\pi}{2}} \sqrt{1 - k^2 \sin^2 z} \cdot dz$$

| $\sin^{-1}k$ | *K* | *E* | $\sin^{-1}k$ | *K* | *E* |
|---|---|---|---|---|---|
| 0° | 1.5 708 | 1.5 708 | 45° | 1.8 541 | 1.3 506 |
| 1° | 1.5 709 | 1.5 707 | 46° | 1.8 691 | 1.3 418 |
| 2° | 1.5 713 | 1.5 703 | 47° | 1.8 848 | 1.3 329 |
| 3° | 1.5 719 | 1.5 697 | 48° | 1.9 011 | 1.3 238 |
| 4° | 1.5 727 | 1.5 689 | 49° | 1.9 180 | 1.3 147 |
| 5° | 1.5 738 | 1.5 678 | 50° | 1.9 356 | 1.3 055 |
| 6° | 1.5 751 | 1.5 665 | 51° | 1.9 539 | 1.2 963 |
| 7° | 1.5 767 | 1.5 649 | 52° | 1.9 729 | 1.2 870 |
| 8° | 1.5 785 | 1.5 632 | 53° | 1.9 927 | 1.2 776 |
| 9° | 1.5 805 | 1.5 611 | 54° | 2.0 133 | 1.2 681 |
| 10° | 1.5 828 | 1.5 589 | 55° | 2.0 347 | 1.2 587 |
| 11° | 1.5 854 | 1.5 564 | 56° | 2.0 571 | 1.2 492 |
| 12° | 1.5 882 | 1.5 537 | 57° | 2.0 804 | 1.2 397 |
| 13° | 1.5 913 | 1.5 507 | 58° | 2.1 047 | 1.2 301 |
| 14° | 1.5 946 | 1.5 476 | 59° | 2.1 300 | 1.2 206 |
| 15° | 1.5 981 | 1.5 442 | 60° | 2.1 565 | 1.2 111 |
| 16° | 1.6 020 | 1.5 405 | 61° | 2.1 842 | 1.2 015 |
| 17° | 1.6 061 | 1.5 367 | 62° | 2.2 132 | 1.1 920 |
| 18° | 1.6 105 | 1.5 326 | 63° | 2.2 435 | 1.1 826 |
| 19° | 1.6 151 | 1.5 283 | 64° | 2.2 754 | 1.1 732 |
| 20° | 1.6 200 | 1.5 238 | 65° | 2.3 088 | 1.1 638 |
| 21° | 1.6 252 | 1.5 191 | 66° | 2.3 439 | 1.1 545 |
| 22° | 1.6 307 | 1.5 141 | 67° | 2.3 809 | 1.1 453 |
| 23° | 1.6 365 | 1.5 090 | 68° | 2.4 198 | 1.1 362 |
| 24° | 1.6 426 | 1.5 037 | 69° | 2.4 610 | 1.1 272 |
| 25° | 1.6 490 | 1.4 981 | 70° | 2.5 046 | 1.1 184 |
| 26° | 1.6 557 | 1.4 924 | 71° | 2.5 507 | 1.1 096 |
| 27° | 1.6 627 | 1.4 864 | 72° | 2.5 998 | 1.1 011 |
| 28° | 1.6 701 | 1.4 803 | 73° | 2.6 521 | 1.0 927 |
| 29° | 1.6 777 | 1.4 740 | 74° | 2.7 081 | 1.0 844 |
| 30° | 1.6 858 | 1.4 675 | 75° | 2.7 681 | 1.0 764 |
| 31° | 1.6 941 | 1.4 608 | 76° | 2.8 327 | 1.0 686 |
| 32° | 1.7 028 | 1.4 539 | 77° | 2.9 026 | 1.0 611 |
| 33° | 1.7 119 | 1.4 469 | 78° | 2.9 786 | 1.0 538 |
| 34° | 1.7 214 | 1.4 397 | 79° | 3.0 617 | 1.0 468 |
| 35° | 1.7 312 | 1.4 323 | 80° | 3.1 534 | 1.0 401 |
| 36° | 1.7 415 | 1.4 248 | 81° | 3.2 553 | 1.0 338 |
| 37° | 1.7 522 | 1.4 171 | 82° | 3.3 699 | 1.0 278 |
| 38° | 1.7 633 | 1.4 092 | 83° | 3.5 004 | 1.0 223 |
| 39° | 1.7 748 | 1.4 013 | 84° | 3.6 519 | 1.0 172 |
| 40° | 1.7 868 | 1.3 931 | 85° | 3.8 317 | 1.0 127 |
| 41° | 1.7 992 | 1.3 849 | 86° | 4.0 528 | 1.0 086 |
| 42° | 1.8 122 | 1.3 765 | 87° | 4.3 387 | 1.0 053 |
| 43° | 1.8 256 | 1.3 680 | 88° | 4.7 427 | 1.0 026 |
| 44° | 1.8 396 | 1.3 594 | 89° | 5.4 349 | 1.0 008 |

## 4. THE ELLIPTIC INTEGRAL OF THE FIRST KIND, $F(k, \phi)$

$$F(k, \phi) = \int_0^\phi \frac{dz}{\sqrt{1 - k^2 \sin^2 z}}$$

| $\phi$ | $\alpha = \sin^{-1}k$ | | | | | | | | |
|---|---|---|---|---|---|---|---|---|---|
| | 0° | 10° | 15° | 30° | 45° | 60° | 75° | 80° | 90° |
| 1° | 0.0 174 | 0.0 174 | 0.0 174 | 0.0 174 | 0.0 174 | 0.0 174 | 0.0 174 | 0.0 174 | 0.0 174 |
| 2° | 0.0 349 | 0.0 349 | 0.0 349 | 0.0 349 | 0.0 349 | 0.0 349 | 0.0 349 | 0.0 349 | 0.0 349 |
| 3° | 0.0 524 | 0.0 524 | 0.0 524 | 0.0 524 | 0.0 524 | 0.0 524 | 0.0 524 | 0.0 524 | 0.0 524 |
| 4° | 0.0 698 | 0.0 698 | 0.0 698 | 0.0 698 | 0.0 698 | 0.0 699 | 0.0 699 | 0.0 699 | 0.0 699 |
| 5° | 0.0 873 | 0.0 873 | 0.0 873 | 0.0 873 | 0.0 873 | 0.0 874 | 0.0 874 | 0.0 874 | 0.0 874 |
| 10° | 0.1 745 | 0.1 746 | 0.1 746 | 0.1 748 | 0.1 750 | 0.1 752 | 0.1 754 | 0.1 754 | 0.1 754 |
| 15° | 0.2 618 | 0.2 619 | 0.2 620 | 0.2 625 | 0.2 633 | 0.2 641 | 0.2 646 | 0.2 647 | 0.2 648 |
| 20° | 0.3 491 | 0.3 493 | 0.3 495 | 0.3 508 | 0.3 526 | 0.3 545 | 0.3 559 | 0.3 562 | 0.3 564 |
| 25° | 0.4 363 | 0.4 367 | 0.4 372 | 0.4 397 | 0.4 433 | 0.4 470 | 0.4 498 | 0.4 504 | 0.4 509 |
| 30° | 0.5 236 | 0.5 243 | 0.5 251 | 0.5 294 | 0.5 356 | 0.5 422 | 0.5 474 | 0.5 484 | 0.5 493 |
| 35° | 0.6 109 | 0.6 119 | 0.6 132 | 0.6 200 | 0.6 300 | 0.6 408 | 0.6 495 | 0.6 513 | 0.6 528 |
| 40° | 0.6 981 | 0.6 997 | 0.7 016 | 0.7 116 | 0.7 267 | 0.7 436 | 0.7 574 | 0.7 604 | 0.7 629 |
| 45° | 0.7 854 | 0.7 876 | 0.7 902 | 0.8 044 | 0.8 260 | 0.8 512 | 0.8 727 | 0.8 774 | 0.8 814 |
| 50° | 0.8 727 | 0.8 756 | 0.8 792 | 0.8 982 | 0.9 283 | 0.9 646 | 0.9 971 | 1.0 044 | 1.0 107 |
| 55° | 0.9 599 | 0.9 637 | 0.9 683 | 0.9 933 | 1.0 337 | 1.0 848 | 1.1 331 | 1.1 444 | 1.1 542 |
| 60° | 1.0 472 | 1.0 519 | 1.0 577 | 1.0 896 | 1.1 424 | 1.2 125 | 1.2 837 | 1.3 014 | 1.3 170 |
| 65° | 1.1 345 | 1.1 402 | 1.1 474 | 1 1 869 | 1.2 545 | 1.3 489 | 1.4 532 | 1.4 810 | 1.5 064 |
| 70° | 1.2 217 | 1.2 286 | 1.2 373 | 1.2 853 | 1.3 697 | 1.4 944 | 1.6 468 | 1.6 918 | 1.7 354 |
| 75° | 1.3 090 | 1.3 171 | 1.3 273 | 1.3 846 | 1.4 879 | 1.6 492 | 1.8 714 | 1.9 468 | 2.0 276 |
| 80° | 1.3 963 | 1.4 056 | 1.4 175 | 1.4 846 | 1.6 085 | 1.8 125 | 2.1 339 | 2.2 653 | 2.4 362 |
| 85° | 1.4 835 | 1.4 942 | 1.5 078 | 1.5 850 | 1.7 308 | 1.9 826 | 2.4 366 | 2.6 694 | 3.1 313 |
| 86° | 1.5 010 | 1.5 120 | 1.5 259 | 1.6 052 | 1.7 554 | 2.0 172 | 2.5 013 | 2.7 612 | 3.3 547 |
| 87° | 1.5 184 | 1.5 297 | 1.5 439 | 1.6 253 | 1.7 801 | 2.0 519 | 2.5 670 | 2.8 561 | 3.6 425 |
| 88° | 1.5 359 | 1.5 474 | 1.5 620 | 1.6 454 | 1.8 047 | 2.0 867 | 2.6 336 | 2.9 537 | 4.0 481 |
| 89° | 1.5 533 | 1.5 651 | 1.5 801 | 1.6 656 | 1.8 294 | 2.1 216 | 2.7 007 | 3.0 530 | 4.7 414 |
| 90° | 1.5 708 | 1.5 828 | 1.5 981 | 1.6 858 | 1.8 541 | 2.1 565 | 2.7 681 | 3.1 534 | Inf. |

## 5. THE ELLIPTIC INTEGRAL OF THE SECOND KIND, $E(k, \phi)$

$$E(k, \phi) = \int_0^\phi \sqrt{1 - k^2 \sin^2 z} \cdot dz$$

| $\phi$ | $\alpha = \sin^{-1}k$ | | | | | | | | |
|---|---|---|---|---|---|---|---|---|---|
| | 0° | 10° | 15° | 30° | 45° | 60° | 75° | 80° | 90° |
| 1° | 0.0 174 | 0.0 174 | 0.0 174 | 0.0 174 | 0.0 174 | 0.0 174 | 0.0 174 | 0.0 174 | 0.0 174 |
| 2° | 0.0 349 | 0.0 349 | 0.0 349 | 0.0 349 | 0.0 349 | 0.0 349 | 0.0 349 | 0.0 349 | 0.0 349 |
| 3° | 0.0 524 | 0.0 524 | 0.0 524 | 0.0 524 | 0.0 524 | 0.0 523 | 0.0 523 | 0.0 523 | 0.0 523 |
| 4° | 0.0 698 | 0.0 698 | 0.0 698 | 0.0 698 | 0.0 698 | 0.0 698 | 0.0 698 | 0.0 698 | 0.0 698 |
| 5° | 0.0 873 | 0.0 873 | 0.0 873 | 0.0 872 | 0.0 872 | 0.0 872 | 0.0 872 | 0.0 872 | 0.0 872 |
| 10° | 0.1 745 | 0.1 745 | 0.1 745 | 0.1 743 | 0.1 741 | 0.1 739 | 0.1 737 | 0.1 737 | 0.1 736 |
| 15° | 0.2 618 | 0.2 617 | 0.2 616 | 0.2 611 | 0.2 603 | 0.2 596 | 0.2 590 | 0.2 589 | 0.2 588 |
| 20° | 0.3 491 | 0.3 489 | 0.3 486 | 0.3 473 | 0.3 456 | 0.3 438 | 0.3 425 | 0.3 422 | 0.3 420 |
| 25° | 0.4 363 | 0.4 359 | 0.4 354 | 0.4 330 | 0.4 296 | 0.4 261 | 0.4 236 | 0.4 230 | 0.4 226 |
| 30° | 0.5 236 | 0.5 229 | 0.5 221 | 0.5 179 | 0.5 120 | 0.5 061 | 0.5 016 | 0.5 007 | 0.5 000 |
| 35° | 0.6 109 | 0.6 098 | 0.6 085 | 0.6 019 | 0.5 928 | 0.5 833 | 0.5 762 | 0.5 748 | 0.5 736 |
| 40° | 0.6 981 | 0.6 966 | 0.6 947 | 0.6 851 | 0.6 715 | 0.6 575 | 0.6 468 | 0.6 446 | 0.6 428 |
| 45° | 0.7 854 | 0.7 832 | 0.7 806 | 0.7 672 | 0.7 482 | 0.7 282 | 0.7 129 | 0.7 097 | 0.7 071 |
| 50° | 0.8 727 | 0.8 698 | 0.8 663 | 0.8 483 | 0.8 226 | 0.7 954 | 0.7 741 | 0.7 697 | 0.7 660 |
| 55° | 0.9 599 | 0.9 562 | 0.9 517 | 0.9 284 | 0.8 949 | 0.8 588 | 0.8 302 | 0.8 242 | 0.8 192 |
| 60° | 1.0 472 | 1.0 426 | 1.0 368 | 0.0 076 | 0.9 650 | 0.9 184 | 0.8 808 | 0.8 728 | 0.8 660 |
| 65° | 1.1 345 | 1.1 288 | 1.1 218 | 1.0 858 | 1.0 329 | 0.9 743 | 0.9 258 | 0.9 152 | 0.9 063 |
| 70° | 1.2 217 | 1.2 149 | 1.2 065 | 1.1 632 | 1.0 990 | 1.0 266 | 0.9 652 | 0.9 514 | 0.9 397 |
| 75° | 1.3 090 | 1.3 010 | 1.2 911 | 1.2 399 | 1.1 635 | 1.0 759 | 0.9 992 | 0.9 814 | 0.9 659 |
| 80° | 1.3 963 | 1.3 870 | 1.3 755 | 1.3 161 | 1.2 266 | 1.1 225 | 1.0 282 | 1.0 054 | 0.9 848 |
| 85° | 1.4 835 | 1.4 729 | 1.4 598 | 1.3 919 | 1.2 889 | 1.1 673 | 1.0 534 | 1.0 244 | 0.9 962 |
| 86° | 1.5 010 | 1.4 901 | 1.4 767 | 1.4 070 | 1.3 012 | 1.1 761 | 1.0 581 | 1.0 277 | 0.9 976 |
| 87° | 1.5 184 | 1.5 073 | 1.4 936 | 1.4 221 | 1.3 136 | 1.1 848 | 1.0 628 | 1.0 309 | 0.9 986 |
| 88° | 1.5 359 | 1.5 245 | 1.5 104 | 1.4 372 | 1.3 260 | 1.1 936 | 1.0 674 | 1.0 340 | 0.9 994 |
| 89° | 1.5 533 | 1.5 417 | 1.5 273 | 1.4 524 | 1.3 383 | 1.2 023 | 1.0 719 | 1.0 371 | 0.9 998 |
| 90° | 1.5 708 | 1.5 589 | 1.5 442 | 1.4 675 | 1.3 506 | 1.2 111 | 1.0 764 | 1.0 401 | 1.0 000 |

## 6. THE GAMMA FUNCTION: $\Gamma(x) = \int_0^\infty u^{x-1}e^{-u}\,da,\ x > 0$

| $x$ | $\Gamma(x)$ | $x$ | $\Gamma(x)$ | $x$ | $\Gamma(x)$ | $x$ | $\Gamma(x)$ | $x$ | $\Gamma(x)$ |
|---|---|---|---|---|---|---|---|---|---|
| 1.01 | 0.99 433 | 1.21 | 0.91 558 | 1.41 | 0.88 676 | 1.61 | 0.89 468 | 1.81 | 0.93 408 |
| 1.02 | 0.98 884 | 1.22 | 0.91 311 | 1.42 | 0.88 636 | 1.62 | 0.89 592 | 1.82 | 0.93 685 |
| 1.03 | 0.98 355 | 1.23 | 0.91 075 | 1.43 | 0.88 604 | 1.63 | 0.89 724 | 1.83 | 0.93 969 |
| 1.04 | 0.97 844 | 1.24 | 0.90 852 | 1.44 | 0.88 581 | 1.64 | 0.89 864 | 1.84 | 0.94 261 |
| 1.05 | 0.97 350 | 1.25 | 0.90 640 | 1.45 | 0.88 566 | 1.65 | 0.90 012 | 1.85 | 0.94 561 |
| 1.06 | 0.96 874 | 1.26 | 0.90 440 | 1.46 | 0.88 560 | 1.66 | 0.90 167 | 1.86 | 0.94 869 |
| 1.07 | 0.96 415 | 1.27 | 0.90 250 | 1.47 | 0.88 563 | 1.67 | 0.90 330 | 1.87 | 0.95 184 |
| 1.08 | 0.95 973 | 1.28 | 0.90 072 | 1.48 | 0.88 575 | 1.68 | 0.90 500 | 1.88 | 0.95 507 |
| 1.09 | 0.95 546 | 1.29 | 0.89 904 | 1.49 | 0.88 595 | 1.69 | 0.90 678 | 1.89 | 0.95 838 |
| **1.10** | 0.95 135 | **1.30** | 0.89 747 | **1.50** | 0.88 623 | **1.70** | 0.90 864 | **1.90** | 0.96 177 |
| 1.11 | 0.94 740 | 1.31 | 0.89 600 | 1.51 | 0.88 659 | 1.71 | 0.91 057 | 1.91 | 0.96 523 |
| 1.12 | 0.94 359 | 1.32 | 0.89 464 | 1.52 | 0.88 704 | 1.72 | 0.91 258 | 1.92 | 0.96 877 |
| 1.13 | 0.93 993 | 1.33 | 0.89 338 | 1.53 | 0.88 757 | 1.73 | 0.91 467 | 1.93 | 0.97 240 |
| 1.14 | 0.93 642 | 1.34 | 0.89 222 | 1.54 | 0.88 818 | 1.74 | 0.91 683 | 1.94 | 0.97 610 |
| 1.15 | 0.93 304 | 1.35 | 0.89 115 | 1.55 | 0.88 887 | 1.75 | 0.91 906 | 1.95 | 0.97 988 |
| 1.16 | 0.92 980 | 1.36 | 0.89 018 | 1.56 | 0.88 964 | 1.76 | 0.92 137 | 1.96 | 0.98 374 |
| 1.17 | 0.92 670 | 1.37 | 0.88 931 | 1.57 | 0.89 049 | 1.77 | 0.92 376 | 1.97 | 0.98 768 |
| 1.18 | 0.92 373 | 1.38 | 0.88 854 | 1.58 | 0.89 142 | 1.78 | 0.92 623 | 1.98 | 0.99 171 |
| 1.19 | 0.92 089 | 1.39 | 0.88 785 | 1.59 | 0.89 243 | 1.79 | 0.92 877 | 1.99 | 0.99 581 |
| **1.20** | 0.91 817 | **1.40** | 0.88 726 | **1.60** | 0.89 352 | **1.80** | 0.93 138 | **2.00** | 1.00 000 |

For larger values of $x$, use the above table with the relation

$$\Gamma(x+1) = x\Gamma(x).$$

For large positive values of $x$, the asymptotic series

$$\Gamma(x) \sim x^x e^{-x}\sqrt{\frac{2\pi}{x}}\left[1 + \frac{1}{12\,x} + \frac{1}{288\,x^2} - \frac{139}{51840\,x^3} - \frac{571}{2488320\,x^4} + \cdots\right]$$

is convenient.

# 7. COMMON LOGARITHM OF THE GAMMA FUNCTION

| x | log Γ(x) | x | log Γ(x) | x | log Γ(x) | x | log Γ(x) | x | log Γ(x) |
|------|-----------|------|-----------|------|-----------|------|-----------|------|------------|
| 1.01 | 9.99 753 | 1.21 | 9.96 169 | 1.41 | 9.94 781 | 1.61 | 9.95 167 | 1.81 | 9.97 038 |
| 1.02 | 9.99 513 | 1.22 | 9.96 052 | 1.42 | 9.94 761 | 1.62 | 9.95 227 | 1.82 | 9.97 167 |
| 1.03 | 9.99 280 | 1.23 | 9.95 940 | 1.43 | 9.94 745 | 1.63 | 9.95 291 | 1.83 | 9.97 298 |
| 1.04 | 9.99 053 | 1.24 | 9.95 833 | 1.44 | 9.94 734 | 1.64 | 9.95 359 | 1.84 | 9.97 433 |
| 1.05 | 9.98 834 | 1.25 | 9.95 732 | 1.45 | 9.94 727 | 1.65 | 9.95 430 | 1.85 | 9.97 571 |
| 1.06 | 9.98 621 | 1.26 | 9.95 636 | 1.46 | 9.94 724 | 1.66 | 9.95 505 | 1.86 | 9.97 712 |
| 1.07 | 9.98 415 | 1.27 | 9.95 545 | 1.47 | 9.94 725 | 1.67 | 9.95 583 | 1.87 | 9.97 856 |
| 1.08 | 9.98 215 | 1.28 | 9.95 459 | 1.48 | 9.94 731 | 1.68 | 9.95 665 | 1.88 | 9.98 004 |
| 1.09 | 9.98 021 | 1.29 | 9.95 378 | 1.49 | 9.94 741 | 1.69 | 9.95 750 | 1.89 | 9.98 154 |
| **1.10** | 9.97 834 | **1.30** | 9.95 302 | **1.50** | 9.94 754 | **1.70** | 9.95 830 | **1.90** | 9.98 307 |
| 1.11 | 9.97 653 | 1.31 | 9.95 231 | 1.51 | 9.94 772 | 1.71 | 9.95 931 | 1.91 | 9.98 463 |
| 1.12 | 9.97 478 | 1.32 | 9.95 165 | 1.52 | 9.94 794 | 1.72 | 9.96 027 | 1.92 | 9.98 622 |
| 1.13 | 9.97 310 | 1.33 | 9.95 104 | 1.53 | 9.94 820 | 1.73 | 9.96 126 | 1.93 | 9.98 784 |
| 1.14 | 9.97 147 | 1.34 | 9.95 047 | 1.54 | 9.94 850 | 1.74 | 9.96 229 | 1.94 | 9.98 949 |
| 1.15 | 9.96 990 | 1.35 | 9.94 995 | 1.55 | 9.94 884 | 1.75 | 9.96 335 | 1.95 | 9.99 117 |
| 1.16 | 9.96 839 | 1.36 | 9.94 948 | 1.56 | 9.94 921 | 1.76 | 9.96 444 | 1.96 | 9.99 288 |
| 1.17 | 9.96 694 | 1.37 | 9.94 905 | 1.57 | 9.94 963 | 1.77 | 9.96 556 | 1.97 | 9.99 462 |
| 1.18 | 9.96 554 | 1.38 | 9.94 868 | 1.58 | 9.95 008 | 1.78 | 9.96 672 | 1.98 | 9.99 638 |
| 1.19 | 9.96 421 | 1.39 | 9.94 834 | 1.59 | 9.95 057 | 1.79 | 9.96 791 | 1.99 | 9.99 818 |
| **1.20** | 9.96 292 | **1.40** | 9.94 805 | **1.60** | 9.95 110 | **1.80** | 9.96 913 | **2.00** | 10.00 000 |

Note. Subtract 10 from each entry.

For larger values of $x$, use the above table with the relation

$$\log_{10} \Gamma(x + 1) = \log_{10} x + \log_{10} \Gamma(x).$$

## 8. EXPONENTIAL AND HYPERBOLIC FUNCTIONS

| x | Value | | | | | Common Logarithm | | |
|---|---|---|---|---|---|---|---|---|
| | $e^x$ | $e^{-x}$ | Sinh x | Cosh x | Tanh x | $e^x$ | Sinh x | Cosh x |
| **0.00** | 1.0 000 | 1.00 000 | 0.0 000 | 1.0 000 | 0.00 000 | 0.00 000 | ———— | 0.00 000 |
| 0.01 | 1.0 101 | 0.99 005 | 0.0 100 | 1.0 001 | 0.01 000 | 0.00 434 | 8.00 001* | 0.00 002 |
| 0.02 | 1.0 202 | 0.98 020 | 0.0 200 | 1.0 002 | 0.02 000 | 0.00 869 | 8.30 106* | 0.00 009 |
| 0.03 | 1.0 305 | 0.97 045 | 0.0 300 | 1.0 005 | 0.02 999 | 0.01 303 | 8.47 719* | 0.00 020 |
| 0.04 | 1.0 408 | 0.96 079 | 0.0 400 | 1.0 008 | 0.03 998 | 0.01 737 | 8.60 218* | 0.00 035 |
| 0.05 | 1.0 513 | 0.95 123 | 0.0 500 | 1.0 013 | 0.04 996 | 0.02 171 | 8.69 915* | 0.00 054 |
| 0.06 | 1.0 618 | 0.94 176 | 0.0 600 | 1.0 018 | 0.05 993 | 0.02 606 | 8.77 841* | 0.00 078 |
| 0.07 | 1.0 725 | 0.93 239 | 0.0 701 | 1.0 025 | 0.06 989 | 0.03 040 | 8.84 545* | 0.00 106 |
| 0.08 | 1.0 833 | 0.92 312 | 0.0 801 | 1.0 032 | 0.07 983 | 0.03 474 | 8.90 355* | 0.00 139 |
| 0.09 | 1.0 942 | 0.91 393 | 0.0 901 | 1.0 041 | 0.08 976 | 0.03 909 | 8.95 483* | 0.00 176 |
| **0.10** | 1.1 052 | 0.90 484 | 0.1 002 | 1.0 050 | 0.09 967 | 0.04 343 | 9.00 072* | 0.00 217 |
| 0.11 | 1.1 163 | 0.89 583 | 0.1 102 | 1.0 061 | 0.10 956 | 0.04 777 | 9.04 227* | 0.00 262 |
| 0.12 | 1.1 275 | 0.88 692 | 0.1 203 | 1.0 072 | 0.11 943 | 0.05 212 | 9.08 022* | 0.00 312 |
| 0.13 | 1.1 388 | 0.87 810 | 0.1 304 | 1.0 085 | 0.12 927 | 0.05 646 | 9.11 517* | 0.00 366 |
| 0.14 | 1.1 503 | 0.86 936 | 0.1 405 | 1.0 098 | 0.13 909 | 0.06 080 | 9.14 755* | 0.00 424 |
| 0.15 | 1.1 618 | 0.86 071 | 0.1 506 | 1.0 113 | 0.14 889 | 0.06 514 | 9.17 772* | 0.00 487 |
| 0.16 | 1.1 735 | 0.85 214 | 0.1 607 | 1.0 128 | 0.15 865 | 0.06 949 | 9.20 597* | 0.00 554 |
| 0.17 | 1.1 853 | 0.84 366 | 0.1 708 | 1.0 145 | 0.16 838 | 0.07 383 | 9.23 254* | 0.00 625 |
| 0.18 | 1.1 972 | 0.83 527 | 0.1 810 | 1.0 162 | 0.17 808 | 0.07 817 | 9.25 762* | 0.00 700 |
| 0.19 | 1.2 092 | 0.82 696 | 0.1 911 | 1.0 181 | 0.18 775 | 0.08 252 | 9.28 136* | 0.00 779 |
| **0.20** | 1.2 214 | 0.81 873 | 0.2 013 | 1.0 201 | 0.19 738 | 0.08 686 | 9.30 392* | 0.00 863 |
| 0.21 | 1.2 337 | 0.81 058 | 0.2 115 | 1.0 221 | 0.20 697 | 0.09 120 | 9.32 541* | 0.00 951 |
| 0.22 | 1.2 461 | 0.80 252 | 0.2 218 | 1.0 243 | 0.21 652 | 0.09 554 | 9.34 592* | 0.01 043 |
| 0.23 | 1.2 586 | 0.79 453 | 0.2 320 | 1.0 266 | 0.22 603 | 0.09 989 | 9.36 555* | 0.01 139 |
| 0.24 | 1.2 712 | 0.78 663 | 0.2 423 | 1.0 289 | 0.23 550 | 0.10 423 | 9.38 437* | 0.01 239 |
| 0.25 | 1.2 840 | 0.77 880 | 0.2 526 | 1.0 314 | 0.24 492 | 0.10 857 | 9.40 245* | 0.01 343 |
| 0.26 | 1.2 969 | 0.77 105 | 0.2 629 | 1.0 340 | 0.25 430 | 0.11 292 | 9.41 986* | 0.01 452 |
| 0.27 | 1.3 100 | 0.76 338 | 0.2 733 | 1.0 367 | 0.26 362 | 0.11 726 | 9.43 663* | 0.01 564 |
| 0.28 | 1.3 231 | 0.75 578 | 0.2 837 | 1.0 395 | 0.27 291 | 0.12 160 | 9.45 282* | 0.01 681 |
| 0.29 | 1.3 364 | 0.74 826 | 0.2 941 | 1.0 423 | 0.28 213 | 0.12 595 | 9.46 847* | 0.01 801 |
| **0.30** | 1.3 499 | 0.74 082 | 0.3 045 | 1.0 453 | 0.29 131 | 0.13 029 | 9.48 362* | 0.01 926 |
| 0.31 | 1.3 634 | 0.73 345 | 0.3 150 | 1.0 484 | 0.30 044 | 0.13 463 | 9.49 830* | 0.02 054 |
| 0.32 | 1.3 771 | 0.72 615 | 0.3 255 | 1.0 516 | 0.30 951 | 0.13 897 | 9.51 254* | 0.02 187 |
| 0.33 | 1.3 910 | 0.71 892 | 0.3 360 | 1.0 549 | 0.31 852 | 0.14 332 | 9.52 637* | 0.02 323 |
| 0.34 | 1.4 049 | 0.71 177 | 0.3 466 | 1.0 584 | 0.32 748 | 0.14 766 | 9.53 981* | 0.02 463 |
| 0.35 | 1.4 191 | 0.70 469 | 0.3 572 | 1.0 619 | 0.33 638 | 0.15 200 | 9.55 290* | 0.02 607 |
| 0.36 | 1.4 333 | 0.69 768 | 0.3 678 | 1.0 655 | 0.34 521 | 0.15 635 | 9.56 564* | 0.02 755 |
| 0.37 | 1.4 477 | 0.69 073 | 0.3 785 | 1.0 692 | 0.35 399 | 0.16 069 | 9.57 807* | 0.02 907 |
| 0.38 | 1.4 623 | 0.68 386 | 0.3 892 | 1.0 731 | 0.36 271 | 0.16 503 | 9.59 019* | 0.03 063 |
| 0.39 | 1.4 770 | 0.67 706 | 0.4 000 | 1.0 770 | 0.37 136 | 0.16 937 | 9.60 202* | 0.03 222 |
| **0.40** | 1.4 918 | 0.67 032 | 0.4 108 | 1.0 811 | 0.37 995 | 0.17 372 | 9.61 358* | 0.03 385 |
| 0.41 | 1.5 068 | 0.66 365 | 0.4 216 | 1.0 852 | 0.38 847 | 0.17 806 | 9.62 488* | 0.03 552 |
| 0.42 | 1.5 220 | 0.65 705 | 0.4 325 | 1.0 895 | 0.39 693 | 0.18 240 | 9.63 594* | 0.03 723 |
| 0.43 | 1.5 373 | 0.65 051 | 0.4 434 | 1.0 939 | 0.40 532 | 0.18 675 | 9.64 677* | 0.03 897 |
| 0.44 | 1.5 527 | 0.64 404 | 0.4 543 | 1.0 984 | 0.41 364 | 0.19 109 | 9.65 738* | 0.04 075 |
| 0.45 | 1.5 683 | 0.63 763 | 0.4 653 | 1.1 030 | 0.42 190 | 0.19 543 | 9.66 777* | 0.04 256 |
| 0.46 | 1.5 841 | 0.63 128 | 0.4 764 | 1.1 077 | 0.43 008 | 0.19 978 | 9.67 797* | 0.04 441 |
| 0.47 | 1.6 000 | 0.62 500 | 0.4 875 | 1.1 125 | 0.43 820 | 0.20 412 | 9.68 797* | 0.04 630 |
| 0.48 | 1.6 161 | 0.61 878 | 0.4 986 | 1.1 174 | 0.44 624 | 0.20 846 | 9.69 779* | 0.04 822 |
| 0.49 | 1.6 323 | 0.61 263 | 0.5 098 | 1.1 225 | 0.45 422 | 0.21 280 | 9.70 744* | 0.05 018 |
| **0.50** | 1.6 487 | 0.60 653 | 0.5 211 | 1.1 276 | 0.46 212 | 0.21 715 | 9.71 692* | 0.05 217 |

*The asterisk indicates that 10 is to be subtracted.

## 8. EXPONENTIAL AND HYPERBOLIC FUNCTIONS

| $x$ | Value | | | | | Common Logarithm | | |
|---|---|---|---|---|---|---|---|---|
| | $e^x$ | $e^{-x}$ | Sinh $x$ | Cosh $x$ | Tanh $x$ | $e^x$ | Sinh $x$ | Cosh $x$ |
| **0.50** | 1.6 487 | 0.60 653 | 0.5 211 | 1.1 276 | 0.46 212 | 0.21 715 | 9.71 692* | 0.05 217 |
| 0.51 | 1.6 653 | 0.60 050 | 0.5 324 | 1.1 329 | 0.46 995 | 0.22 149 | 9.72 624* | 0.05 419 |
| 0.52 | 1.6 820 | 0.59 452 | 0.5 438 | 1.1 383 | 0.47 770 | 0.22 583 | 9.73 540* | 0.05 625 |
| 0.53 | 1.6 989 | 0.58 860 | 0.5 552 | 1.1 438 | 0.48 538 | 0.23 018 | 9.74 442* | 0.05 834 |
| 0.54 | 1.7 160 | 0.58 275 | 0.5 666 | 1.1 494 | 0.49 299 | 0.23 452 | 9.75 330* | 0.06 046 |
| 0.55 | 1.7 333 | 0.57 695 | 0.5 782 | 1.1 551 | 0.50 052 | 0.23 886 | 9.76 204* | 0.06 262 |
| 0.56 | 1.7 507 | 0.57 121 | 0.5 897 | 1.1 609 | 0.50 798 | 0.24 320 | 9.77 065* | 0.06 481 |
| 0.57 | 1.7 683 | 0.56 553 | 0.6 014 | 1.1 669 | 0.51 536 | 0.24 755 | 9.77 914* | 0.06 703 |
| 0.58 | 1.7 860 | 0.55 990 | 0.6 131 | 1.1 730 | 0.52 267 | 0.25 189 | 9.78 751* | 0.06 929 |
| 0.59 | 1.8 040 | 0.55 433 | 0.6 248 | 1.1 792 | 0.52 990 | 0.25 623 | 9.79 576* | 0.07 157 |
| **0.60** | 1.8 221 | 0.54 881 | 0.6 367 | 1.1 855 | 0.53 705 | 0.26 058 | 9.80 390* | 0.07 389 |
| 0.61 | 1.8 404 | 0.54 335 | 0.6 485 | 1.1 919 | 0.54 413 | 0.26 492 | 9.81 194* | 0.07 624 |
| 0.62 | 1.8 589 | 0.53 794 | 0.6 605 | 1.1 984 | 0.55 113 | 0.26 926 | 9.81 987* | 0.07 861 |
| 0.63 | 1.8 776 | 0.53 259 | 0.6 725 | 1.2 051 | 0.55 805 | 0.27 361 | 9.82 770* | 0.08 102 |
| 0.64 | 1.8 965 | 0.52 729 | 0.6 846 | 1.2 119 | 0.56 490 | 0.27 795 | 9.83 543* | 0.08 346 |
| 0.65 | 1.9 155 | 0.52 205 | 0.6 967 | 1.2 188 | 0.57 167 | 0.28 229 | 9.84 308* | 0.08 593 |
| 0.66 | 1.9 348 | 0.51 685 | 0.7 090 | 1.2 258 | 0.57 836 | 0.28 663 | 9.85 063* | 0.08 843 |
| 0.67 | 1.9 542 | 0.51 171 | 0.7 213 | 1.2 330 | 0.58 498 | 0.29 098 | 9.85 809* | 0.09 095 |
| 0.68 | 1.9 739 | 0.50 662 | 0.7 336 | 1.2 402 | 0.59 152 | 0.29 532 | 9.86 548* | 0.09 351 |
| 0.69 | 1.9 937 | 0.50 158 | 0.7 461 | 1.2 476 | 0.59 798 | 0.29 966 | 9.87 278* | 0.09 609 |
| **0.70** | 2.0 138 | 0.49 659 | 0.7 586 | 1.2 552 | 0.60 437 | 0.30 401 | 9.88 000* | 0.09 870 |
| 0.71 | 2.0 340 | 0.49 164 | 0.7 712 | 1.2 628 | 0.61 068 | 0.30 835 | 9.88 715* | 0.10 134 |
| 0.72 | 2.0 544 | 0.48 675 | 0.7 838 | 1.2 706 | 0.61 691 | 0.31 269 | 9.89 423* | 0.10 401 |
| 0.73 | 2.0 751 | 0.48 191 | 0.7 966 | 1.2 785 | 0.62 307 | 0.31 703 | 9.90 123* | 0.10 670 |
| 0.74 | 2.0 959 | 0.47 711 | 0.8 094 | 1.2 865 | 0.62 915 | 0.32 138 | 9.90 817* | 0.10 942 |
| 0.75 | 2.1 170 | 0.47 237 | 0.8 223 | 1.2 947 | 0.63 515 | 0.32 572 | 9.91 504* | 0.11 216 |
| 0.76 | 2.1 383 | 0.46 767 | 0.8 353 | 1.3 030 | 0.64 108 | 0.33 006 | 9.92 185* | 0.11 493 |
| 0.77 | 2.1 598 | 0.46 301 | 0.8 484 | 1.3 114 | 0.64 693 | 0.33 441 | 9.92 859* | 0.11 773 |
| 0.78 | 2.1 815 | 0.45 841 | 0.8 615 | 1.3 199 | 0.65 271 | 0.33 875 | 9.93 527* | 0.12 055 |
| 0.79 | 2.2 034 | 0.45 384 | 0.8 748 | 1.3 286 | 0.65 841 | 0.34 309 | 9.94 190* | 0.12 340 |
| **0.80** | 2.2 255 | 0.44 933 | 0.8 881 | 1.3 374 | 0.66 404 | 0.34 744 | 9.94 846* | 0.12 627 |
| 0.81 | 2.2 479 | 0.44 486 | 0.9 015 | 1.3 464 | 0.66 959 | 0.35 178 | 9.95 498* | 0.12 917 |
| 0.82 | 2.2 705 | 0.44 043 | 0.9 150 | 1.3 555 | 0.67 507 | 0.35 612 | 9.96 144* | 0.13 209 |
| 0.83 | 2.2 933 | 0.43 605 | 0.9 286 | 1.3 647 | 0.68 048 | 0.36 046 | 9.96 784* | 0.13 503 |
| 0.84 | 2.3 164 | 0.43 171 | 0.9 423 | 1.3 740 | 0.68 581 | 0.36 481 | 9.97 420* | 0.13 800 |
| 0.85 | 2.3 396 | 0.42 741 | 0.9 561 | 1.3 835 | 0.69 107 | 0.36 915 | 9.98 051* | 0.14 099 |
| 0.86 | 2.3 632 | 0.42 316 | 0.9 700 | 1.3 932 | 0.69 626 | 0.37 349 | 9.98 677* | 0.14 400 |
| 0.87 | 2.3 869 | 0.41 895 | 0.9 840 | 1.4 029 | 0.70 137 | 0.37 784 | 9.99 299* | 0.14 704 |
| 0.88 | 2.4 109 | 0.41 478 | 0.9 981 | 1.4 128 | 0.70 642 | 0.38 218 | 9.99 916* | 0.15 009 |
| 0.89 | 2.4 351 | 0.41 066 | 1.0 122 | 1.4 229 | 0.71 139 | 0.38 652 | 0.00 528 | 0.15 317 |
| **0.90** | 2.4 596 | 0.40 657 | 1.0 265 | 1.4 331 | 0.71 630 | 0.39 087 | 0.01 137 | 0.15 627 |
| 0.91 | 2.4 843 | 0.40 252 | 1.0 409 | 1.4 434 | 0.72 113 | 0.39 521 | 0.01 741 | 0.15 939 |
| 0.92 | 2.5 093 | 0.39 852 | 1.0 554 | 1.4 539 | 0.72 590 | 0.39 955 | 0.02 341 | 0.16 254 |
| 0.93 | 2.5 345 | 0.39 455 | 1.0 700 | 1.4 645 | 0.73 059 | 0.40 389 | 0.02 937 | 0.16 570 |
| 0.94 | 2.5 600 | 0.39 063 | 1.0 847 | 1.4 753 | 0.73 522 | 0.40 824 | 0.03 530 | 0.16 888 |
| 0.95 | 2.5 857 | 0.38 674 | 1.0 995 | 1.4 862 | 0.73 978 | 0.41 258 | 0.04 119 | 0.17 208 |
| 0.96 | 2.6 117 | 0.38 289 | 1.1 144 | 1.4 973 | 0.74 428 | 0.41 692 | 0.04 704 | 0.17 531 |
| 0.97 | 2.6 379 | 0.37 908 | 1.1 294 | 1.5 085 | 0.74 870 | 0.42 127 | 0.05 286 | 0.17 855 |
| 0.98 | 2.6 645 | 0.37 531 | 1.1 446 | 1.5 199 | 0.75 307 | 0.42 561 | 0.05 864 | 0.18 181 |
| 0.99 | 2.6 912 | 0.37 158 | 1.1 598 | 1.5 314 | 0.75 736 | 0.42 995 | 0.06 439 | 0.18 509 |
| **1.00** | 2.7 183 | 0.36 788 | 1.1 752 | 1.5 431 | 0.76 159 | 0.43 429 | 0.07 011 | 0.18 839 |

*The asterisk indicates that 10 is to be subtracted.

## 8. EXPONENTIAL AND HYPERBOLIC FUNCTIONS

| x | Value | | | | | Common Logarithm | | |
|---|---|---|---|---|---|---|---|---|
| | $e^x$ | $e^{-x}$ | Sinh x | Cosh x | Tanh x | $e^x$ | Sinh x | Cosh x |
| **1.00** | 2.7 183 | 0.36 788 | 1.1 752 | 1.5 431 | 0.76 159 | 0.43 429 | 0.07 011 | 0.18 839 |
| 1.01 | 2.7 456 | 0.36 422 | 1.1 907 | 1.5 549 | 0.76 576 | 0.43 864 | 0.07 580 | 0.19 171 |
| 1.02 | 2.7 732 | 0.36 059 | 1.2 063 | 1.5 669 | 0.76 987 | 0.44 298 | 0.08 146 | 0.19 504 |
| 1.03 | 2.8 011 | 0.35 701 | 1.2 220 | 1.5 790 | 0.77 391 | 0.44 732 | 0.08 708 | 0.19 839 |
| 1.04 | 2.8 292 | 0.35 345 | 1.2 379 | 1.5 913 | 0.77 789 | 0.45 167 | 0.09 268 | 0.20 176 |
| 1.05 | 2.8 577 | 0.34 994 | 1.2 539 | 1.6 038 | 0.78 181 | 0.45 601 | 0.09 825 | 0.20 515 |
| 1.06 | 2.8 864 | 0.34 646 | 1.2 700 | 1.6 164 | 0.78 566 | 0.46 035 | 0.10 379 | 0.20 855 |
| 1.07 | 2.9 154 | 0.34 301 | 1.2 862 | 1.6 292 | 0.78 946 | 0.46 470 | 0.10 930 | 0.21 197 |
| 1.08 | 2.9 447 | 0.33 960 | 1.3 025 | 1.6 421 | 0.79 320 | 0.46 904 | 0.11 479 | 0.21 541 |
| 1.09 | 2.9 743 | 0.33 622 | 1.3 190 | 1.6 552 | 0.79 688 | 0.47 338 | 0.12 025 | 0.21 886 |
| **1.10** | 3.0 042 | 0.33 287 | 1.3 356 | 1.6 685 | 0.80 050 | 0.47 772 | 0.12 569 | 0.22 233 |
| 1.11 | 3.0 344 | 0.32 956 | 1.3 524 | 1.6 820 | 0.80 406 | 0.48 207 | 0.13 111 | 0.22 582 |
| 1.12 | 3.0 649 | 0.32 628 | 1.3 693 | 1.6 956 | 0.80 757 | 0.48 641 | 0.13 649 | 0.22 931 |
| 1.13 | 3.0 957 | 0.32 303 | 1.3 863 | 1.7 093 | 0.81 102 | 0.49 075 | 0.14 186 | 0.23 283 |
| 1.14 | 3.1 268 | 0.31 982 | 1.4 035 | 1.7 233 | 0.81 441 | 0.49 510 | 0.14 720 | 0.23 636 |
| 1.15 | 3.1 582 | 0.31 664 | 1.4 208 | 1.7 374 | 0.81 775 | 0.49 944 | 0.15 253 | 0.23 990 |
| 1.16 | 3.1 899 | 0.31 349 | 1.4 382 | 1.7 517 | 0.82 104 | 0.50 378 | 0.15 783 | 0.24 346 |
| 1.17 | 3.2 220 | 0.31 037 | 1.4 558 | 1.7 662 | 0.82 427 | 0.50 812 | 0.16 311 | 0.24 703 |
| 1.18 | 3.2 544 | 0.30 728 | 1.4 735 | 1.7 808 | 0.82 745 | 0.51 247 | 0.16 836 | 0.25 062 |
| 1.19 | 3.2 871 | 0.30 422 | 1.4 914 | 1.7 957 | 0.83 058 | 0.51 681 | 0.17 360 | 0.25 422 |
| **1.20** | 3.3 201 | 0.30 119 | 1.5 095 | 1.8 107 | 0.83 365 | 0.52 115 | 0.17 882 | 0.25 784 |
| 1.21 | 3.3 535 | 0.29 820 | 1.5 276 | 1.8 258 | 0.83 668 | 0.52 550 | 0.18 402 | 0.26 146 |
| 1.22 | 3.3 872 | 0.29 523 | 1.5 460 | 1.8 412 | 0.83 965 | 0.52 984 | 0.18 920 | 0.26 510 |
| 1.23 | 3.4 212 | 0.29 229 | 1.5 645 | 1.8 568 | 0.84 258 | 0.53 418 | 0.19 437 | 0.26 876 |
| 1.24 | 3.4 556 | 0.28 938 | 1.5 831 | 1.8 725 | 0.84 546 | 0.53 853 | 0.19 951 | 0.27 242 |
| 1.25 | 3.4 903 | 0.28 650 | 1.6 019 | 1.8 884 | 0.84 828 | 0.54 287 | 0.20 464 | 0.27 610 |
| 1.26 | 3.5 254 | 0.28 365 | 1.6 209 | 1.9 045 | 0.85 106 | 0.54 721 | 0.20 975 | 0.27 979 |
| 1.27 | 3.5 609 | 0.28 083 | 1.6 400 | 1.9 208 | 0.85 380 | 0.55 155 | 0.21 485 | 0.28 349 |
| 1.28 | 3.5 966 | 0.27 804 | 1.6 593 | 1.9 373 | 0.85 648 | 0.55 590 | 0.21 993 | 0.28 721 |
| 1.29 | 3.6 328 | 0.27 527 | 1.6 788 | 1.9 540 | 0.85 913 | 0.56 024 | 0.22 499 | 0.29 093 |
| **1.30** | 3.6 693 | 0.27 253 | 1.6 984 | 1.9 709 | 0.86 172 | 0.56 458 | 0.23 004 | 0.29 467 |
| 1.31 | 3.7 062 | 0.26 982 | 1.7 182 | 1.9 880 | 0.86 428 | 0.56 893 | 0.23 507 | 0.29 842 |
| 1.32 | 3.7 434 | 0.26 714 | 1.7 381 | 2.0 053 | 0.86 678 | 0.57 327 | 0.24 009 | 0.30 217 |
| 1.33 | 3.7 810 | 0.26 448 | 1.7 583 | 2.0 228 | 0.86 925 | 0.57 761 | 0.24 509 | 0.30 594 |
| 1.34 | 3.8 190 | 0.26 185 | 1.7 786 | 2.0 404 | 0.87 167 | 0.58 195 | 0.25 008 | 0.30 972 |
| 1.35 | 3.8 574 | 0.25 924 | 1.7 991 | 2.0 583 | 0.87 405 | 0.58 630 | 0.25 505 | 0.31 352 |
| 1.36 | 3.8 962 | 0.25 666 | 1.8 198 | 2.0 764 | 0.87 639 | 0.59 064 | 0.26 002 | 0.31 732 |
| 1.37 | 3.9 354 | 0.25 411 | 1.8 406 | 2.0 947 | 0.87 869 | 0.59 498 | 0.26 496 | 0.32 113 |
| 1.38 | 3.9 749 | 0.25 158 | 1.8 617 | 2.1 132 | 0.88 095 | 0.59 933 | 0.26 990 | 0.32 495 |
| 1.39 | 4.0 149 | 0.24 908 | 1.8 829 | 2.1 320 | 0.88 317 | 0.60 367 | 0.27 482 | 0.32 878 |
| **1.40** | 4.0 552 | 0.24 660 | 1.9 043 | 2.1 509 | 0.88 535 | 0.60 801 | 0.27 974 | 0.33 262 |
| 1.41 | 4.0 960 | 0.24 414 | 1.9 259 | 2.1 700 | 0.88 749 | 0.61 236 | 0.28 464 | 0.33 647 |
| 1.42 | 4.1 371 | 0.24 171 | 1.9 477 | 2.1 894 | 0.88 960 | 0.61 670 | 0.28 952 | 0.34 033 |
| 1.43 | 4.1 787 | 0.23 931 | 1.9 697 | 2.2 090 | 0.89 167 | 0.62 104 | 0.29 440 | 0.34 420 |
| 1.44 | 4.2 207 | 0.23 693 | 1.9 919 | 2.2 288 | 0.89 370 | 0.62 538 | 0.29 926 | 0.34 807 |
| 1.45 | 4.2 631 | 0.23 457 | 2.0 143 | 2.2 488 | 0.89 569 | 0.62 973 | 0.30 412 | 0.35 196 |
| 1.46 | 4.3 060 | 0.23 224 | 2.0 369 | 2.2 691 | 0.89 765 | 0.63 407 | 0.30 896 | 0.35 585 |
| 1.47 | 4.3 492 | 0.22 993 | 2.0 597 | 2.2 896 | 0.89 958 | 0.63 841 | 0.31 379 | 0.35 976 |
| 1.48 | 4.3 929 | 0.22 764 | 2.0 827 | 2.3 103 | 0.90 147 | 0.64 276 | 0.31 862 | 0.36 367 |
| 1.49 | 4.4 371 | 0.22 537 | 2.1 059 | 2.3 312 | 0.90 332 | 0.64 710 | 0.32 343 | 0.36 759 |
| **1.50** | 4.4 817 | 0.22 313 | 2.1 293 | 2.3 524 | 0.90 515 | 0.65 144 | 0.32 823 | 0.37 151 |

## 8. EXPONENTIAL AND HYPERBOLIC FUNCTIONS

| x | Value | | | | | Common Logarithm | | |
|---|---|---|---|---|---|---|---|---|
| | $e^x$ | $e^{-x}$ | Sinh x | Cosh x | Tanh x | $e^x$ | Sinh x | Cosh x |
| **1.50** | 4.4 817 | 0.22 313 | 2.1 293 | 2.3 524 | 0.90 515 | 0.65 144 | 0.32 823 | 0.37 151 |
| 1.51 | 4.5 267 | 0.22 091 | 2.1 529 | 2.3 738 | 0.90 694 | 0.65 578 | 0.33 303 | 0.37 545 |
| 1.52 | 4.5 722 | 0.21 871 | 2.1 768 | 2.3 955 | 0.90 870 | 0.66 013 | 0.33 781 | 0.37 939 |
| 1.53 | 4.6 182 | 0.21 654 | 2.2 008 | 2.4 174 | 0.91 042 | 0.66 447 | 0.34 258 | 0.38 334 |
| 1.54 | 4.6 646 | 0.21 438 | 2.2 251 | 2.4 395 | 0.91 212 | 0.66 881 | 0.34 735 | 0.38 730 |
| 1.55 | 4.7 115 | 0.21 225 | 2.2 496 | 2.4 619 | 0.91 379 | 0.67 316 | 0.35 211 | 0.39 126 |
| 1.56 | 4.7 588 | 0.21 014 | 2.2 743 | 2.4 845 | 0.91 542 | 0.67 750 | 0.35 686 | 0.39 524 |
| 1.57 | 4.8 066 | 0.20 805 | 2.2 993 | 2.5 073 | 0.91 703 | 0.68 184 | 0.36 160 | 0.39 921 |
| 1.58 | 4.8 550 | 0.20 598 | 2.3 245 | 2.5 305 | 0.91 860 | 0.68 619 | 0.36 633 | 0.40 320 |
| 1.59 | 4.9 037 | 0.20 393 | 2.3 499 | 2.5 538 | 0.92 015 | 0.69 053 | 0.37 105 | 0.40 719 |
| **1.60** | 4.9 530 | 0.20 190 | 2.3 756 | 2.5 775 | 0.92 167 | 0.69 487 | 0.37 577 | 0.41 119 |
| 1.61 | 5.0 028 | 0.19 989 | 2.4 015 | 2.6 013 | 0.92 316 | 0.69 921 | 0.38 048 | 0.41 520 |
| 1.62 | 5.0 531 | 0.19 790 | 2.4 276 | 2.6 255 | 0.92 462 | 0.70 356 | 0.38 518 | 0.41 921 |
| 1.63 | 5.1 039 | 0.19 593 | 2.4 540 | 2.6 499 | 0.92 606 | 0.70 790 | 0.38 987 | 0.42 323 |
| 1.64 | 5.1 552 | 0.19 398 | 2.4 806 | 2.6 746 | 0.92 747 | 0.71 224 | 0.39 456 | 0.42 725 |
| 1.65 | 5.2 070 | 0.19 205 | 2.5 075 | 2.6 995 | 0.92 886 | 0.71 659 | 0.39 923 | 0.43 129 |
| 1.66 | 5.2 593 | 0.19 014 | 2.5 346 | 2.7 247 | 0.93 022 | 0.72 093 | 0.40 391 | 0.43 532 |
| 1.67 | 5.3 122 | 0.18 825 | 2.5 620 | 2.7 502 | 0.93 155 | 0.72 527 | 0.40 857 | 0.43 937 |
| 1.68 | 5.3 656 | 0.18 637 | 2.5 896 | 2.7 760 | 0.93 286 | 0.72 961 | 0.41 323 | 0.44 341 |
| 1.69 | 5.4 195 | 0.18 452 | 2.6 175 | 2.8 020 | 0.93 415 | 0.73 396 | 0.41 788 | 0.44 747 |
| **1.70** | 5.4 739 | 0.18 268 | 2.6 456 | 2.8 283 | 0.93 541 | 0.73 830 | 0.42 253 | 0.45 153 |
| 1.71 | 5.5 290 | 0.18 087 | 2.6 740 | 2.8 549 | 0.93 665 | 0.74 264 | 0.42 717 | 0.45 559 |
| 1.72 | 5.5 845 | 0.17 907 | 2.7 027 | 2.8 818 | 0.93 786 | 0.74 699 | 0.43 180 | 0.45 966 |
| 1.73 | 5.6 407 | 0.17 728 | 2.7 317 | 2.9 090 | 0.93 906 | 0.75 133 | 0.43 643 | 0.46 374 |
| 1.74 | 5.6 973 | 0.17 552 | 2.7 609 | 2.9 364 | 0.94 023 | 0.75 567 | 0.44 105 | 0.46 782 |
| 1.75 | 5.7 546 | 0.17 377 | 2.7 904 | 2.9 642 | 0.94 138 | 0.76 002 | 0.44 567 | 0.47 191 |
| 1.76 | 5.8 124 | 0.17 204 | 2.8 202 | 2.9 922 | 0.94 250 | 0.76 436 | 0.45 028 | 0.47 600 |
| 1.77 | 5.8 709 | 0.17 033 | 2.8 503 | 3.0 206 | 0.94 361 | 0.76 870 | 0.45 488 | 0.48 009 |
| 1.78 | 5.9 299 | 0.16 864 | 2.8 806 | 3.0 492 | 0.94 470 | 0.77 304 | 0.45 948 | 0.48 419 |
| 1.79 | 5.9 895 | 0.16 696 | 2.9 112 | 3.0 782 | 0.94 576 | 0.77 739 | 0.46 408 | 0.48 830 |
| **1.80** | 6.0 496 | 0.16 530 | 2.9 422 | 3.1 075 | 0.94 681 | 0.78 173 | 0.46 867 | 0.49 241 |
| 1.81 | 6.1 104 | 0.16 365 | 2.9 734 | 3.1 371 | 0.94 783 | 0.78 607 | 0.47 325 | 0.49 652 |
| 1.82 | 6.1 719 | 0.16 203 | 3.0 049 | 3.1 669 | 0.94 884 | 0.79 042 | 0.47 783 | 0.50 064 |
| 1.83 | 6.2 339 | 0.16 041 | 3.0 367 | 3.1 972 | 0.94 983 | 0.79 476 | 0.48 241 | 0.50 476 |
| 1.84 | 6.2 965 | 0.15 882 | 3.0 689 | 3.2 277 | 0.95 080 | 0.79 910 | 0.48 698 | 0.50 889 |
| 1.85 | 6.3 598 | 0.15 724 | 3.1 013 | 3.2 585 | 0.95 175 | 0.80 344 | 0.49 154 | 0.51 302 |
| 1.86 | 6.4 237 | 0.15 567 | 3.1 340 | 3.2 897 | 0.95 268 | 0.80 779 | 0.49 610 | 0.51 716 |
| 1.87 | 6.4 883 | 0.15 412 | 3.1 671 | 3.3 212 | 0.95 359 | 0.81 213 | 0.50 066 | 0.52 130 |
| 1.88 | 6.5 535 | 0.15 259 | 3.2 005 | 3.3 530 | 0.95 449 | 0.81 647 | 0.50 521 | 0.52 544 |
| 1.89 | 6.6 194 | 0.15 107 | 3.2 341 | 3.3 852 | 0.95 537 | 0.82 082 | 0.50 976 | 0.52 959 |
| **1.90** | 6.6 859 | 0.14 957 | 3.2 682 | 3.4 177 | 0.95 624 | 0.82 516 | 0.51 430 | 0.53 374 |
| 1.91 | 6.7 531 | 0.14 808 | 3.3 025 | 3.4 506 | 0.95 709 | 0.82 950 | 0.51 884 | 0.53 789 |
| 1.92 | 6.8 210 | 0.14 661 | 3.3 372 | 3.4 838 | 0.95 792 | 0.83 385 | 0.52 338 | 0.54 205 |
| 1.93 | 6.8 895 | 0.14 515 | 3.3 722 | 3.5 173 | 0.95 873 | 0.83 819 | 0.52 791 | 0.54 621 |
| 1.94 | 6.9 588 | 0.14 370 | 3.4 075 | 3.5 512 | 0.95 953 | 0.84 253 | 0.53 244 | 0.55 038 |
| 1.95 | 7.0 287 | 0.14 227 | 3.4 432 | 3.5 855 | 0.96 032 | 0.84 687 | 0.53 696 | 0.55 455 |
| 1.96 | 7.0 993 | 0.14 086 | 3.4 792 | 3.6 201 | 0.96 109 | 0.85 122 | 0.54 148 | 0.55 872 |
| 1.97 | 7.1 707 | 0.13 946 | 3.5 156 | 3.6 551 | 0.96 185 | 0.85 556 | 0.54 600 | 0.56 290 |
| 1.98 | 7.2 427 | 0.13 807 | 3.5 523 | 3.6 904 | 0.96 259 | 0.85 990 | 0.55 051 | 0.56 707 |
| 1.99 | 7.3 155 | 0.13 670 | 3.5 894 | 3.7 261 | 0.96 331 | 0.86 425 | 0.55 502 | 0.57 126 |
| **2.00** | 7.3 891 | 0.13 534 | 3.6 269 | 3.7 622 | 0.96 403 | 0.86 859 | 0.55 953 | 0.57 544 |

## 8. EXPONENTIAL AND HYPERBOLIC FUNCTIONS

| x | Value | | | | | Common Logarithm | | |
|---|---|---|---|---|---|---|---|---|
| | $e^x$ | $e^{-x}$ | Sinh x | Cosh x | Tanh x | $e^x$ | Sinh x | Cosh x |
| 2.00 | 7.3 891 | 0.13 534 | 3.6 269 | 3.7 622 | 0.96 403 | 0.86 859 | 0.55 953 | 0.57 544 |
| 2.01 | 7.4 633 | 0.13 399 | 3.6 647 | 3.7 987 | 0.96 473 | 0.87 293 | 0.56 403 | 0.57 963 |
| 2.02 | 7.5 383 | 0.13 266 | 3.7 028 | 3.8 355 | 0.96 541 | 0.87 727 | 0.56 853 | 0.58 382 |
| 2.03 | 7.6 141 | 0.13 134 | 3.7 414 | 3.8 727 | 0.96 609 | 0.88 162 | 0.57 303 | 0.58 802 |
| 2.04 | 7.6 906 | 0.13 003 | 3.7 803 | 3.9 103 | 0.96 675 | 0.88 596 | 0.57 753 | 0.59 221 |
| 2.05 | 7.7 679 | 0.12 873 | 3.8 196 | 3.9 483 | 0.96 740 | 0.89 030 | 0.58 202 | 0.59 641 |
| 2.06 | 7.8 460 | 0.12 745 | 3.8 593 | 3.9 867 | 0.96 803 | 0.89 465 | 0.58 650 | 0.60 061 |
| 2.07 | 7.9 248 | 0.12 619 | 3.8 993 | 4.0 255 | 0.96 865 | 0.89 899 | 0.59 099 | 0.60 482 |
| 2.08 | 8.0 045 | 0.12 493 | 3.9 398 | 4.0 647 | 0.96 926 | 0.90 333 | 0.59 547 | 0.60 903 |
| 2.09 | 8.0 849 | 0.12 369 | 3.9 806 | 4.1 043 | 0.96 986 | 0.90 768 | 0.59 995 | 0.61 324 |
| 2.10 | 8.1 662 | 0.12 246 | 4.0 219 | 4.1 443 | 0.97 045 | 0.91 202 | 0.60 443 | 0.61 745 |
| 2.11 | 8.2 482 | 0.12 124 | 4.0 635 | 4.1 847 | 0.97 103 | 0.91 636 | 0.60 890 | 0.62 167 |
| 2.12 | 8.3 311 | 0.12 003 | 4.1 056 | 4.2 256 | 0.97 159 | 0.92 070 | 0.61 337 | 0.62 589 |
| 2.13 | 8.4 149 | 0.11 884 | 4.1 480 | 4.2 669 | 0.97 215 | 0.92 505 | 0.61 784 | 0.63 011 |
| 2.14 | 8.4 994 | 0.11 765 | 4.1 909 | 4.3 085 | 0.97 269 | 0.92 939 | 0.62 231 | 0.63 433 |
| 2.15 | 8.5 849 | 0.11 648 | 4.2 342 | 4.3 507 | 0.97 323 | 0.93 373 | 0.62 677 | 0.63 856 |
| 2.16 | 8.6 711 | 0.11 533 | 4.2 779 | 4.3 932 | 0.97 375 | 0.93 808 | 0.63 123 | 0.64 278 |
| 2.17 | 8.7 583 | 0.11 418 | 4.3 221 | 4.4 362 | 0.97 426 | 0.94 242 | 0.63 569 | 0.64 701 |
| 2.18 | 8.8 463 | 0.11 304 | 4.3 666 | 4.4 797 | 0.97 477 | 0.94 676 | 0.64 015 | 0.65 125 |
| 2.19 | 8.9 352 | 0.11 192 | 4.4 116 | 4.5 236 | 0.97 526 | 0.95 110 | 0.64 460 | 0.65 548 |
| 2.20 | 9.0 250 | 0.11 080 | 4.4 571 | 4.5 679 | 0.97 574 | 0.95 545 | 0.64 905 | 0.65 972 |
| 2.21 | 9.1 157 | 0.10 970 | 4.5 030 | 4.6 127 | 0.97 622 | 0.95 979 | 0.65 350 | 0.66 396 |
| 2.22 | 9.2 073 | 0.10 861 | 4.5 494 | 4.6 580 | 0.97 668 | 0.96 413 | 0.65 795 | 0.66 820 |
| 2.23 | 9.2 999 | 0.10 753 | 4.5 962 | 4.7 037 | 0.97 714 | 0.96 848 | 0.66 240 | 0.67 244 |
| 2.24 | 9.3 933 | 0.10 646 | 4.6 434 | 4.7 499 | 0.97 759 | 0.97 282 | 0.66 684 | 0.67 668 |
| 2.25 | 9.4 877 | 0.10 540 | 4.6 912 | 4.7 966 | 0.97 803 | 0.97 716 | 0.67 128 | 0.68 093 |
| 2.26 | 9.5 831 | 0.10 435 | 4.7 394 | 4.8 437 | 0.97 846 | 0.98 151 | 0.67 572 | 0.68 518 |
| 2.27 | 9.6 794 | 0.10 331 | 4.7 880 | 4.8 914 | 0.97 888 | 0.98 585 | 0.68 016 | 0.68 943 |
| 2.28 | 9.7 767 | 0.10 228 | 4.8 372 | 4.9 395 | 0.97 929 | 0.99 019 | 0.68 459 | 0.69 368 |
| 2.29 | 9.8 749 | 0.10 127 | 4.8 868 | 4.9 881 | 0.97 970 | 0.99 453 | 0.68 903 | 0.69 794 |
| 2.30 | 9.9 742 | 0.10 026 | 4.9 370 | 5.0 372 | 0.98 010 | 0.99 888 | 0.69 346 | 0.70 219 |
| 2.31 | 10 .074 | 0.09 926 | 4.9 876 | 5.0 868 | 0.98 049 | 1.00 322 | 0.69 789 | 0.70 645 |
| 2.32 | 10 .176 | 0.09 827 | 5.0 387 | 5.1 370 | 0.98 087 | 1.00 756 | 0.70 232 | 0.71 071 |
| 2.33 | 10 .278 | 0.09 730 | 5.0 903 | 5.1 876 | 0.98 124 | 1.01 191 | 0.70 675 | 0.71 497 |
| 2.34 | 10 .381 | 0.09 633 | 5.1 425 | 5.2 388 | 0.98 161 | 1.01 625 | 0.71 117 | 0.71 923 |
| 2.35 | 10 .486 | 0.09 537 | 5.1 951 | 5.2 905 | 0.98 197 | 1.02 059 | 0.71 559 | 0.72 349 |
| 2.36 | 10 .591 | 0.09 442 | 5.2 483 | 5.3 427 | 0.98 233 | 1.02 493 | 0.72 002 | 0.72 776 |
| 2.37 | 10 .697 | 0.09 348 | 5.3 020 | 5.3 954 | 0.98 267 | 1.02 928 | 0.72 444 | 0.73 203 |
| 2.38 | 10 .805 | 0.09 255 | 5.3 562 | 5.4 487 | 0.98 301 | 1.03 362 | 0.72 885 | 0.73 630 |
| 2.39 | 10 .913 | 0.09 163 | 5.4 109 | 5.5 026 | 0.98 335 | 1.03 796 | 0.73 327 | 0.74 056 |
| 2.40 | 11 .023 | 0.09 072 | 5.4 662 | 5.5 569 | 0.98 367 | 1.04 231 | 0.73 769 | 0.74 484 |
| 2.41 | 11 .134 | 0.08 982 | 5.5 221 | 5.6 119 | 0.98 400 | 1.04 665 | 0.74 210 | 0.74 911 |
| 2.42 | 11 .246 | 0.08 892 | 5.5 785 | 5.6 674 | 0.98 431 | 1.05 099 | 0.74 652 | 0.75 338 |
| 2.43 | 11 .359 | 0.08 804 | 5.6 354 | 5.7 235 | 0.98 462 | 1.05 534 | 0.75 093 | 0.75 766 |
| 2.44 | 11 .473 | 0.08 716 | 5.6 929 | 5.7 801 | 0.98 492 | 1.05 968 | 0.75 534 | 0.76 194 |
| 2.45 | 11 .588 | 0.08 629 | 5.7 510 | 5.8 373 | 0.98 522 | 1.06 402 | 0.75 975 | 0.76 621 |
| 2.46 | 11 .705 | 0.08 543 | 5.8 097 | 5.8 951 | 0.98 551 | 1.06 836 | 0.76 415 | 0.77 049 |
| 2.47 | 11 .822 | 0.08 458 | 5.8 689 | 5.9 535 | 0.98 579 | 1.07 271 | 0.76 856 | 0.77 477 |
| 2.48 | 11 .941 | 0.08 374 | 5.9 288 | 6.0 125 | 0.98 607 | 1.07 705 | 0.77 296 | 0.77 906 |
| 2.49 | 12 .061 | 0.08 291 | 5.9 892 | 6.0 721 | 0.98 635 | 1.08 139 | 0.77 737 | 0.78 334 |
| 2.50 | 12 .182 | 0.08 208 | 6.0 502 | 6.1 323 | 0.98 661 | 1.08 574 | 0.78 177 | 0.78 762 |

## 8. EXPONENTIAL AND HYPERBOLIC FUNCTIONS

| x | Value | | | | | Common Logarithm | | |
|---|---|---|---|---|---|---|---|---|
| | $e^x$ | $e^{-x}$ | Sinh x | Cosh x | Tanh x | $e^x$ | Sinh x | Cosh x |
| 2.50 | 12 .182 | 0.08 208 | 6.0 502 | 6.1 323 | 0.98 661 | 1.08 574 | 0.78 177 | 0.78 762 |
| 2.51 | 12 .305 | 0.08 127 | 6.1 118 | 6.1 931 | 0.98 688 | 1.09 008 | 0.78 617 | 0.79 191 |
| 2.52 | 12 .429 | 0.08 046 | 6.1 741 | 6.2 545 | 0.98 714 | 1.09 442 | 0.79 057 | 0.79 619 |
| 2.53 | 12 .554 | 0.07 966 | 6.2 369 | 6.3 166 | 0.98 739 | 1.09 877 | 0.79 497 | 0.80 048 |
| 2.54 | 12 .680 | 0.07 887 | 6.3 004 | 6.3 793 | 0.98 764 | 1.10 311 | 0.79 937 | 0.80 477 |
| 2.55 | 12 .807 | 0.07 808 | 6.3 645 | 6.4 426 | 0.98 788 | 1.10 745 | 0.80 377 | 0.80 906 |
| 2.56 | 12 .936 | 0.07 730 | 6.4 293 | 6.5 066 | 0.98 812 | 1.11 179 | 0.80 816 | 0.81 335 |
| 2.57 | 13 .066 | 0.07 654 | 6.4 946 | 6.5 712 | 0.98 835 | 1.11 614 | 0.81 256 | 0.81 764 |
| 2.58 | 13 .197 | 0.07 577 | 6.5 607 | 6.6 365 | 0.98 858 | 1.12 048 | 0.81 695 | 0.82 194 |
| 2.59 | 13 .330 | 0.07 502 | 6.6 274 | 6.7 024 | 0.98 881 | 1.12 482 | 0.82 134 | 0.82 623 |
| 2.60 | 13 .464 | 0.07 427 | 6.6 947 | 6.7 690 | 0.98 903 | 1.12 917 | 0.82 573 | 0.83 052 |
| 2.61 | 13 .599 | 0.07 353 | 6.7 628 | 6.8 363 | 0.98 924 | 1.13 351 | 0.83 012 | 0.83 482 |
| 2.62 | 13 .736 | 0.07 280 | 6.8 315 | 6.9 043 | 0.98 946 | 1.13 785 | 0.83 451 | 0.83 912 |
| 2.63 | 13 .874 | 0.07 208 | 6.9 008 | 6.9 729 | 0.98 966 | 1.14 219 | 0.83 890 | 0.84 341 |
| 2.64 | 14 .013 | 0.07 136 | 6.9 709 | 7.0 423 | 0.98 987 | 1.14 654 | 0.84 329 | 0.84 771 |
| 2.65 | 14 .154 | 0.07 065 | 7.0 417 | 7.1 123 | 0.99 007 | 1.15 088 | 0.84 768 | 0.85 201 |
| 2.66 | 14 .296 | 0.06 995 | 7.1 132 | 7.1 831 | 0.99 026 | 1.15 522 | 0.85 206 | 0.85 631 |
| 2.67 | 14 .440 | 0.06 925 | 7.1 854 | 7.2 546 | 0.99 045 | 1.15 957 | 0.85 645 | 0.86 061 |
| 2.68 | 14 .585 | 0.06 856 | 7.2 583 | 7.3 268 | 0.99 064 | 1.16 391 | 0.86 083 | 0.86 492 |
| 2.69 | 14 .732 | 0.06 788 | 7.3 319 | 7.3 998 | 0.99 083 | 1.16 825 | 0.86 522 | 0.86 922 |
| 2.70 | 14 .880 | 0.06 721 | 7.4 063 | 7.4 735 | 0.99 101 | 1.17 260 | 0.86 960 | 0.87 352 |
| 2.71 | 15 .029 | 0.06 654 | 7.4 814 | 7.5 479 | 0.99 118 | 1.17 694 | 0.87 398 | 0.87 783 |
| 2.72 | 15 .180 | 0.06 587 | 7.5 572 | 7.6 231 | 0.99 136 | 1.18 128 | 0.87 836 | 0.88 213 |
| 2.73 | 15 .333 | 0.06 522 | 7.6 338 | 7.6 991 | 0.99 153 | 1.18 562 | 0.88 274 | 0.88 644 |
| 2.74 | 15 .487 | 0.06 457 | 7.7 112 | 7.7 758 | 0.99 170 | 1.18 997 | 0.88 712 | 0.89 074 |
| 2.75 | 15 .643 | 0.06 393 | 7.7 894 | 7.8 533 | 0.99 186 | 1.19 431 | 0.89 150 | 0.89 505 |
| 2.76 | 15 .800 | 0.06 329 | 7.8 683 | 7.9 316 | 0.99 202 | 1.19 865 | 0.89 588 | 0.89 936 |
| 2.77 | 15 .959 | 0.06 266 | 7.9 480 | 8.0 106 | 0.99 218 | 1.20 300 | 0.90 026 | 0.90 367 |
| 2.78 | 16 .119 | 0.06 204 | 8.0 285 | 8.0 905 | 0.99 233 | 1.20 734 | 0.90 463 | 0.90 798 |
| 2.79 | 16 .281 | 0.06 142 | 8.1 098 | 8.1 712 | 0.99 248 | 1.21 168 | 0.90 901 | 0.91 229 |
| 2.80 | 16 .445 | 0.06 081 | 8.1 919 | 8.2 527 | 0.99 263 | 1.21 602 | 0.91 339 | 0.91 660 |
| 2.81 | 16 .610 | 0.06 020 | 8.2 749 | 8.3 351 | 0.99 278 | 1.22 037 | 0.91 776 | 0.92 091 |
| 2.82 | 16 .777 | 0.05 961 | 8.3 586 | 8.4 182 | 0.99 292 | 1.22 471 | 0.92 213 | 0.92 522 |
| 2.83 | 16 .945 | 0.05 901 | 8.4 432 | 8.5 022 | 0.99 306 | 1.22 905 | 0.92 651 | 0.92 953 |
| 2.84 | 17 .116 | 0.05 843 | 8.5 287 | 8.5 871 | 0.99 320 | 1.23 340 | 0.93 088 | 0.93 385 |
| 2.85 | 17 .288 | 0.05 784 | 8.6 150 | 8.6 728 | 0.99 333 | 1.23 774 | 0.93 525 | 0.93 816 |
| 2.86 | 17 .462 | 0.05 727 | 8.7 021 | 8.7 594 | 0.99 346 | 1.24 208 | 0.93 963 | 0.94 247 |
| 2.87 | 17 .637 | 0.05 670 | 8.7 902 | 8.8 469 | 0.99 359 | 1.24 643 | 0.94 400 | 0.94 679 |
| 2.88 | 17 .814 | 0.05 613 | 8.8 791 | 8.9 352 | 0.99 372 | 1.25 077 | 0.94 837 | 0.95 110 |
| 2.89 | 17 .993 | 0.05 558 | 8.9 689 | 9.0 244 | 0.99 384 | 1.25 511 | 0.95 274 | 0.95 542 |
| 2.90 | 18 .174 | 0.05 502 | 9.0 596 | 9.1 146 | 0.99 396 | 1.25 945 | 0.95 711 | 0.95 974 |
| 2.91 | 18 .357 | 0.05 448 | 9.1 512 | 9.2 056 | 0.99 408 | 1.26 380 | 0.96 148 | 0.96 405 |
| 2.92 | 18 .541 | 0.05 393 | 9.2 437 | 9.2 976 | 0.99 420 | 1.26 814 | 0.96 584 | 0.96 837 |
| 2.93 | 18 .728 | 0.05 340 | 9.3 371 | 9.3 905 | 0.99 431 | 1.27 248 | 0.97 021 | 0.97 269 |
| 2.94 | 18 .916 | 0.05 287 | 9.4 315 | 9.4 844 | 0.99 443 | 1.27 683 | 0.97 458 | 0.97 701 |
| 2.95 | 19 .106 | 0.05 234 | 9.5 268 | 9.5 791 | 0.99 454 | 1.28 117 | 0.97 895 | 0.98 133 |
| 2.96 | 19 .298 | 0.05 182 | 9.6 231 | 9.6 749 | 0.99 464 | 1.28 551 | 0.98 331 | 0.98 565 |
| 2.97 | 19 .492 | 0.05 130 | 9.7 203 | 9.7 716 | 0.99 475 | 1.28 985 | 0.98 768 | 0.98 997 |
| 2.98 | 19 .688 | 0.05 079 | 9.8 185 | 9.8 693 | 0.99 485 | 1.29 420 | 0.99 205 | 0.99 429 |
| 2.99 | 19 .886 | 0.05 029 | 9.9 177 | 9.9 680 | 0.99 496 | 1.29 854 | 0.99 641 | 0.99 861 |
| 3.00 | 20 .086 | 0.04 979 | 10 .018 | 10 .068 | 0.99 505 | 1.30 288 | 1.00 078 | 1.00 293 |

## 8. EXPONENTIAL AND HYPERBOLIC FUNCTIONS

| x | Value | | | | | Common Logarithm | | |
|---|---|---|---|---|---|---|---|---|
| | $e^x$ | $e^{-x}$ | Sinh x | Cosh x | Tanh x | $e^x$ | Sinh x | Cosh x |
| **3.00** | 20 .086 | 0.04 979 | 10 .018 | 10 .068 | 0.99 505 | 1.30 288 | 1.00 078 | 1.00 293 |
| 3.01 | 20 .287 | 0.04 929 | 10 .119 | 10 .168 | 0.99 515 | 1.30 723 | 1.00 514 | 1.00 725 |
| 3.02 | 20 .491 | 0.04 880 | 10 .221 | 10 .270 | 0.99 525 | 1.31 157 | 1.00 950 | 1.01 157 |
| 3.03 | 20 .697 | 0.04 832 | 10 .324 | 10 .373 | 0.99 534 | 1.31 591 | 1.01 387 | 1.01 589 |
| 3.04 | 20 .905 | 0.04 783 | 10 .429 | 10 .477 | 0.99 543 | 1.32 026 | 1.01 823 | 1.02 022 |
| 3.05 | 21 .115 | 0.04 736 | 10 .534 | 10 .581 | 0.99 552 | 1.32 460 | 1.02 259 | 1.02 454 |
| 3.06 | 21 .328 | 0.04 689 | 10 .640 | 10 .687 | 0.99 561 | 1.32 894 | 1.02 696 | 1.02 886 |
| 3.07 | 21 .542 | 0.04 642 | 10 .748 | 10 .794 | 0.99 570 | 1.33 328 | 1.03 132 | 1.03 319 |
| 3.08 | 21 .758 | 0.04 596 | 10 .856 | 10 .902 | 0.99 578 | 1.33 763 | 1.03 568 | 1.03 751 |
| 3.09 | 21 .977 | 0.04 550 | 10 .966 | 11 .011 | 0.99 587 | 1.34 197 | 1.04 004 | 1.04 184 |
| **3.10** | 22 .198 | 0.04 505 | 11 .076 | 11 .122 | 0.99 595 | 1.34 631 | 1.04 440 | 1.04 616 |
| 3.11 | 22 .421 | 0.04 460 | 11 .188 | 11 .233 | 0.99 603 | 1.35 066 | 1.04 876 | 1.05 049 |
| 3.12 | 22 .646 | 0.04 416 | 11 .301 | 11 .345 | 0.99 611 | 1.35 500 | 1.05 312 | 1.05 481 |
| 3.13 | 22 .874 | 0.04 372 | 11 .415 | 11 .459 | 0.99 618 | 1.35 934 | 1.05 748 | 1.05 914 |
| 3.14 | 23 .104 | 0.04 328 | 11 .530 | 11 .574 | 0.99 626 | 1.36 368 | 1.06 184 | 1.06 347 |
| 3.15 | 23 .336 | 0.04 285 | 11 .647 | 11 .689 | 0.99 633 | 1.36 803 | 1.06 620 | 1.06 779 |
| 3.16 | 23 .571 | 0.04 243 | 11 .764 | 11 .807 | 0.99 641 | 1.37 237 | 1.07 056 | 1.07 212 |
| 3.17 | 23 .807 | 0.04 200 | 11 .883 | 11 .925 | 0.99 648 | 1.37 671 | 1.07 492 | 1.07 645 |
| 3.18 | 24 .047 | 0.04 159 | 12 .003 | 12 .044 | 0.99 655 | 1.38 106 | 1.07 927 | 1.08 078 |
| 3.19 | 24 .288 | 0.04 117 | 12 .124 | 12 .165 | 0.99 662 | 1.38 540 | 1.08 363 | 1.08 510 |
| **3.20** | 24 .533 | 0.04 076 | 12 .246 | 12 .287 | 0.99 668 | 1.38 974 | 1.08 799 | 1.08 943 |
| 3.21 | 24 .779 | 0.04 036 | 12 .369 | 12 .410 | 0.99 675 | 1.39 409 | 1.09 235 | 1.09 376 |
| 3.22 | 25 .028 | 0.03 996 | 12 .494 | 12 .534 | 0.99 681 | 1.39 843 | 1.09 670 | 1.09 809 |
| 3.23 | 25 .280 | 0.03 956 | 12 .620 | 12 .660 | 0.99 688 | 1.40 277 | 1.10 106 | 1.10 242 |
| 3.24 | 25 .534 | 0.03 916 | 12 .747 | 12 .786 | 0.99 694 | 1.40 711 | 1.10 542 | 1.10 675 |
| 3.25 | 25 .790 | 0.03 877 | 12 .876 | 12 .915 | 0.99 700 | 1.41 146 | 1.10 977 | 1.11 108 |
| 3.26 | 26 .050 | 0.03 839 | 13 .006 | 13 .044 | 0.99 706 | 1.41 580 | 1.11 413 | 1.11 541 |
| 3.27 | 26 .311 | 0.03 801 | 13 .137 | 13 .175 | 0.99 712 | 1.42 014 | 1.11 849 | 1.11 974 |
| 3.28 | 26 .576 | 0.03 763 | 13 .269 | 13 .307 | 0.99 717 | 1.42 449 | 1.12 284 | 1.12 407 |
| 3.29 | 26 .843 | 0.03 725 | 13 .403 | 13 .440 | 0.99 723 | 1.42 883 | 1.12 720 | 1.12 840 |
| **3.30** | 27 .113 | 0.03 688 | 13 .538 | 13 .575 | 0.99 728 | 1.43 317 | 1.13 155 | 1.13 273 |
| 3.31 | 27 .385 | 0.03 652 | 13 .674 | 13 .711 | 0.99 734 | 1.43 751 | 1.13 591 | 1.13 706 |
| 3.32 | 27 .660 | 0.03 615 | 13 .812 | 13 .848 | 0.99 739 | 1.44 186 | 1.14 026 | 1.14 139 |
| 3.33 | 27 .938 | 0.03 579 | 13 .951 | 13 .987 | 0.99 744 | 1.44 620 | 1.14 461 | 1.14 573 |
| 3.34 | 28 .219 | 0.03 544 | 14 .092 | 14 .127 | 0.99 749 | 1.45 054 | 1.14 897 | 1.15 006 |
| 3.35 | 28 .503 | 0.03 508 | 14 .234 | 14 .269 | 0.99 754 | 1.45 489 | 1.15 332 | 1.15 439 |
| 3.36 | 28 .789 | 0.03 474 | 14 .377 | 14 .412 | 0.99 759 | 1.45 923 | 1.15 768 | 1.15 872 |
| 3.37 | 29 .079 | 0.03 439 | 14 .522 | 14 .556 | 0.99 764 | 1.46 357 | 1.16 203 | 1.16 306 |
| 3.38 | 29 .371 | 0.03 405 | 14 .668 | 14 .702 | 0.99 768 | 1.46 792 | 1.16 638 | 1.16 739 |
| 3.39 | 29 .666 | 0.03 371 | 14 .816 | 14 .850 | 0.99 773 | 1.47 226 | 1.17 073 | 1.17 172 |
| **3.40** | 29 .964 | 0.03 337 | 14 .965 | 14 .999 | 0.99 777 | 1.47 660 | 1.17 509 | 1.17 605 |
| 3.41 | 30 .265 | 0.03 304 | 15 .116 | 15 .149 | 0.99 782 | 1.48 094 | 1.17 944 | 1.18 039 |
| 3.42 | 30 .569 | 0.03 271 | 15 .268 | 15 .301 | 0.99 786 | 1.48 529 | 1.18 379 | 1.18 472 |
| 3.43 | 30 .877 | 0.03 239 | 15 .422 | 15 .455 | 0.99 790 | 1.48 963 | 1.18 814 | 1.18 906 |
| 3.44 | 31 .187 | 0.03 206 | 15 .577 | 15 .610 | 0.99 795 | 1.49 397 | 1.19 250 | 1.19 339 |
| 3.45 | 31 .500 | 0.03 175 | 15 .734 | 15 .766 | 0.99 799 | 1.49 832 | 1.19 685 | 1.19 772 |
| 3.46 | 31 .817 | 0.03 143 | 15 .893 | 15 .924 | 0.99 803 | 1.50 266 | 1.20 120 | 1.20 206 |
| 3.47 | 32 .137 | 0.03 112 | 16 .053 | 16 .084 | 0.99 807 | 1.50 700 | 1.20 555 | 1.20 639 |
| 3.48 | 32 .460 | 0.03 081 | 16 .214 | 16 .245 | 0.99 810 | 1.51 134 | 1.20 990 | 1.21 073 |
| 3.49 | 32 .786 | 0.03 050 | 16 .378 | 16 .408 | 0.99 814 | 1.51 569 | 1.21 425 | 1.21 506 |
| **3.50** | 33 .115 | 0.03 020 | 16 .543 | 16 .573 | 0.99 818 | 1.52 003 | 1.21 860 | 1.21 940 |

# 8. EXPONENTIAL AND HYPERBOLIC FUNCTIONS

| x | Value | | | | | Common Logarithm | | |
|---|---|---|---|---|---|---|---|---|
| | $e^x$ | $e^{-x}$ | Sinh x | Cosh x | Tanh x | $e^x$ | Sinh x | Cosh x |
| 3.50 | 33 .115 | 0.03 020 | 16 .543 | 16 .573 | 0.99 818 | 1.52 003 | 1.21 860 | 1.21 940 |
| 3.51 | 33 .448 | 0.02 990 | 16 .709 | 16 .739 | 0.99 821 | 1.52 437 | 1.22 296 | 1.22 373 |
| 3.52 | 33 .784 | 0.02 960 | 16 .877 | 16 .907 | 0.99 825 | 1.52 872 | 1.22 731 | 1.22 807 |
| 3.53 | 34 .124 | 0.02 930 | 17 .047 | 17 .077 | 0.99 828 | 1.53 306 | 1.23 166 | 1.23 240 |
| 3.54 | 34 .467 | 0.02 901 | 17 .219 | 17 .248 | 0.99 832 | 1.53 740 | 1.23 601 | 1.23 674 |
| 3.55 | 34 .813 | 0.02 872 | 17 .392 | 17 .421 | 0.99 835 | 1.54 175 | 1.24 036 | 1.24 107 |
| 3.56 | 35 .163 | 0.02 844 | 17 .567 | 17 .596 | 0.99 838 | 1.54 609 | 1.24 471 | 1.24 541 |
| 3.57 | 35 .517 | 0.02 816 | 17 .744 | 17 .772 | 0.99 842 | 1.55 043 | 1.24 906 | 1.24 975 |
| 3.58 | 35 .874 | 0.02 788 | 17 .923 | 17 .951 | 0.99 845 | 1.55 477 | 1.25 341 | 1.25 408 |
| 3.59 | 36 .234 | 0.02 760 | 18 .103 | 18 .131 | 0.99 848 | 1.55 912 | 1.25 776 | 1.25 842 |
| 3.60 | 36 .598 | 0.02 732 | 18 .285 | 18 .313 | 0.99 851 | 1.56 346 | 1.26 211 | 1.26 275 |
| 3.61 | 36 .966 | 0.02 705 | 18 .470 | 18 .497 | 0.99 854 | 1.56 780 | 1.26 646 | 1.26 709 |
| 3.62 | 37 .338 | 0.02 678 | 18 .655 | 18 .682 | 0.99 857 | 1.57 215 | 1.27 080 | 1.27 143 |
| 3.63 | 37 .713 | 0.02 652 | 18 .843 | 18 .870 | 0.99 859 | 1.57 649 | 1.27 515 | 1.27 576 |
| 3.64 | 38 .092 | 0.02 625 | 19 .033 | 19 .059 | 0.99 862 | 1.58 083 | 1.27 950 | 1.28 010 |
| 3.65 | 38 .475 | 0.02 599 | 19 .224 | 19 .250 | 0.99 865 | 1.58 517 | 1.28 385 | 1.28 444 |
| 3.66 | 38. 861 | 0.02 573 | 19 .418 | 19 .444 | 0.99 868 | 1.58 952 | 1.28 820 | 1.28 878 |
| 3.67 | 39 .252 | 0.02 548 | 19 .613 | 19 .639 | 0.99 870 | 1.59 386 | 1.29 255 | 1.29 311 |
| 3.68 | 39 .646 | 0.02 522 | 19 .811 | 19 .836 | 0.99 873 | 1.59 820 | 1.29 690 | 1.29 745 |
| 3.69 | 40 .045 | 0.02 497 | 20 .010 | 20 .035 | 0.99 875 | 1.60 255 | 1.30 125 | 1.30 179 |
| 3.70 | 40 .447 | 0.02 472 | 20 .211 | 20 .236 | 0.99 878 | 1.60 689 | 1.30 559 | 1.30 612 |
| 3.71 | 40 .854 | 0.02 448 | 20 .415 | 20 .439 | 0.99 880 | 1.61 123 | 1.30 994 | 1.31 046 |
| 3.72 | 41 .264 | 0.02 423 | 20 .620 | 20 .644 | 0.99 883 | 1.61 558 | 1.31 429 | 1.31 480 |
| 3.73 | 41 .679 | 0.02 399 | 20 .828 | 20 .852 | 0.99 885 | 1.61 992 | 1.31 864 | 1.31 914 |
| 3.74 | 42 .098 | 0.02 375 | 21 .037 | 21 .061 | 0.99 887 | 1.62 426 | 1.32 299 | 1.32 348 |
| 3.75 | 42 .521 | 0.02 352 | 21 .249 | 21 .272 | 0.99 889 | 1.62 860 | 1.32 733 | 1.32 781 |
| 3.76 | 42 .948 | 0.02 328 | 21 .463 | 21 .486 | 0.99 892 | 1.63 295 | 1.33 168 | 1.33 215 |
| 3.77 | 43 .380 | 0.02 305 | 21 .679 | 21 .702 | 0.99 894 | 1.63 729 | 1.33 603 | 1.33 649 |
| 3.78 | 43 .816 | 0.02 282 | 21 .897 | 21 .919 | 0.99 896 | 1.64 163 | 1.34 038 | 1.34 083 |
| 3.79 | 44 .256 | 0.02 260 | 22 .117 | 22 .139 | 0.99 898 | 1.64 598 | 1.34 472 | 1.34 517 |
| 3.80 | 44 .701 | 0.02 237 | 22 .339 | 22 .362 | 0.99 900 | 1.65 032 | 1.34 907 | 1.34 951 |
| 3.81 | 45 .150 | 0.02 215 | 22 .564 | 22 .586 | 0.99 902 | 1.65 466 | 1.35 342 | 1.35 384 |
| 3.82 | 45 .604 | 0.02 193 | 22 .791 | 22 .813 | 0.99 904 | 1.65 900 | 1.35 777 | 1.35 818 |
| 3.83 | 46 .063 | 0.02 171 | 23 .020 | 23 .042 | 0.99 906 | 1.66 335 | 1.36 211 | 1.36 252 |
| 3.84 | 46 .525 | 0.02 149 | 23 .252 | 23 .273 | 0.99 908 | 1.66 769 | 1.36 646 | 1.36 686 |
| 3.85 | 46 .993 | 0.02 128 | 23 .486 | 23 .507 | 0.99 909 | 1.67 203 | 1.37 081 | 1.37 120 |
| 3.86 | 47 .465 | 0.02 107 | 23 .722 | 23 .743 | 0.99 911 | 1.67 638 | 1.37 515 | 1.37 554 |
| 3.87 | 47 .942 | 0.02 086 | 23 .961 | 23 .982 | 0.99 913 | 1.68 072 | 1.37 950 | 1.37 988 |
| 3.88 | 48 .424 | 0.02 065 | 24 .202 | 24 .222 | 0.99 915 | 1.68 506 | 1.38 385 | 1.38 422 |
| 3.89 | 48 .911 | 0.02 045 | 24 .445 | 24 .466 | 0.99 916 | 1.68 941 | 1.38 819 | 1.38 856 |
| 3.90 | 49 .402 | 0.02 024 | 24 .691 | 24 .711 | 0.99 918 | 1.69 375 | 1.39 254 | 1.39 290 |
| 3.91 | 49 .899 | 0.02 004 | 24 .939 | 24 .959 | 0.99 920 | 1.69 809 | 1.39 689 | 1.39 724 |
| 3.92 | 50 .400 | 0.01 984 | 25 .190 | 25 .210 | 0.99 921 | 1.70 243 | 1.40 123 | 1.40 158 |
| 3.93 | 50 .907 | 0.01 964 | 25 .444 | 25 .463 | 0.99 923 | 1.70 678 | 1.40 558 | 1.40 591 |
| 3.94 | 51 .419 | 0.01 945 | 25 .700 | 25 .719 | 0.99 924 | 1.71 112 | 1.40 993 | 1.41 025 |
| 3.95 | 51 .935 | 0.01 925 | 25 .958 | 25 .977 | 0.99 926 | 1.71 546 | 1.41 427 | 1.41 459 |
| 3.96 | 52 .457 | 0.01 906 | 26 .219 | 26 .238 | 0.99 927 | 1.71 981 | 1.41 862 | 1.41 893 |
| 3.97 | 52 .985 | 0.01 887 | 26 .483 | 26 .502 | 0.99 929 | 1.72 415 | 1.42 296 | 1.42 327 |
| 3.98 | 53 .517 | 0.01 869 | 26 .749 | 26 .768 | 0.99 930 | 1.72 849 | 1.42 731 | 1.42 761 |
| 3.99 | 54 .055 | 0.01 850 | 27 .018 | 27 .037 | 0.99 932 | 1.73 284 | 1.43 166 | 1.43 195 |
| 4.00 | 54 .598 | 0.01 832 | 27 .290 | 27 .308 | 0.99 933 | 1.73 718 | 1.43 600 | 1.43 629 |

## 8. EXPONENTIAL AND HYPERBOLIC FUNCTIONS

| x | Value | | | | | Common Logarithm | | |
|---|---|---|---|---|---|---|---|---|
| | $e^x$ | $e^{-x}$ | Sinh x | Cosh x | Tanh x | $e^x$ | Sinh x | Cosh x |
| **4.00** | 54 .598 | 0.01 832 | 27 .290 | 27 .308 | 0.99 933 | 1.73 718 | 1.43 600 | 1.43 629 |
| 4.01 | 55 .147 | 0.01 813 | 27 .564 | 27 .583 | 0.99 934 | 1.74 152 | 1.44 035 | 1.44 063 |
| 4.02 | 55 .701 | 0.01 795 | 27 .842 | 27 .860 | 0.99 936 | 1.74 586 | 1.44 469 | 1.44 497 |
| 4.03 | 56 .261 | 0.01 777 | 28 .122 | 28 .139 | 0.99 937 | 1.75 021 | 1.44 904 | 1.44 931 |
| 4.04 | 56 .826 | 0.01 760 | 28 .404 | 28 .422 | 0.99 938 | 1.75 455 | 1.45 339 | 1.45 365 |
| 4.05 | 57 .397 | 0.01 742 | 28 .690 | 28 .707 | 0.99 939 | 1.75 889 | 1.45 773 | 1.45 799 |
| 4.06 | 57 .974 | 0.01 725 | 28 .979 | 28 .996 | 0.99 941 | 1.76 324 | 1.46 208 | 1.46 233 |
| 4.07 | 58 .557 | 0.01 708 | 29 .270 | 29 .287 | 0.99 942 | 1.76 758 | 1.46 642 | 1.46 668 |
| 4.08 | 59 .145 | 0.01 691 | 29 .564 | 29 .581 | 0.99 943 | 1.77 192 | 1.47 077 | 1.47 102 |
| 4.09 | 59 .740 | 0.01 674 | 29 .862 | 29 .878 | 0.99 944 | 1.77 626 | 1.47 511 | 1.47 536 |
| **4.10** | 60 .340 | 0.01 657 | 30 .162 | 30 .178 | 0.99 945 | 1.78 061 | 1.47 946 | 1.47 970 |
| 4.11 | 60 .947 | 0.01 641 | 30 .465 | 30 .482 | 0.99 946 | 1.78 495 | 1.48 380 | 1.48 404 |
| 4.12 | 61 .559 | 0.01 624 | 30 .771 | 30 .788 | 0.99 947 | 1.78 929 | 1.48 815 | 1.48 838 |
| 4.13 | 62 .178 | 0.01 608 | 31 .081 | 31 .097 | 0.99 948 | 1.79 364 | 1.49 249 | 1.49 272 |
| 4.14 | 62 .803 | 0.01 592 | 31 .393 | 31 .409 | 0.99 949 | 1.79 798 | 1.49 684 | 1.49 706 |
| 4.15 | 63 .434 | 0.01 576 | 31 .709 | 31 .725 | 0.99 950 | 1.80 232 | 1.50 118 | 1.50 140 |
| 4.16 | 64 .072 | 0.01 561 | 32 .028 | 32 .044 | 0.99 951 | 1.80 667 | 1.50 553 | 1.50 574 |
| 4.17 | 64 .715 | 0.01 545 | 32 .350 | 32 .365 | 0.99 952 | 1.81 101 | 1.50 987 | 1.51 008 |
| 4.18 | 65 .366 | 0.01 530 | 32 .675 | 32 .691 | 0.99 953 | 1.81 535 | 1.51 422 | 1.51 442 |
| 4.19 | 66 .023 | 0.01 515 | 33 .004 | 33 .019 | 0.99 954 | 1.81 969 | 1.51 856 | 1.51 876 |
| **4.20** | 66 .686 | 0.01 500 | 33 .336 | 33 .351 | 0.99 955 | 1.82 404 | 1.52 291 | 1.52 310 |
| 4.21 | 67 .357 | 0.01 485 | 33 .671 | 33 .686 | 0.99 956 | 1.82 838 | 1.52 725 | 1.52 745 |
| 4.22 | 68 .033 | 0.01 470 | 34 .009 | 34 .024 | 0.99 957 | 1.83 272 | 1.53 160 | 1.53 179 |
| 4.23 | 68 .717 | 0.01 455 | 34 .351 | 34 .366 | 0.99 958 | 1.83 707 | 1.53 594 | 1.53 613 |
| 4.24 | 69 .408 | 0.01 441 | 34 .697 | 34 .711 | 0.99 958 | 1.84 141 | 1.54 029 | 1.54 047 |
| 4.25 | 70 .105 | 0.01 426 | 35 .046 | 35 .060 | 0.99 959 | 1.84 575 | 1.54 463 | 1.54 481 |
| 4.26 | 70 .810 | 0.01 412 | 35 .398 | 35 .412 | 0.99 960 | 1.85 009 | 1.54 898 | 1.54 915 |
| 4.27 | 71 .522 | 0.01 398 | 35 .754 | 35 .768 | 0.99 961 | 1.85 444 | 1.55 332 | 1.55 349 |
| 4.28 | 72 .240 | 0.01 384 | 36 .113 | 36 .127 | 0.99 962 | 1.85 878 | 1.55 767 | 1.55 783 |
| 4.29 | 72 .966 | 0.01 370 | 36 .476 | 36 .490 | 0.99 962 | 1.86 312 | 1.56 201 | 1.56 217 |
| **4.30** | 73 .700 | 0.01 357 | 36 .843 | 36 .857 | 0.99 963 | 1.86 747 | 1.56 636 | 1.56 652 |
| 4.31 | 74 .440 | 0.01 343 | 37 .214 | 37 .227 | 0.99 964 | 1.87 181 | 1.57 070 | 1.57 086 |
| 4.32 | 75 .189 | 0.01 330 | 37 .588 | 37 .601 | 0.99 965 | 1.87 615 | 1.57 505 | 1.57 520 |
| 4.33 | 75 .944 | 0.01 317 | 37 .966 | 37 .979 | 0.99 965 | 1.88 050 | 1.57 939 | 1.57 954 |
| 4.34 | 76 .708 | 0.01 304 | 38 .347 | 38 .360 | 0.99 966 | 1.88 484 | 1.58 373 | 1.58 388 |
| 4.35 | 77 .478 | 0.01 291 | 38 .733 | 38 .746 | 0.99 967 | 1.88 918 | 1.58 808 | 1.58 822 |
| 4.36 | 78 .257 | 0.01 278 | 39 .122 | 39 .135 | 0.99 967 | 1.89 352 | 1.59 242 | 1.59 256 |
| 4.37 | 79 .044 | 0.01 265 | 39 .515 | 39 .528 | 0.99 968 | 1.89 787 | 1.59 677 | 1.59 691 |
| 4.38 | 79 .838 | 0.01 253 | 39 .913 | 39 .925 | 0.99 969 | 1.90 221 | 1.60 111 | 1.60 125 |
| 4.39 | 80 .640 | 0.01 240 | 40 .314 | 40 .326 | 0.99 969 | 1.90 655 | 1.60 546 | 1.60 559 |
| **4.40** | 81 .451 | 0.01 228 | 40 .719 | 40 .732 | 0.99 970 | 1.91 090 | 1.60 980 | 1.60 993 |
| 4.41 | 82 .269 | 0.01 216 | 41 .129 | 41 .141 | 0.99 970 | 1.91 524 | 1.61 414 | 1.61 427 |
| 4.42 | 83 .096 | 0.01 203 | 41 .542 | 41 .554 | 0.99 971 | 1.91 958 | 1.61 849 | 1.61 861 |
| 4.43 | 83 .931 | 0.01 191 | 41 .960 | 41 .972 | 0.99 972 | 1.92 392 | 1.62 283 | 1.62 296 |
| 4.44 | 84 .775 | 0.01 180 | 42 .382 | 42 .393 | 0.99 972 | 1.92 827 | 1.62 718 | 1.62 730 |
| 4.45 | 85 .627 | 0.01 168 | 42 .808 | 42 .819 | 0.99 973 | 1.93 261 | 1.63 152 | 1.63 164 |
| 4.46 | 86 .488 | 0.01 156 | 43 .238 | 43 .250 | 0.99 973 | 1.93 695 | 1.63 587 | 1.63 598 |
| 4.47 | 87 .357 | 0.01 145 | 43 .673 | 43 .684 | 0.99 974 | 1.94 130 | 1.64 021 | 1.64 032 |
| 4.48 | 88 .235 | 0.01 133 | 44 .112 | 44 .123 | 0.99 974 | 1.94 564 | 1.64 455 | 1.64 467 |
| 4.49 | 89 .121 | 0.01 122 | 44 .555 | 44 .566 | 0.99 975 | 1.94 998 | 1.64 890 | 1.64 901 |
| **4.50** | 90 .017 | 0.01 111 | 45 .003 | 45 .014 | 0.99 975 | 1.95 433 | 1.65 324 | 1.65 335 |

## 8. EXPONENTIAL AND HYPERBOLIC FUNCTIONS

| $x$ | Value $e^x$ | $e^{-x}$ | Sinh $x$ | Cosh $x$ | Tanh $x$ | Common Logarithm $e^x$ | Sinh $x$ | Cosh $x$ |
|---|---|---|---|---|---|---|---|---|
| **4.50** | 90 .017 | 0.01 111 | 45 .003 | 45 .014 | 0.99 975 | 1.95 433 | 1.65 324 | 1.65 335 |
| 4.51 | 90 .922 | 0.01 100 | 45 .455 | 45 .466 | 0.99 976 | 1.95 867 | 1.65 759 | 1.65 769 |
| 4.52 | 91 .836 | 0.01 089 | 45 .912 | 45 .923 | 0.99 976 | 1.96 301 | 1.66 193 | 1.66 203 |
| 4.53 | 92 .759 | 0.01 078 | 46 .374 | 46 .385 | 0.99 977 | 1.96 735 | 1.66 627 | 1.66 637 |
| 4.54 | 93 .691 | 0.01 067 | 46 .840 | 46 .851 | 0.99 977 | 1.97 170 | 1.67 062 | 1.67 072 |
| 4.55 | 94 .632 | 0.01 057 | 47 .311 | 47 .321 | 0.99 978 | 1.97 604 | 1.67 496 | 1.67 506 |
| 4.56 | 95 .583 | 0.01 046 | 47 .787 | 47 .797 | 0.99 978 | 1.98 038 | 1.67 931 | 1.67 940 |
| 4.57 | 96 .544 | 0.01 036 | 48 .267 | 48 .277 | 0.99 979 | 1.98 473 | 1.68 365 | 1.68 374 |
| 4.58 | 97 .514 | 0.01 025 | 48 .752 | 48 .762 | 0.99 979 | 1.98 907 | 1.68 799 | 1.68 808 |
| 4.59 | 98 .494 | 0.01 015 | 49 .242 | 49 .252 | 0.99 979 | 1.99 341 | 1.69 234 | 1.69 243 |
| **4.60** | 99 .484 | 0.01 005 | 49 .737 | 49 .747 | 0.99 980 | 1.99 775 | 1.69 668 | 1.69 677 |
| 4.61 | 100 .48 | 0.00 995 | 50 .237 | 50 .247 | 0.99 980 | 2.00 210 | 1.70 102 | 1.70 111 |
| 4.62 | 101 .49 | 0.00 985 | 50 .742 | 50 .752 | 0.99 981 | 2.00 644 | 1.70 537 | 1.70 545 |
| 4.63 | 102 .51 | 0.00 975 | 51 .252 | 51 .262 | 0.99 981 | 2.01 078 | 1.70 971 | 1.70 979 |
| 4.64 | 103 .54 | 0.00 966 | 51 .767 | 51 .777 | 0.99 981 | 2.01 513 | 1.71 406 | 1.71 414 |
| 4.65 | 104 .58 | 0.00 956 | 52 .288 | 52 .297 | 0.99 982 | 2.01 947 | 1.71 840 | 1.71 848 |
| 4.66 | 105 .64 | 0.00 947 | 52 .813 | 52 .823 | 0.99 982 | 2.02 381 | 1.72 274 | 1.72 282 |
| 4.67 | 106 .70 | 0.00 937 | 53 .344 | 53 .354 | 0.99 982 | 2.02 816 | 1.72 709 | 1.72 716 |
| 4.68 | 107 .77 | 0.00 928 | 53 .880 | 53 .890 | 0.99 983 | 2.03 250 | 1.73 143 | 1.73 151 |
| 4.69 | 108 .85 | 0.00 919 | 54 .422 | 54 .431 | 0.99 983 | 2.03 684 | 1.73 577 | 1.73 585 |
| **4.70** | 109 .95 | 0.00 910 | 54 .969 | 54 .978 | 0.99 983 | 2.04 118 | 1.74 012 | 1.74 019 |
| 4.71 | 111 .05 | 0.00 900 | 55 .522 | 55 .531 | 0.99 984 | 2.04 553 | 1.74 446 | 1.74 453 |
| 4.72 | 112 .17 | 0.00 892 | 56 .080 | 56 .089 | 0.99 984 | 2.04 987 | 1.74 881 | 1.74 887 |
| 4.73 | 113 .30 | 0.00 883 | 56 .643 | 56 .652 | 0.99 984 | 2.05 421 | 1.75 315 | 1.75 322 |
| 4.74 | 114 .43 | 0.00 874 | 57 .213 | 57 .221 | 0.99 985 | 2.05 856 | 1.75 749 | 1.75 756 |
| 4.75 | 115 .58 | 0.00 865 | 57 .788 | 57 .796 | 0.99 985 | 2.06 290 | 1.76 184 | 1.76 190 |
| 4.76 | 116 .75 | 0.00 857 | 58 .369 | 58 .377 | 0.99 985 | 2.06 724 | 1.76 618 | 1.76 624 |
| 4.77 | 117 .92 | 0.00 848 | 58 .955 | 58 .964 | 0.99 986 | 2.07 158 | 1.77 052 | 1.77 059 |
| 4.78 | 119 .10 | 0.00 840 | 59 .548 | 59 .556 | 0.99 986 | 2.07 593 | 1.77 487 | 1.77 493 |
| 4.79 | 120 .30 | 0.00 831 | 60 .147 | 60 .155 | 0.99 986 | 2.08 027 | 1.77 921 | 1.77 927 |
| **4.80** | 121 .51 | 0.00 823 | 60 .751 | 60 .759 | 0.99 986 | 2.08 461 | 1.78 355 | 1.78 361 |
| 4.81 | 122 .73 | 0.00 815 | 61 .362 | 61 .370 | 0.99 987 | 2.08 896 | 1.78 790 | 1.78 796 |
| 4.82 | 123 .97 | 0.00 807 | 61 .979 | 61 .987 | 0.99 987 | 2.09 330 | 1.79 224 | 1.79 230 |
| 4.83 | 125 .21 | 0.00 799 | 62 .601 | 62 .609 | 0.99 987 | 2.09 764 | 1.79 658 | 1.79 664 |
| 4.84 | 126 .47 | 0.00 791 | 63 .231 | 63 .239 | 0.99 987 | 2.10 199 | 1.80 093 | 1.80 098 |
| 4.85 | 127 .74 | 0.00 783 | 63 .866 | 63 .874 | 0.99 988 | 2.10 633 | 1.80 527 | 1.80 532 |
| 4.86 | 129 .02 | 0.00 775 | 64 .508 | 64 .516 | 0.99 988 | 2.11 067 | 1.80 962 | 1.80 967 |
| 4.87 | 130 .32 | 0.00 767 | 65 .157 | 65 .164 | 0.99 988 | 2.11 501 | 1.81 396 | 1.81 401 |
| 4.88 | 131 .63 | 0.00 760 | 65 .812 | 65 .819 | 0.99 988 | 2.11 936 | 1.81 830 | 1.81 835 |
| 4.89 | 132 .95 | 0.00 752 | 66 .473 | 66 .481 | 0.99 989 | 2.12 370 | 1.82 265 | 1.82 269 |
| **4.90** | 134 .29 | 0.00 745 | 67 .141 | 67 .149 | 0.99 989 | 2.12 804 | 1.82 699 | 1.82 704 |
| 4.91 | 135 .64 | 0.00 737 | 67 .816 | 67 .823 | 0.99 989 | 2.13 239 | 1.83 133 | 1.83 138 |
| 4.92 | 137 .00 | 0.00 730 | 68 .498 | 68 .505 | 0.99 989 | 2.13 673 | 1.83 568 | 1.83 572 |
| 4.93 | 138 .38 | 0.00 723 | 69 .186 | 69 .193 | 0.99 990 | 2.14 107 | 1.84 002 | 1.84 006 |
| 4.94 | 139 .77 | 0.00 715 | 69 .882 | 69 .889 | 0.99 990 | 2.14 541 | 1.84 436 | 1.84 441 |
| 4.95 | 141 .17 | 0.00 708 | 70 .584 | 70 .591 | 0.99 990 | 2.14 976 | 1.84 871 | 1.84 875 |
| 4.96 | 142 .59 | 0.00 701 | 71 .293 | 71 .300 | 0.99 990 | 2.15 410 | 1.85 305 | 1.85 309 |
| 4.97 | 144 .03 | 0.00 694 | 72 .010 | 72 .017 | 0.99 990 | 2.15 844 | 1.85 739 | 1.85 743 |
| 4.98 | 145 .47 | 0.00 687 | 72 .734 | 72 .741 | 0.99 991 | 2.16 279 | 1.86 174 | 1.86 178 |
| 4.99 | 146 .94 | 0.00 681 | 73 .465 | 73 .472 | 0.99 991 | 2.16 713 | 1.86 608 | 1.86 612 |
| **5.00** | 148 .41 | 0.00 674 | 74 .203 | 74 .210 | 0.99 991 | 2.17 147 | 1.87 042 | 1.87 046 |

## 8. EXPONENTIAL AND HYPERBOLIC FUNCTIONS

| x | Value | | | | | Common Logarithm | | |
|---|---|---|---|---|---|---|---|---|
| | $e^x$ | $e^{-x}$ | Sinh x | Cosh x | Tanh x | $e^x$ | Sinh x | Cosh x |
| 5.00 | 148 .41 | 0.00 674 | 74 .203 | 74 .210 | 0.99 991 | 2.17 147 | 1.87 042 | 1.87 046 |
| 5.01 | 149 .90 | 0.00 667 | 74 .949 | 74 .956 | 0.99 991 | 2.17 582 | 1.87 477 | 1.87 480 |
| 5.02 | 151 .41 | 0.00 660 | 75 .702 | 75 .709 | 0.99 991 | 2.18 016 | 1.87 911 | 1.87 915 |
| 5.03 | 152 .93 | 0.00 654 | 76 .463 | 76 .470 | 0.99 991 | 2.18 450 | 1.88 345 | 1.88 349 |
| 5.04 | 154 .47 | 0.00 647 | 77 .232 | 77 .238 | 0.99 992 | 2.18 884 | 1.88 780 | 1.88 783 |
| 5.05 | 156 .02 | 0.00 641 | 78 .008 | 78 .014 | 0.99 992 | 2.19 319 | 1.89 214 | 1.89 217 |
| 5.06 | 157 .59 | 0.00 635 | 78 .792 | 78 .798 | 0.99 992 | 2.19 753 | 1.89 648 | 1.89 652 |
| 5.07 | 159 .17 | 0.00 628 | 79 .584 | 79 .590 | 0.99 992 | 2.20 187 | 1.90 083 | 1.90 086 |
| 5.08 | 160 .77 | 0.00 622 | 80 .384 | 80 .390 | 0.99 992 | 2.20 622 | 1.90 517 | 1.90 520 |
| 5.09 | 162 .39 | 0.00 616 | 81 .192 | 81 .198 | 0.99 992 | 2.21 056 | 1.90 951 | 1.90 955 |
| 5.10 | 164 .02 | 0.00 610 | 82 .008 | 82 .014 | 0.99 993 | 2.21 490 | 1.91 386 | 1.91 389 |
| 5.11 | 165 .67 | 0.00 604 | 82 .832 | 82 .838 | 0.99 993 | 2.21 924 | 1.91 820 | 1.91 823 |
| 5.12 | 167 .34 | 0.00 598 | 83 .665 | 83 .671 | 0.99 993 | 2.22 359 | 1.92 254 | 1.92 257 |
| 5.13 | 169 .02 | 0.00 592 | 84 .506 | 84 .512 | 0.99 993 | 2.22 793 | 1.92 689 | 1.92 692 |
| 5.14 | 170 .72 | 0.00 586 | 85 .355 | 85 .361 | 0.99 993 | 2.23 227 | 1.93 123 | 1.93 126 |
| 5.15 | 172 .43 | 0.00 580 | 86 .213 | 86 .219 | 0.99 993 | 2.23 662 | 1.93 557 | 1.93 560 |
| 5.16 | 174 .16 | 0.00 574 | 87 .079 | 87 .085 | 0.99 993 | 2.24 096 | 1.93 992 | 1.93 994 |
| 5.17 | 175 .91 | 0.00 568 | 87 .955 | 87 .960 | 0.99 994 | 2.24 530 | 1.94 426 | 1.94 429 |
| 5.18 | 177 .68 | 0.00 563 | 88 .839 | 88 .844 | 0.99 994 | 2.24 965 | 1.94 860 | 1.94 863 |
| 5.19 | 179 .47 | 0.00 557 | 89 .731 | 89 .737 | 0.99 994 | 2.25 399 | 1.95 294 | 1.95 297 |
| 5.20 | 181 .27 | 0.00 552 | 90 .633 | 90 .639 | 0.99 994 | 2.25 833 | 1.95 729 | 1.95 731 |
| 5.21 | 183 .09 | 0.00 546 | 91 .544 | 91 .550 | 0.99 994 | 2.26 267 | 1.96 163 | 1.96 166 |
| 5.22 | 184 .93 | 0.00 541 | 92 .464 | 92 .470 | 0.99 994 | 2.26 702 | 1.96 597 | 1.96 600 |
| 5.23 | 186 .79 | 0.00 535 | 93 .394 | 93 .399 | 0.99 994 | 2.27 136 | 1.97 032 | 1.97 034 |
| 5.24 | 188 .67 | 0.00 530 | 94 .332 | 94 .338 | 0.99 994 | 2.27 570 | 1.97 466 | 1.97 469 |
| 5.25 | 190 .57 | 0.00 525 | 95 .281 | 95 .286 | 0.99 994 | 2.28 005 | 1.97 900 | 1.97 903 |
| 5.26 | 192 .48 | 0.00 520 | 96 .238 | 96 .243 | 0.99 995 | 2.28 439 | 1.98 335 | 1.98 337 |
| 5.27 | 194 .42 | 0.00 514 | 97 .205 | 97 .211 | 0.99 995 | 2.28 873 | 1.98 769 | 1.98 771 |
| 5.28 | 196 .37 | 0.00 509 | 98 .182 | 98 .187 | 0.99 995 | 2.29 307 | 1.99 203 | 1.99 206. |
| 5.29 | 198 .34 | 0.00 504 | 99 .169 | 99 .174 | 0.99 995 | 2.29 742 | 1.99 638 | 1.99 640 |
| 5.30 | 200 .34 | 0.00 499 | 100 .17 | 100 .17 | 0.99 995 | 2.30 176 | 2.00 072 | 2.00 074 |
| 5.31 | 202 .35 | 0.00 494 | 101 .17 | 101 .18 | 0.99 995 | 2.30 610 | 2.00 506 | 2.00 508 |
| 5.32 | 204 .38 | 0.00 489 | 102 .19 | 102 .19 | 0.99 995 | 2.31 045 | 2.00 941 | 2.00 943 |
| 5.33 | 206 .44 | 0.00 484 | 103 .22 | 103 .22 | 0.99 995 | 2.31 479 | 2.01 375 | 2.01 377 |
| 5.34 | 208 .51 | 0.00 480 | 104 .25 | 104 .26 | 0.99 995 | 2.31 913 | 2.01 809 | 2.01 811 |
| 5.35 | 210 .61 | 0.00 475 | 105 .30 | 105 .31 | 0.99 995 | 2.32 348 | 2.02 244 | 2.02 246 |
| 5.36 | 212 .72 | 0.00 470 | 106 .36 | 106 .36 | 0.99 996 | 2.32 782 | 2.02 678 | 2.02 680 |
| 5.37 | 214 .86 | 0.00 465 | 107 .43 | 107 .43 | 0.99 996 | 2.33 216 | 2.03 112 | 2.03 114 |
| 5.38 | 217 .02 | 0.00 461 | 108 .51 | 108 .51 | 0.99 996 | 2.33 650 | 2.03 547 | 2.03 548 |
| 5.39 | 219 .20 | 0.00 456 | 109 .60 | 109 .60 | 0.99 996 | 2.34 085 | 2.03 981 | 2.03 983 |
| 5.40 | 221 .41 | 0.00 452 | 110 .70 | 110 .71 | 0.99 996 | 2.34 519 | 2.04 415 | 2.04 417 |
| 5.41 | 223 .63 | 0.00 447 | 111 .81 | 111 .82 | 0.99 996 | 2.34 953 | 2.04 849 | 2.04 851 |
| 5.42 | 225 .88 | 0.00 443 | 112 .94 | 112 .94 | 0.99 996 | 2.35 388 | 2.05 284 | 2.05 285 |
| 5.43 | 228 .15 | 0.00 438 | 114 .07 | 114 .08 | 0.99 996 | 2.35 822 | 2.05 718 | 2.05 720 |
| 5.44 | 230 .44 | 0.00 434 | 115 .22 | 115 .22 | 0.99 996 | 2.36 256 | 2.06 152 | 2.06 154 |
| 5.45 | 232 .76 | 0.00 430 | 116 .38 | 116 .38 | 0.99 996 | 2.36 690 | 2.06 587 | 2.06 588 |
| 5.46 | 235 .10 | 0.00 425 | 117 .55 | 117 .55 | 0.99 996 | 2.37 125 | 2.07 021 | 2.07 023 |
| 5.47 | 237 .46 | 0.00 421 | 118 .73 | 118 .73 | 0.99 996 | 2.37 559 | 2.07 455 | 2.07 457 |
| 5.48 | 239 .85 | 0.00 417 | 119 .92 | 119 .93 | 0.99 997 | 2.37 993 | 2.07 890 | 2.07 891 |
| 5.49 | 242 .26 | 0.00 413 | 121 .13 | 121 .13 | 0.99 997 | 2.38 428 | 2.08 324 | 2.08 325 |
| 5.50 | 244 .69 | 0.00 409 | 122 .34 | 122 .35 | 0.99 997 | 2.38 862 | 2.08 758 | 2.08 760 |

## 8. EXPONENTIAL AND HYPERBOLIC FUNCTIONS

| x | Value | | | | | Common Logarithm | | |
|---|---|---|---|---|---|---|---|---|
| | $e^x$ | $e^{-x}$ | Sinh x | Cosh x | Tanh x | $e^x$ | Sinh x | Cosh x |
| **5.50** | 244 .69 | 0.00 409 | 122 .34 | 122 .35 | 0.99 997 | 2.38 862 | 2.08 758 | 2.08 760 |
| 5.51 | 247 .15 | 0.00 405 | 123 .57 | 123 .58 | 0.99 997 | 2.39 296 | 2.09 193 | 2.09 194 |
| 5.52 | 249 .64 | 0.00 401 | 124 .82 | 124 .82 | 0.99 997 | 2.39 731 | 2.09 627 | 2.09 628 |
| 5.53 | 252 .14 | 0.00 397 | 126 .07 | 126 .07 | 0.99 997 | 2.40 165 | 2.10 061 | 2.10 063 |
| 5.54 | 254 .68 | 0.00 393 | 127 .34 | 127 .34 | 0.99 997 | 2.40 599 | 2.10 495 | 2.10 497 |
| 5.55 | 257 .24 | 0.00 389 | 128 .62 | 128 .62 | 0.99 997 | 2.41 033 | 2.10 930 | 2.10 931 |
| 5.56 | 259 .82 | 0.00 385 | 129. 91 | 129 .91 | 0.99 997 | 2.41 468 | 2.11 364 | 2.11 365 |
| 5.57 | 262 .43 | 0.00 381 | 131 .22 | 131 .22 | 0.99 997 | 2.41 902 | 2.11 798 | 2.11 800 |
| 5.58 | 265 .07 | 0.00 377 | 132 .53 | 132 .54 | 0.99 997 | 2.42 336 | 2.12 233 | 2.12 234 |
| 5.59 | 267 .74 | 0.00 374 | 133 .87 | 133 .87 | 0.99 997 | 2.42 771 | 2.12 667 | 2.12 668 |
| **5.60** | 270 .43 | 0.00 370 | 135 .21 | 135 .22 | 0.99 997 | 2.43 205 | 2.13 101 | 2.13 103 |
| 5.61 | 273 .14 | 0.00 366 | 136 .57 | 136 .57 | 0.99 997 | 2.43 639 | 2.13 536 | 2.13 537 |
| 5.62 | 275 .89 | 0.00 362 | 137 .94 | 137 .95 | 0.99 997 | 2.44 073 | 2.13 970 | 2.13 971 |
| 5.63 | 278 .66 | 0.00 359 | 139 .33 | 139 .33 | 0.99 997 | 2.44 508 | 2.14 404 | 2.14 405 |
| 5.64 | 281 .46 | 0.00 355 | 140 .73 | 140 .73 | 0.99 997 | 2.44 942 | 2.14 839 | 2.14 840 |
| 5.65 | 284 .29 | 0.00 352 | 142 .14 | 142 .15 | 0.99 998 | 2.45 376 | 2.15 273 | 2.15 274 |
| 5.66 | 287 .15 | 0.00 348 | 143 .57 | 143 .58 | 0.99 998 | 2.45 811 | 2.15 707 | 2.15 708 |
| 5.67 | 290 .03 | 0.00 345 | 145 .02 | 145 .02 | 0.99 998 | 2.46 245 | 2.16 141 | 2.16 142 |
| 5.68 | 292 .95 | 0.00 341 | 146 .47 | 146 .48 | 0.99 998 | 2.46 679 | 2.16 576 | 2.16 577 |
| 5.69 | 295 .89 | 0.00 338 | 147 .95 | 147 .95 | 0.99 998 | 2.47 114 | 2.17 010 | 2.17 011 |
| **5.70** | 298 .87 | 0.00 335 | 149 .43 | 149 .44 | 0.99 998 | 2.47 548 | 2.17 444 | 2.17 445 |
| 5.71 | 301 .87 | 0.00 331 | 150 .93 | 150 .94 | 0.99 998 | 2.47 982 | 2.17 879 | 2.17 880 |
| 5.72 | 304 .90 | 0.00 328 | 152 .45 | 152 .45 | 0.99 998 | 2.48 416 | 2.18 313 | 2.18 314 |
| 5.73 | 307 .97 | 0.00 325 | 153 .98 | 153 .99 | 0.99 998 | 2.48 851 | 2.18 747 | 2.18 748 |
| 5.74 | 311 .06 | 0.00 321 | 155 .53 | 155 .53 | 0.99 998 | 2.49 285 | 2.19 182 | 2.19 182 |
| 5.75 | 314 .19 | 0.00 318 | 157 .09 | 157 .10 | 0.99 998 | 2.49 719 | 2.19 616 | 2.19 617 |
| 5.76 | 317 .35 | 0.00 315 | 158 .67 | 158 .68 | 0.99 998 | 2.50 154 | 2.20 050 | 2.20 051 |
| 5.77 | 320 .54 | 0.00 312 | 160 .27 | 160 .27 | 0.99 998 | 2.50 588 | 2.20 484 | 2.20 485 |
| 5.78 | 323 .76 | 0.00 309 | 161 .88 | 161 .88 | 0.99 998 | 2.51 022 | 2.20 919 | 2.20 920 |
| 5.79 | 327 .01 | 0.00 306 | 163 .50 | 163 .51 | 0.99 998 | 2.51 457 | 2.21 353 | 2.21 354 |
| **5.80** | 330 .30 | 0.00 303 | 165 .15 | 165 .15 | 0.99 998 | 2.51 891 | 2.21 787 | 2.21 788 |
| 5.81 | 333 .62 | 0.00 300 | 166 .81 | 166 .81 | 0.99 998 | 2.52 325 | 2.22 222 | 2.22 222 |
| 5.82 | 336 .97 | 0.00 297 | 168 .48 | 168 .49 | 0.99 998 | 2.52 759 | 2.22 656 | 2.22 657 |
| 5.83 | 340 .36 | 0.00 294 | 170 .18 | 170 .18 | 0.99 998 | 2.53 194 | 2.23 090 | 2.23 091 |
| 5.84 | 343 .78 | 0.00 291 | 171 .89 | 171 .89 | 0.99 998 | 2.53 628 | 2.23 525 | 2.23 525 |
| 5.85 | 347 .23 | 0.00 288 | 173 .62 | 173 .62 | 0.99 998 | 2.54 062 | 2.23 959 | 2.23 960 |
| 5.86 | 350 .72 | 0.00 285 | 175 .36 | 175 .36 | 0.99 998 | 2.54 497 | 2.24 393 | 2.24 394 |
| 5.87 | 354 .25 | 0.00 282 | 177 .12 | 177 .13 | 0.99 998 | 2.54 931 | 2.24 828 | 2.24 828 |
| 5.88 | 357 .81 | 0.00 279 | 178 .90 | 178 .91 | 0.99 998 | 2.55 365 | 2.25 262 | 2.25 262 |
| 5.89 | 361 .41 | 0.00 277 | 180 .70 | 180 .70 | 0.99 998 | 2.55 799 | 2.25 696 | 2.25 697 |
| **5.90** | 365 .04 | 0.00 274 | 182 .52 | 182 .52 | 0.99 998 | 2.56 234 | 2.26 130 | 2.26 131 |
| 5.91 | 368 .71 | 0.00 271 | 184 .35 | 184 .35 | 0.99 999 | 2.56 668 | 2.26 565 | 2.26 565 |
| 5.92 | 372 .41 | 0.00 269 | 186 .20 | 186 .21 | 0.99 999 | 2.57 102 | 2.26 999 | 2.27 000 |
| 5.93 | 376 .15 | 0.00 266 | 188 .08 | 188 .08 | 0.99 999 | 2.57 537 | 2.27 433 | 2.27 434 |
| 5.94 | 379 .93 | 0.00 263 | 189 .97 | 189 .97 | 0.99 999 | 2.57 971 | 2.27 868 | 2.27 868 |
| 5.95 | 383 .75 | 0.00 261 | 191 .88 | 191 .88 | 0.99 999 | 2.58 405 | 2.28 302 | 2.28 303 |
| 5.96 | 387 .61 | 0.00 258 | 193 .80 | 193 .81 | 0.99 999 | 2.58 840 | 2.28 736 | 2.28 737 |
| 5.97 | 391 .51 | 0.00 255 | 195 .75 | 195 .75 | 0.99 999 | 2.59 274 | 2.29 171 | 2.29 171 |
| 5.98 | 395 .44 | 0.00 253 | 197 .72 | 197 .72 | 0.99 999 | 2.59 708 | 2.29 605 | 2.29 605 |
| 5.99 | 399 .41 | 0.00 250 | 199 .71 | 199 .71 | 0.99 999 | 2.60 142 | 2.30 039 | 2.30 040 |
| **6.00** | 403 .43 | 0.00 248 | 201 .71 | 201 .72 | 0.99 999 | 2.60 577 | 2.30 473 | 2.30 474 |

## 9. FIVE-PLACE NATURAL LOGARITHMS

| No. | 0 | 1 | 2 | 3 | 4 | 5 | 6 | 7 | 8 | 9 | D |
|---|---|---|---|---|---|---|---|---|---|---|---|
| 1.00 | 0.0 0000 | 0100 | 0200 | 0300 | 0399 | 0499 | 0598 | 0698 | 0797 | 0896 | 100–99 |
| 1.01 | 0.0 0995 | 1094 | 1193 | 1292 | 1390 | 1489 | 1587 | 1686 | 1784 | 1882 | 99–98 |
| 1.02 | 0.0 1980 | 2078 | 2176 | 2274 | 2372 | 2469 | 2567 | 2664 | 2762 | 2859 | 98–97 |
| 1.03 | 0.0 2956 | 3053 | 3150 | 3247 | 3343 | 3440 | 3537 | 3633 | 3730 | 3826 | 97–96 |
| 1.04 | 0.0 3922 | 4018 | 4114 | 4210 | 4306 | 4402 | 4497 | 4593 | 4688 | 4784 | 96–95 |
| 1.05 | 0.0 4879 | 4974 | 5069 | 5164 | 5259 | 5354 | 5449 | 5543 | 5638 | 5733 | 95–94 |
| 1.06 | 0.0 5827 | 5921 | 6015 | 6110 | 6204 | 6297 | 6391 | 6485 | 6579 | 6672 | 94 |
| 1.07 | 0.0 6766 | 6859 | 6953 | 7046 | 7139 | 7232 | 7325 | 7418 | 7511 | 7603 | 93 |
| 1.08 | 0.0 7696 | 7789 | 7881 | 7973 | 8066 | 8158 | 8250 | 8342 | 8434 | 8526 | 93–92 |
| 1.09 | 0.0 8618 | 8709 | 8801 | 8893 | 8984 | 9075 | 9167 | 9258 | 9349 | 9440 | 92–91 |
| 1.10 | 0.0 9531 | 9622 | 9713 | 9803 | 9894 | 9985 | *0075 | *0165 | *0256 | *0346 | 91–90 |
| 1.11 | 0.1 0436 | 0526 | 0616 | 0706 | 0796 | 0885 | 0975 | 1065 | 1154 | 1244 | 90–89 |
| 1.12 | 0.1 1333 | 1422 | 1511 | 1600 | 1689 | 1778 | 1867 | 1956 | 2045 | 2133 | 89 |
| 1.13 | 0.1 2222 | 2310 | 2399 | 2487 | 2575 | 2663 | 2751 | 2839 | 2927 | 3015 | 88 |
| 1.14 | 0.1 3103 | 3191 | 3278 | 3366 | 3453 | 3540 | 3628 | 3715 | 3802 | 3889 | 88–87 |
| 1.15 | 0.1 3976 | 4063 | 4150 | 4237 | 4323 | 4410 | 4497 | 4583 | 4669 | 4756 | 87–86 |
| 1.16 | 0.1 4842 | 4928 | 5014 | 5100 | 5186 | 5272 | 5358 | 5444 | 5529 | 5615 | 86 |
| 1.17 | 0.1 5700 | 5786 | 5871 | 5956 | 6042 | 6127 | 6212 | 6297 | 6382 | 6467 | 85 |
| 1.18 | 0.1 6551 | 6636 | 6721 | 6805 | 6890 | 6974 | 7059 | 7143 | 7227 | 7311 | 85–84 |
| 1.19 | 0.1 7395 | 7479 | 7563 | 7647 | 7731 | 7815 | 7898 | 7982 | 8065 | 8149 | 84–83 |
| 1.20 | 0.1 8232 | 8315 | 8399 | 8482 | 8565 | 8648 | 8731 | 8814 | 8897 | 8979 | 83 |
| 1.21 | 0.1 9062 | 9145 | 9227 | 9310 | 9392 | 9474 | 9557 | 9639 | 9721 | 9803 | 83–82 |
| 1.22 | 0.1 9885 | 9967 | *0049 | *0131 | *0212 | *0294 | *0376 | *0457 | *0539 | *0620 | 82–81 |
| 1.23 | 0.2 0701 | 0783 | 0864 | 0945 | 1026 | 1107 | 1188 | 1269 | 1350 | 1430 | 81 |
| 1.24 | 0.2 1511 | 1592 | 1672 | 1753 | 1833 | 1914 | 1994 | 2074 | 2154 | 2234 | 81–80 |
| 1.25 | 0.2 2314 | 2394 | 2474 | 2554 | 2634 | 2714 | 2793 | 2873 | 2952 | 3032 | 80–79 |
| 1.26 | 0.2 3111 | 3191 | 3270 | 3349 | 3428 | 3507 | 3586 | 3665 | 3744 | 3823 | 79 |
| 1.27 | 0.2 3902 | 3980 | 4059 | 4138 | 4216 | 4295 | 4373 | 4451 | 4530 | 4608 | 79–78 |
| 1.28 | 0.2 4686 | 4764 | 4842 | 4920 | 4998 | 5076 | 5154 | 5231 | 5309 | 5387 | 78 |
| 1.29 | 0.2 5464 | 5542 | 5619 | 5697 | 5774 | 5851 | 5928 | 6005 | 6082 | 6159 | 77 |
| 1.30 | 0.2 6236 | 6313 | 6390 | 6467 | 6544 | 6620 | 6697 | 6773 | 6850 | 6926 | 77–76 |
| 1.31 | 0.2 7003 | 7079 | 7155 | 7231 | 7308 | 7384 | 7460 | 7536 | 7612 | 7687 | 76 |
| 1.32 | 0.2 7763 | 7839 | 7915 | 7990 | 8066 | 8141 | 8217 | 8292 | 8367 | 8443 | 76–75 |
| 1.33 | 0.2 8518 | 8593 | 8668 | 8743 | 8818 | 8893 | 8968 | 9043 | 9118 | 9192 | 75 |
| 1.34 | 0.2 9267 | 9342 | 9416 | 9491 | 9565 | 9639 | 9714 | 9788 | 9862 | 9936 | 75–74 |
| 1.35 | 0.3 0010 | 0085 | 0158 | 0232 | 0306 | 0380 | 0454 | 0528 | 0601 | 0675 | 74 |
| 1.36 | 0.3 0748 | 0822 | 0895 | 0969 | 1042 | 1115 | 1189 | 1262 | 1335 | 1408 | 74–73 |
| 1.37 | 0.3 1481 | 1554 | 1627 | 1700 | 1773 | 1845 | 1918 | 1991 | 2063 | 2136 | 73–72 |
| 1.38 | 0.3 2208 | 2281 | 2353 | 2426 | 2498 | 2570 | 2642 | 2714 | 2786 | 2858 | 72 |
| 1.39 | 0.3 2930 | 3002 | 3074 | 3146 | 3218 | 3289 | 3361 | 3433 | 3504 | 3576 | 72–71 |
| 1.40 | 0.3 3647 | 3719 | 3790 | 3861 | 3933 | 4004 | 4075 | 4146 | 4217 | 4288 | 71 |
| 1.41 | 0.3 4359 | 4430 | 4501 | 4572 | 4642 | 4713 | 4784 | 4854 | 4925 | 4995 | 71–70 |
| 1.42 | 0.3 5066 | 5136 | 5206 | 5277 | 5347 | 5417 | 5487 | 5557 | 5627 | 5697 | 70 |
| 1.43 | 0.3 5767 | 5837 | 5907 | 5977 | 6047 | 6116 | 6186 | 6256 | 6325 | 6395 | 70–69 |
| 1.44 | 0.3 6464 | 6534 | 6603 | 6672 | 6742 | 6811 | 6880 | 6949 | 7018 | 7087 | 69 |
| 1.45 | 0.3 7156 | 7225 | 7294 | 7363 | 7432 | 7501 | 7569 | 7638 | 7707 | 7775 | 69 |
| 1.46 | 0.3 7844 | 7912 | 7981 | 8049 | 8117 | 8186 | 8254 | 8322 | 8390 | 8458 | 68 |
| 1.47 | 0.3 8526 | 8594 | 8662 | 8730 | 8798 | 8866 | 8934 | 9001 | 9069 | 9137 | 68 |
| 1.48 | 0.3 9204 | 9272 | 9339 | 9407 | 9474 | 9541 | 9609 | 9676 | 9743 | 9810 | 68–67 |
| 1.49 | 0.3 9878 | 9945 | *0012 | *0079 | *0146 | *0213 | *0279 | *0346 | *0413 | *0480 | 67 |
| 1.50 | 0.4 0547 | 0613 | 0680 | 0746 | 0813 | 0879 | 0946 | 1012 | 1078 | 1145 | 67–66 |

*Note change in first decimal place.

## 9. FIVE-PLACE NATURAL LOGARITHMS

| No. | 0 | 1 | 2 | 3 | 4 | 5 | 6 | 7 | 8 | 9 | D |
|---|---|---|---|---|---|---|---|---|---|---|---|
| 1.50 | 0.4 0547 | 0613 | 0680 | 0746 | 0813 | 0879 | 0946 | 1012 | 1078 | 1145 | 67-66 |
| 1.51 | 0.4 1211 | 1277 | 1343 | 1409 | 1476 | 1542 | 1608 | 1673 | 1739 | 1805 | 66 |
| 1.52 | 0.4 1871 | 1937 | 2003 | 2068 | 2134 | 2199 | 2265 | 2331 | 2396 | 2461 | 66-65 |
| 1.53 | 0.4 2527 | 2592 | 2657 | 2723 | 2788 | 2853 | 2918 | 2983 | 3048 | 3113 | 65 |
| 1.54 | 0.4 3178 | 3243 | 3308 | 3373 | 3438 | 3502 | 3567 | 3632 | 3696 | 3761 | 65-64 |
| 1.55 | 0.4 3825 | 3890 | 3954 | 4019 | 4083 | 4148 | 4212 | 4276 | 4340 | 4404 | 64 |
| 1.56 | 0.4 4469 | 4533 | 4597 | 4661 | 4725 | 4789 | 4852 | 4916 | 4980 | 5044 | 64 |
| 1.57 | 0.4 5108 | 5171 | 5235 | 5298 | 5362 | 5426 | 5489 | 5552 | 5616 | 5679 | 64-63 |
| 1.58 | 0.4 5742 | 5806 | 5869 | 5932 | 5995 | 6058 | 6122 | 6185 | 6248 | 6310 | 63 |
| 1.59 | 0.4 6373 | 6436 | 6499 | 6562 | 6625 | 6687 | 6750 | 6813 | 6875 | 6938 | 63 |
| 1.60 | 0.4 7000 | 7063 | 7125 | 7188 | 7250 | 7312 | 7375 | 7437 | 7499 | 7561 | 62 |
| 1.61 | 0.4 7623 | 7686 | 7748 | 7810 | 7872 | 7933 | 7995 | 8057 | 8119 | 8181 | 62 |
| 1.62 | 0.4 8243 | 8304 | 8366 | 8428 | 8489 | 8551 | 8612 | 8674 | 8735 | 8797 | 62-61 |
| 1.63 | 0.4 8858 | 8919 | 8981 | 9042 | 9103 | 9164 | 9225 | 9287 | 9348 | 9409 | 61 |
| 1.64 | 0.4 9470 | 9531 | 9592 | 9652 | 9713 | 9774 | 9835 | 9896 | 9956 | *0017 | 61 |
| 1.65 | 0.5 0078 | 0138 | 0199 | 0259 | 0320 | 0380 | 0441 | 0501 | 0561 | 0622 | 61-60 |
| 1.66 | 0.5 0682 | 0742 | 0802 | 0862 | 0922 | 0983 | 1043 | 1103 | 1163 | 1222 | 60 |
| 1.67 | 0.5 1282 | 1342 | 1402 | 1462 | 1522 | 1581 | 1641 | 1701 | 1760 | 1820 | 60 |
| 1.68 | 0.5 1879 | 1939 | 1998 | 2058 | 2117 | 2177 | 2236 | 2295 | 2354 | 2414 | 60-59 |
| 1.69 | 0.5 2473 | 2532 | 2591 | 2650 | 2709 | 2768 | 2827 | 2886 | 2945 | 3004 | 59 |
| 1.70 | 0.5 3063 | 3122 | 3180 | 3239 | 3298 | 3357 | 3415 | 3474 | 3532 | 3591 | 59-58 |
| 1.71 | 0.5 3649 | 3708 | 3766 | 3825 | 3883 | 3941 | 4000 | 4058 | 4116 | 4174 | 58 |
| 1.72 | 0.5 4232 | 4291 | 4349 | 4407 | 4465 | 4523 | 4581 | 4639 | 4696 | 4754 | 58 |
| 1.73 | 0.5 4812 | 4870 | 4928 | 4985 | 5043 | 5101 | 5158 | 5216 | 5274 | 5331 | 58-57 |
| 1.74 | 0.5 5389 | 5446 | 5503 | 5561 | 5618 | 5675 | 5733 | 5790 | 5847 | 5904 | 57 |
| 1.75 | 0.5 5962 | 6019 | 6076 | 6133 | 6190 | 6247 | 6304 | 6361 | 6418 | 6475 | 57 |
| 1.76 | 0.5 6531 | 6588 | 6645 | 6702 | 6758 | 6815 | 6872 | 6928 | 6985 | 7041 | 57 |
| 1.77 | 0.5 7098 | 7154 | 7211 | 7267 | 7324 | 7380 | 7436 | 7493 | 7549 | 7605 | 56 |
| 1.78 | 0.5 7661 | 7718 | 7774 | 7830 | 7886 | 7942 | 7998 | 8054 | 8110 | 8166 | 56 |
| 1.79 | 0.5 8222 | 8277 | 8333 | 8389 | 8445 | 8501 | 8556 | 8612 | 8667 | 8723 | 56 |
| 1.80 | 0.5 8779 | 8834 | 8890 | 8945 | 9001 | 9056 | 9111 | 9167 | 9222 | 9277 | 56-55 |
| 1.81 | 0.5 9333 | 9388 | 9443 | 9498 | 9553 | 9609 | 9664 | 9719 | 9774 | 9829 | 55 |
| 1.82 | 0.5 9884 | 9939 | 9993 | *0048 | *0103 | *0158 | *0213 | *0268 | *0322 | *0377 | 55 |
| 1.83 | 0.6 0432 | 0486 | 0541 | 0595 | 0650 | 0704 | 0759 | 0813 | 0868 | 0922 | 55-54 |
| 1.84 | 0.6 0977 | 1031 | 1085 | 1139 | 1194 | 1248 | 1302 | 1356 | 1410 | 1464 | 54 |
| 1.85 | 0.6 1519 | 1573 | 1627 | 1681 | 1735 | 1788 | 1842 | 1896 | 1950 | 2004 | 54 |
| 1.86 | 0.6 2058 | 2111 | 2165 | 2219 | 2272 | 2326 | 2380 | 2433 | 2487 | 2540 | 54-53 |
| 1.87 | 0.6 2594 | 2647 | 2701 | 2754 | 2808 | 2861 | 2914 | 2967 | 3021 | 3074 | 53 |
| 1.88 | 0.6 3127 | 3180 | 3234 | 3287 | 3340 | 3393 | 3446 | 3499 | 3552 | 3605 | 53 |
| 1.89 | 0.6 3658 | 3711 | 3763 | 3816 | 3869 | 3922 | 3975 | 4027 | 4080 | 4133 | 53 |
| 1.90 | 0.6 4185 | 4238 | 4291 | 4343 | 4396 | 4448 | 4501 | 4553 | 4606 | 4658 | 53-52 |
| 1.91 | 0.6 4710 | 4763 | 4815 | 4867 | 4920 | 4972 | 5024 | 5076 | 5128 | 5180 | 52 |
| 1.92 | 0.6 5233 | 5285 | 5337 | 5389 | 5441 | 5493 | 5545 | 5596 | 5648 | 5700 | 52 |
| 1.93 | 0.6 5752 | 5804 | 5856 | 5907 | 5959 | 6011 | 6062 | 6114 | 6166 | 6217 | 52 |
| 1.94 | 0.6 6269 | 6320 | 6372 | 6423 | 6475 | 6526 | 6578 | 6629 | 6680 | 6732 | 52-51 |
| 1.95 | 0.6 6783 | 6834 | 6885 | 6937 | 6988 | 7039 | 7090 | 7141 | 7192 | 7243 | 51 |
| 1.96 | 0.6 7294 | 7345 | 7396 | 7447 | 7498 | 7549 | 7600 | 7651 | 7702 | 7753 | 51 |
| 1.97 | 0.6 7803 | 7854 | 7905 | 7956 | 8006 | 8057 | 8107 | 8158 | 8209 | 8259 | 51 |
| 1.98 | 0.6 8310 | 8360 | 8411 | 8461 | 8512 | 8562 | 8612 | 8663 | 8713 | 8763 | 50 |
| 1.99 | 0.6 8813 | 8864 | 8914 | 8964 | 9014 | 9064 | 9115 | 9165 | 9215 | 9265 | 50 |
| 2.00 | 0.6 9315 | 9365 | 9415 | 9465 | 9515 | 9564 | 9614 | 9664 | 9714 | 9764 | 50 |

*Note change in first decimal place.

## 9. FIVE-PLACE NATURAL LOGARITHMS

| No. | 0 | 1 | 2 | 3 | 4 | 5 | 6 | 7 | 8 | 9 | D |
|---|---|---|---|---|---|---|---|---|---|---|---|
| **2.00** | 0.6 9315 | 9365 | 9415 | 9465 | 9515 | 9564 | 9614 | 9664 | 9714 | 9764 | 50 |
| 2.01 | 0.6 9813 | 9863 | 9913 | 9963 | *0012 | *0062 | *0112 | *0161 | *0211 | *0260 | 50 |
| 2.02 | 0.7 0310 | 0359 | 0409 | 0458 | 0508 | 0557 | 0606 | 0656 | 0705 | 0754 | 49 |
| 2.03 | 0.7 0804 | 0853 | 0902 | 0951 | 1000 | 1050 | 1099 | 1148 | 1197 | 1246 | 49 |
| 2.04 | 0.7 1295 | 1344 | 1393 | 1442 | 1491 | 1540 | 1589 | 1638 | 1686 | 1735 | 49 |
| 2.05 | 0.7 1784 | 1833 | 1881 | 1930 | 1979 | 2028 | 2076 | 2125 | 2173 | 2222 | 49 |
| 2.06 | 0.7 2271 | 2319 | 2368 | 2416 | 2465 | 2513 | 2561 | 2610 | 2658 | 2707 | 49–48 |
| 2.07 | 0.7 2755 | 2803 | 2851 | 2900 | 2948 | 2996 | 3044 | 3092 | 3141 | 3189 | 48 |
| 2.08 | 0.7 3237 | 3285 | 3333 | 3381 | 3429 | 3477 | 3525 | 3573 | 3621 | 3669 | 48 |
| 2.09 | 0.7 3716 | 3764 | 3812 | 3860 | 3908 | 3955 | 4003 | 4051 | 4098 | 4146 | 48 |
| **2.10** | 0.7 4194 | 4241 | 4289 | 4336 | 4384 | 4432 | 4479 | 4527 | 4574 | 4621 | 48–47 |
| 2.11 | 0.7 4669 | 4716 | 4764 | 4811 | 4858 | 4905 | 4953 | 5000 | 5047 | 5094 | 47 |
| 2.12 | 0.7 5142 | 5189 | 5236 | 5283 | 5330 | 5377 | 5424 | 5471 | 5518 | 5565 | 47 |
| 2.13 | 0.7 5612 | 5659 | 5706 | 5753 | 5800 | 5847 | 5893 | 5940 | 5987 | 6034 | 47 |
| 2.14 | 0.7 6081 | 6127 | 6174 | 6221 | 6267 | 6314 | 6361 | 6407 | 6454 | 6500 | 47 |
| 2.15 | 0.7 6547 | 6593 | 6640 | 6686 | 6733 | 6779 | 6825 | 6872 | 6918 | 6965 | 47–46 |
| 2.16 | 0.7 7011 | 7057 | 7103 | 7150 | 7196 | 7242 | 7288 | 7334 | 7381 | 7427 | 46 |
| 2.17 | 0.7 7473 | 7519 | 7565 | 7611 | 7657 | 7703 | 7749 | 7795 | 7841 | 7887 | 46 |
| 2.18 | 0.7 7932 | 7978 | 8024 | 8070 | 8116 | 8162 | 8207 | 8253 | 8299 | 8344 | 46 |
| 2.19 | 0.7 8390 | 8436 | 8481 | 8527 | 8573 | 8618 | 8664 | 8709 | 8755 | 8800 | 46–45 |
| **2.20** | 0.7 8846 | 8891 | 8937 | 8982 | 9027 | 9073 | 9118 | 9163 | 9209 | 9254 | 45 |
| 2.21 | 0.7 9299 | 9344 | 9390 | 9435 | 9480 | 9525 | 9570 | 9615 | 9661 | 9706 | 45 |
| 2.22 | 0.7 9751 | 9796 | 9841 | 9886 | 9931 | 9976 | *0021 | *0066 | *0110 | *0155 | 45 |
| 2.23 | 0.8 0200 | 0245 | 0290 | 0335 | 0379 | 0424 | 0469 | 0514 | 0558 | 0603 | 45 |
| 2.24 | 0.8 0648 | 0692 | 0737 | 0781 | 0826 | 0871 | 0915 | 0960 | 1004 | 1049 | 45–44 |
| 2.25 | 0.8 1093 | 1137 | 1182 | 1226 | 1271 | 1315 | 1359 | 1404 | 1448 | 1492 | 44 |
| 2.26 | 0.8 1536 | 1581 | 1625 | 1669 | 1713 | 1757 | 1802 | 1846 | 1890 | 1934 | 44 |
| 2.27 | 0.8 1978 | 2022 | 2066 | 2110 | 2154 | 2198 | 2242 | 2286 | 2330 | 2374 | 44 |
| 2.28 | 0.8 2418 | 2461 | 2505 | 2549 | 2593 | 2637 | 2680 | 2724 | 2768 | 2812 | 44 |
| 2.29 | 0.8 2855 | 2899 | 2942 | 2986 | 3030 | 3073 | 3117 | 3160 | 3204 | 3247 | 44–43 |
| **2.30** | 0.8 3291 | 3334 | 3378 | 3421 | 3465 | 3508 | 3551 | 3595 | 3638 | 3681 | 43 |
| 2.31 | 0.8 3725 | 3768 | 3811 | 3855 | 3898 | 3941 | 3984 | 4027 | 4070 | 4114 | 43 |
| 2.32 | 0.8 4157 | 4200 | 4243 | 4286 | 4329 | 4372 | 4415 | 4458 | 4501 | 4544 | 43 |
| 2.33 | 0.8 4587 | 4630 | 4673 | 4715 | 4758 | 4801 | 4844 | 4887 | 4930 | 4972 | 43 |
| 2.34 | 0.8 5015 | 5058 | 5101 | 5143 | 5186 | 5229 | 5271 | 5314 | 5356 | 5399 | 43 |
| 2.35 | 0.8 5442 | 5484 | 5527 | 5569 | 5612 | 5654 | 5697 | 5739 | 5781 | 5824 | 43–42 |
| 2.36 | 0.8 5866 | 5909 | 5951 | 5993 | 6036 | 6078 | 6120 | 6162 | 6205 | 6247 | 42 |
| 2.37 | 0.8 6289 | 6331 | 6373 | 6415 | 6458 | 6500 | 6542 | 6584 | 6626 | 6668 | 42 |
| 2.38 | 0.8 6710 | 6752 | 6794 | 6836 | 6878 | 6920 | 6962 | 7004 | 7046 | 7087 | 42 |
| 2.39 | 0.8 7129 | 7171 | 7213 | 7255 | 7297 | 7338 | 7380 | 7422 | 7464 | 7505 | 42 |
| **2.40** | 0.8 7547 | 7589 | 7630 | 7672 | 7713 | 7755 | 7797 | 7838 | 7880 | 7921 | 42 |
| 2.41 | 0.8 7963 | 8004 | 8046 | 8087 | 8129 | 8170 | 8211 | 8253 | 8294 | 8335 | 41 |
| 2.42 | 0.8 8377 | 8418 | 8459 | 8501 | 8542 | 8583 | 8624 | 8666 | 8707 | 8748 | 41 |
| 2.43 | 0.8 8789 | 8830 | 8871 | 8913 | 8954 | 8995 | 9036 | 9077 | 9118 | 9159 | 41 |
| 2.44 | 0.8 9200 | 9241 | 9282 | 9323 | 9364 | 9405 | 9445 | 9486 | 9527 | 9568 | 41 |
| 2.45 | 0.8 9609 | 9650 | 9690 | 9731 | 9772 | 9813 | 9853 | 9894 | 9935 | 9975 | 41 |
| 2.46 | 0.9 0016 | 0057 | 0097 | 0138 | 0179 | 0219 | 0260 | 0300 | 0341 | 0381 | 41–40 |
| 2.47 | 0.9 0422 | 0462 | 0503 | 0543 | 0584 | 0624 | 0664 | 0705 | 0745 | 0786 | 40 |
| 2.48 | 0.9 0826 | 0866 | 0906 | 0947 | 0987 | 1027 | 1067 | 1108 | 1148 | 1188 | 40 |
| 2.49 | 0.9 1228 | 1268 | 1309 | 1349 | 1389 | 1429 | 1469 | 1509 | 1549 | 1589 | 40 |
| **2.50** | 0.9 1629 | 1669 | 1709 | 1749 | 1789 | 1829 | 1869 | 1909 | 1949 | 1988 | 40 |

*Note change in first decimal place.

## 9. FIVE-PLACE NATURAL LOGARITHMS

| No. | 0 | 1 | 2 | 3 | 4 | 5 | 6 | 7 | 8 | 9 | D |
|---|---|---|---|---|---|---|---|---|---|---|---|
| 2.50 | 0.9 1629 | 1669 | 1709 | 1749 | 1789 | 1829 | 1869 | 1909 | 1949 | 1988 | 40 |
| 2.51 | 0.9 2028 | 2068 | 2108 | 2148 | 2188 | 2227 | 2267 | 2307 | 2346 | 2386 | 40 |
| 2.52 | 0.9 2426 | 2466 | 2505 | 2545 | 2584 | 2624 | 2664 | 2703 | 2743 | 2782 | 40 |
| 2.53 | 0.9 2822 | 2861 | 2901 | 2940 | 2980 | 3019 | 3059 | 3098 | 3138 | 3177 | 40–39 |
| 2.54 | 0.9 3216 | 3256 | 3295 | 3334 | 3374 | 3413 | 3452 | 3492 | 3531 | 3570 | 39 |
| 2.55 | 0.9 3609 | 3649 | 3688 | 3727 | 3766 | 3805 | 3844 | 3883 | 3923 | 3962 | 39 |
| 2.56 | 0.9 4001 | 4040 | 4079 | 4118 | 4157 | 4196 | 4235 | 4274 | 4313 | 4352 | 39 |
| 2.57 | 0.9 4391 | 4429 | 4468 | 4507 | 4546 | 4585 | 4624 | 4663 | 4701 | 4740 | 39 |
| 2.58 | 0.9 4779 | 4818 | 4856 | 4895 | 4934 | 4973 | 5011 | 5050 | 5089 | 5127 | 39 |
| 2.59 | 0.9 5166 | 5204 | 5243 | 5282 | 5320 | 5359 | 5397 | 5436 | 5474 | 5513 | 39–38 |
| 2.60 | 0.9 5551 | 5590 | 5628 | 5666 | 5705 | 5743 | 5782 | 5820 | 5858 | 5897 | 38 |
| 2.61 | 0.9 5935 | 5973 | 6012 | 6050 | 6088 | 6126 | 6165 | 6203 | 6241 | 6279 | 38 |
| 2.62 | 0.9 6317 | 6356 | 6394 | 6432 | 6470 | 6508 | 6546 | 6584 | 6622 | 6660 | 38 |
| 2.63 | 0.9 6698 | 6736 | 6774 | 6812 | 6850 | 6888 | 6926 | 6964 | 7002 | 7040 | 38 |
| 2.64 | 0.9 7078 | 7116 | 7154 | 7191 | 7229 | 7267 | 7305 | 7343 | 7380 | 7418 | 38 |
| 2.65 | 0.9 7456 | 7494 | 7531 | 7569 | 7607 | 7644 | 7682 | 7720 | 7757 | 7795 | 38 |
| 2.66 | 0.9 7833 | 7870 | 7908 | 7945 | 7983 | 8020 | 8058 | 8095 | 8133 | 8170 | 38–37 |
| 2.67 | 0.9 8208 | 8245 | 8283 | 8320 | 8358 | 8395 | 8432 | 8470 | 8507 | 8544 | 37 |
| 2.68 | 0.9 8582 | 8619 | 8656 | 8694 | 8731 | 8768 | 8805 | 8843 | 8880 | 8917 | 37 |
| 2.69 | 0.9 8954 | 8991 | 9028 | 9066 | 9103 | 9140 | 9177 | 9214 | 9251 | 9288 | 37 |
| 2.70 | 0.9 9325 | 9362 | 9399 | 9436 | 9473 | 9510 | 9547 | 9584 | 9621 | 9658 | 37 |
| 2.71 | 0.9 9695 | 9732 | 9769 | 9806 | 9842 | 9879 | 9916 | 9953 | 9990 | *0026 | 37 |
| 2.72 | 1.0 0063 | 0100 | 0137 | 0173 | 0210 | 0247 | 0284 | 0320 | 0357 | 0394 | 37 |
| 2.73 | 1.0 0430 | 0467 | 0503 | 0540 | 0577 | 0613 | 0650 | 0686 | 0723 | 0759 | 37 |
| 2.74 | 1.0 0796 | 0832 | 0869 | 0905 | 0942 | 0978 | 1015 | 1051 | 1087 | 1124 | 36 |
| 2.75 | 1.0 1160 | 1196 | 1233 | 1269 | 1305 | 1342 | 1378 | 1414 | 1451 | 1487 | 36 |
| 2.76 | 1.0 1523 | 1559 | 1596 | 1632 | 1668 | 1704 | 1740 | 1776 | 1813 | 1849 | 36 |
| 2.77 | 1.0 1885 | 1921 | 1957 | 1993 | 2029 | 2065 | 2101 | 2137 | 2173 | 2209 | 36 |
| 2.78 | 1.0 2245 | 2281 | 2317 | 2353 | 2389 | 2425 | 2461 | 2497 | 2532 | 2568 | 36 |
| 2.79 | 1.0 2604 | 2640 | 2676 | 2712 | 2747 | 2783 | 2819 | 2855 | 2890 | 2926 | 36 |
| 2.80 | 1.0 2962 | 2998 | 3033 | 3069 | 3105 | 3140 | 3176 | 3212 | 3247 | 3283 | 36 |
| 2.81 | 1.0 3318 | 3354 | 3390 | 3425 | 3461 | 3496 | 3532 | 3567 | 3603 | 3638 | 36–35 |
| 2.82 | 1.0 3674 | 3709 | 3745 | 3780 | 3815 | 3851 | 3886 | 3922 | 3957 | 3992 | 35 |
| 2.83 | 1.0 4028 | 4063 | 4098 | 4134 | 4169 | 4204 | 4239 | 4275 | 4310 | 4345 | 35 |
| 2.84 | 1.0 4380 | 4416 | 4451 | 4486 | 4521 | 4556 | 4591 | 4627 | 4662 | 4697 | 35 |
| 2.85 | 1.0 4732 | 4767 | 4802 | 4837 | 4872 | 4907 | 4942 | 4977 | 5012 | 5047 | 35 |
| 2.86 | 1.0 5082 | 5117 | 5152 | 5187 | 5222 | 5257 | 5292 | 5327 | 5361 | 5396 | 35 |
| 2.87 | 1.0 5431 | 5466 | 5501 | 5536 | 5570 | 5605 | 5640 | 5675 | 5710 | 5744 | 35 |
| 2.88 | 1.0 5779 | 5814 | 5848 | 5883 | 5918 | 5952 | 5987 | 6022 | 6056 | 6091 | 35 |
| 2.89 | 1.0 6126 | 6160 | 6195 | 6229 | 6264 | 6299 | 6333 | 6368 | 6402 | 6437 | 35–34 |
| 2.90 | 1.0 6471 | 6506 | 6540 | 6574 | 6609 | 6643 | 6678 | 6712 | 6747 | 6781 | 34 |
| 2.91 | 1.0 6815 | 6850 | 6884 | 6918 | 6953 | 6987 | 7021 | 7056 | 7090 | 7124 | 34 |
| 2.92 | 1.0 7158 | 7193 | 7227 | 7261 | 7295 | 7329 | 7364 | 7398 | 7432 | 7466 | 34 |
| 2.93 | 1.0 7500 | 7534 | 7568 | 7603 | 7637 | 7671 | 7705 | 7739 | 7773 | 7807 | 34 |
| 2.94 | 1.0 7841 | 7875 | 7909 | 7943 | 7977 | 8011 | 8045 | 8079 | 8113 | 8147 | 34 |
| 2.95 | 1.0 8181 | 8214 | 8248 | 8282 | 8316 | 8350 | 8384 | 8418 | 8451 | 8485 | 34 |
| 2.96 | 1.0 8519 | 8553 | 8586 | 8620 | 8654 | 8688 | 8721 | 8755 | 8789 | 8823 | 34 |
| 2.97 | 1.0 8856 | 8890 | 8924 | 8957 | 8991 | 9024 | 9058 | 9092 | 9125 | 9159 | 34 |
| 2.98 | 1.0 9192 | 9226 | 9259 | 9293 | 9326 | 9360 | 9393 | 9427 | 9460 | 9494 | 34–33 |
| 2.99 | 1.0 9527 | 9561 | 9594 | 9628 | 9661 | 9694 | 9728 | 9761 | 9795 | 9828 | 33 |
| 3.00 | 1.0 9861 | 9895 | 9928 | 9961 | 9994 | *0028 | 0061 | 0094 | 0128 | 0161 | 33 |

*Note change in first decimal place.

## 9. FIVE-PLACE NATURAL LOGARITHMS

| No. | 0 | 1 | 2 | 3 | 4 | 5 | 6 | 7 | 8 | 9 | D |
|---|---|---|---|---|---|---|---|---|---|---|---|
| **3.00** | 1.0 9861 | 9895 | 9928 | 9961 | 9994 | *0028 | *0061 | *0094 | *0128 | *0161 | 33 |
| 3.01 | 1.1 0194 | 0227 | 0260 | 0294 | 0327 | 0360 | 0393 | 0426 | 0459 | 0493 | 33 |
| 3.02 | 1.1 0526 | 0559 | 0592 | 0625 | 0658 | 0691 | 0724 | 0757 | 0790 | 0823 | 33 |
| 3.03 | 1.1 0856 | 0889 | 0922 | 0955 | 0988 | 1021 | 1054 | 1087 | 1120 | 1153 | 33 |
| 3.04 | 1.1 1186 | 1219 | 1252 | 1284 | 1317 | 1350 | 1383 | 1416 | 1449 | 1481 | 33 |
| 3.05 | 1.1 1514 | 1547 | 1580 | 1612 | 1645 | 1678 | 1711 | 1743 | 1776 | 1809 | 33 |
| 3.06 | 1.1 1841 | 1874 | 1907 | 1939 | 1972 | 2005 | 2037 | 2070 | 2103 | 2135 | 33 |
| 3.07 | 1.1 2168 | 2200 | 2233 | 2265 | 2298 | 2330 | 2363 | 2396 | 2428 | 2460 | 33–32 |
| 3.08 | 1.1 2493 | 2525 | 2558 | 2590 | 2623 | 2655 | 2688 | 2720 | 2752 | 2785 | 32 |
| 3.09 | 1.1 2817 | 2849 | 2882 | 2914 | 2946 | 2979 | 3011 | 3043 | 3076 | 3108 | 32 |
| **3.10** | 1.1 3140 | 3172 | 3205 | 3237 | 3269 | 3301 | 3334 | 3366 | 3398 | 3430 | 32 |
| 3.11 | 1.1 3462 | 3494 | 3527 | 3559 | 3591 | 3623 | 3655 | 3687 | 3719 | 3751 | 32 |
| 3.12 | 1.1 3783 | 3815 | 3847 | 3879 | 3911 | 3943 | 3975 | 4007 | 4039 | 4071 | 32 |
| 3.13 | 1.1 4103 | 4135 | 4167 | 4199 | 4231 | 4263 | 4295 | 4327 | 4359 | 4390 | 32 |
| 3.14 | 1.1 4422 | 4454 | 4486 | 4518 | 4550 | 4581 | 4613 | 4645 | 4677 | 4708 | 32 |
| 3.15 | 1.1 4740 | 4772 | 4804 | 4835 | 4867 | 4899 | 4931 | 4962 | 4994 | 5026 | 32 |
| 3.16 | 1.1 5057 | 5089 | 5120 | 5152 | 5184 | 5215 | 5247 | 5278 | 5310 | 5342 | 32 |
| 3.17 | 1.1 5373 | 5405 | 5436 | 5468 | 5499 | 5531 | 5562 | 5594 | 5625 | 5657 | 32–31 |
| 3.18 | 1.1 5688 | 5720 | 5751 | 5782 | 5814 | 5845 | 5877 | 5908 | 5939 | 5971 | 31 |
| 3.19 | 1.1 6002 | 6033 | 6065 | 6096 | 6127 | 6159 | 6190 | 6221 | 6253 | 6284 | 31 |
| **3.20** | 1.1 6315 | 6346 | 6378 | 6409 | 6440 | 6471 | 6502 | 6534 | 6565 | 6596 | 31 |
| 3.21 | 1.1 6627 | 6658 | 6689 | 6721 | 6752 | 6783 | 6814 | 6845 | 6876 | 6907 | 31 |
| 3.22 | 1.1 6938 | 6969 | 7000 | 7031 | 7062 | 7093 | 7124 | 7155 | 7186 | 7217 | 31 |
| 3.23 | 1.1 7248 | 7279 | 7310 | 7341 | 7372 | 7403 | 7434 | 7465 | 7496 | 7526 | 31 |
| 3.24 | 1.1 7557 | 7588 | 7619 | 7650 | 7681 | 7712 | 7742 | 7773 | 7804 | 7835 | 31 |
| 3.25 | 1.1 7865 | 7896 | 7927 | 7958 | 7989 | 8019 | 8050 | 8081 | 8111 | 8142 | 31 |
| 3.26 | 1.1 8173 | 8203 | 8234 | 8265 | 8295 | 8326 | 8357 | 8387 | 8418 | 8448 | 31 |
| 3.27 | 1.1 8479 | 8510 | 8540 | 8571 | 8601 | 8632 | 8662 | 8693 | 8723 | 8754 | 31–30 |
| 3.28 | 1.1 8784 | 8815 | 8845 | 8876 | 8906 | 8937 | 8967 | 8998 | 9028 | 9058 | 30 |
| 3.29 | 1.1 9089 | 9119 | 9150 | 9180 | 9210 | 9241 | 9271 | 9301 | 9332 | 9362 | 30 |
| **3.30** | 1.1 9392 | 9423 | 9453 | 9483 | 9513 | 9544 | 9574 | 9604 | 9634 | 9665 | 30 |
| 3.31 | 1.1 9695 | 9725 | 9755 | 9785 | 9816 | 9846 | 9876 | 9906 | 9936 | 9966 | 30 |
| 3.32 | 1.1 9996 | *0027 | *0057 | *0087 | *0117 | *0147 | *0177 | *0207 | *0237 | *0267 | 30 |
| 3.33 | 1.2 0297 | 0327 | 0357 | 0387 | 0417 | 0447 | 0477 | 0507 | 0537 | 0567 | 30 |
| 3.34 | 1.2 0597 | 0627 | 0657 | 0687 | 0717 | 0747 | 0777 | 0806 | 0836 | 0866 | 30 |
| 3.35 | 1.2 0896 | 0926 | 0956 | 0986 | 1015 | 1045 | 1075 | 1105 | 1135 | 1164 | 30 |
| 3.36 | 1.2 1194 | 1224 | 1254 | 1283 | 1313 | 1343 | 1373 | 1402 | 1432 | 1462 | 30 |
| 3.37 | 1.2 1491 | 1521 | 1551 | 1580 | 1610 | 1640 | 1669 | 1699 | 1728 | 1758 | 30 |
| 3.38 | 1.2 1788 | 1817 | 1847 | 1876 | 1906 | 1935 | 1965 | 1994 | 2024 | 2053 | 30 |
| 3.39 | 1.2 2083 | 2112 | 2142 | 2171 | 2201 | 2230 | 2260 | 2289 | 2319 | 2348 | 29 |
| **3.40** | 1.2 2378 | 2407 | 2436 | 2466 | 2495 | 2524 | 2554 | 2583 | 2613 | 2642 | 29 |
| 3.41 | 1.2 2671 | 2701 | 2730 | 2759 | 2788 | 2818 | 2847 | 2876 | 2906 | 2935 | 29 |
| 3.42 | 1.2 2964 | 2993 | 3023 | 3052 | 3081 | 3110 | 3139 | 3169 | 3198 | 3227 | 29 |
| 3.43 | 1.2 3256 | 3285 | 3314 | 3343 | 3373 | 3402 | 3431 | 3460 | 3489 | 3518 | 29 |
| 3.44 | 1.2 3547 | 3576 | 3605 | 3634 | 3663 | 3692 | 3721 | 3750 | 3779 | 3808 | 29 |
| 3.45 | 1.2 3837 | 3866 | 3895 | 3924 | 3953 | 3982 | 4011 | 4040 | 4069 | 4098 | 29 |
| 3.46 | 1.2 4127 | 4156 | 4185 | 4214 | 4242 | 4271 | 4300 | 4329 | 4358 | 4387 | 29 |
| 3.47 | 1.2 4415 | 4444 | 4473 | 4502 | 4531 | 4559 | 4588 | 4617 | 4646 | 4674 | 29 |
| 3.48 | 1.2 4703 | 4732 | 4761 | 4789 | 4818 | 4847 | 4875 | 4904 | 4933 | 4962 | 29 |
| 3.49 | 1.2 4990 | 5019 | 5047 | 5076 | 5105 | 5133 | 5162 | 5191 | 5219 | 5248 | 29 |
| **3.50** | 1.2 5276 | 5305 | 5333 | 5362 | 5391 | 5419 | 5448 | 5476 | 5505 | 5533 | 29–28 |

*Note change in first decimal place.

## 9. FIVE-PLACE NATURAL LOGARITHMS

| No. | 0 | 1 | 2 | 3 | 4 | 5 | 6 | 7 | 8 | 9 | D |
|-----|---|---|---|---|---|---|---|---|---|---|---|
| 3.50 | 1.2 5276 | 5305 | 5333 | 5362 | 5391 | 5419 | 5448 | 5476 | 5505 | 5533 | 29–28 |
| 3.51 | 1.2 5562 | 5590 | 5619 | 5647 | 5675 | 5704 | 5732 | 5761 | 5789 | 5818 | 28 |
| 3.52 | 1.2 5846 | 5875 | 5903 | 5931 | 5960 | 5988 | 6016 | 6045 | 6073 | 6101 | 28 |
| 3.53 | 1.2 6130 | 6158 | 6186 | 6215 | 6243 | 6271 | 6300 | 6328 | 6356 | 6384 | 28 |
| 3.54 | 1.2 6413 | 6441 | 6469 | 6497 | 6526 | 6554 | 6582 | 6610 | 6638 | 6667 | 28 |
| 3.55 | 1.2 6695 | 6723 | 6751 | 6779 | 6807 | 6836 | 6864 | 6892 | 6920 | 6948 | 28 |
| 3.56 | 1.2 6976 | 7004 | 7032 | 7060 | 7088 | 7116 | 7144 | 7172 | 7201 | 7229 | 28 |
| 3.57 | 1.2 7257 | 7285 | 7313 | 7341 | 7369 | 7397 | 7424 | 7452 | 7480 | 7508 | 28 |
| 3.58 | 1.2 7536 | 7564 | 7592 | 7620 | 7648 | 7676 | 7704 | 7732 | 7759 | 7787 | 28 |
| 3.59 | 1.2 7815 | 7843 | 7871 | 7899 | 7927 | 7954 | 7982 | 8010 | 8038 | 8066 | 28 |
| 3.60 | 1.2 8093 | 8121 | 8149 | 8177 | 8204 | 8232 | 8260 | 8288 | 8315 | 8343 | 28 |
| 3.61 | 1.2 8371 | 8398 | 8426 | 8454 | 8482 | 8509 | 8537 | 8564 | 8592 | 8620 | 28 |
| 3.62 | 1.2 8647 | 8675 | 8703 | 8730 | 8758 | 8785 | 8813 | 8841 | 8868 | 8896 | 28 |
| 3.63 | 1.2 8923 | 8951 | 8978 | 9006 | 9033 | 9061 | 9088 | 9116 | 9143 | 9171 | 28–27 |
| 3.64 | 1.2 9198 | 9226 | 9253 | 9281 | 9308 | 9336 | 9363 | 9390 | 9418 | 9445 | 27 |
| 3.65 | 1.2 9473 | 9500 | 9527 | 9555 | 9582 | 9610 | 9637 | 9664 | 9692 | 9719 | 27 |
| 3.66 | 1.2 9746 | 9774 | 9801 | 9828 | 9856 | 9883 | 9910 | 9937 | 9965 | 9992 | 27 |
| 3.67 | 1.3 0019 | 0046 | 0074 | 0101 | 0128 | 0155 | 0183 | 0210 | 0237 | 0264 | 27 |
| 3.68 | 1.3 0291 | 0318 | 0346 | 0373 | 0400 | 0427 | 0454 | 0481 | 0508 | 0536 | 27 |
| 3.69 | 1.3 0563 | 0590 | 0617 | 0644 | 0671 | 0698 | 0725 | 0752 | 0779 | 0806 | 27 |
| 3.70 | 1.3 0833 | 0860 | 0887 | 0914 | 0941 | 0968 | 0995 | 1022 | 1049 | 1076 | 27 |
| 3.71 | 1.3 1103 | 1130 | 1157 | 1184 | 1211 | 1238 | 1265 | 1292 | 1319 | 1345 | 27 |
| 3.72 | 1.3 1372 | 1399 | 1426 | 1453 | 1480 | 1507 | 1534 | 1560 | 1587 | 1614 | 27 |
| 3.73 | 1.3 1641 | 1668 | 1694 | 1721 | 1748 | 1775 | 1802 | 1828 | 1855 | 1882 | 27 |
| 3.74 | 1.3 1909 | 1935 | 1962 | 1989 | 2015 | 2042 | 2069 | 2096 | 2122 | 2149 | 27 |
| 3.75 | 1.3 2176 | 2202 | 2229 | 2256 | 2282 | 2309 | 2335 | 2362 | 2389 | 2415 | 27 |
| 3.76 | 1.3 2442 | 2468 | 2495 | 2522 | 2548 | 2575 | 2601 | 2628 | 2654 | 2681 | 27 |
| 3.77 | 1.3 2708 | 2734 | 2761 | 2787 | 2814 | 2840 | 2867 | 2893 | 2919 | 2946 | 27–26 |
| 3.78 | 1.3 2972 | 2999 | 3025 | 3052 | 3078 | 3105 | 3131 | 3157 | 3184 | 3210 | 26 |
| 3.79 | 1.3 3237 | 3263 | 3289 | 3316 | 3342 | 3368 | 3395 | 3421 | 3447 | 3474 | 26 |
| 3.80 | 1.3 3500 | 3526 | 3553 | 3579 | 3605 | 3632 | 3658 | 3684 | 3710 | 3737 | 26 |
| 3.81 | 1.3 3763 | 3789 | 3815 | 3842 | 3868 | 3894 | 3920 | 3946 | 3973 | 3999 | 26 |
| 3.82 | 1.3 4025 | 4051 | 4077 | 4104 | 4130 | 4156 | 4182 | 4208 | 4234 | 4260 | 26 |
| 3.83 | 1.3 4286 | 4313 | 4339 | 4365 | 4391 | 4417 | 4443 | 4469 | 4495 | 4521 | 26 |
| 3.84 | 1.3 4547 | 4573 | 4599 | 4625 | 4651 | 4677 | 4703 | 4729 | 4755 | 4781 | 26 |
| 3.85 | 1.3 4807 | 4833 | 4859 | 4885 | 4911 | 4937 | 4963 | 4989 | 5015 | 5041 | 26 |
| 3.86 | 1.3 5067 | 5093 | 5119 | 5144 | 5170 | 5196 | 5222 | 5248 | 5274 | 5300 | 26 |
| 3.87 | 1.3 5325 | 5351 | 5377 | 5403 | 5429 | 5455 | 5480 | 5506 | 5532 | 5558 | 26 |
| 3.88 | 1.3 5584 | 5609 | 5635 | 5661 | 5687 | 5712 | 5738 | 5764 | 5789 | 5815 | 26 |
| 3.89 | 1.3 5841 | 5867 | 5892 | 5918 | 5944 | 5969 | 5995 | 6021 | 6046 | 6072 | 26 |
| 3.90 | 1.3 6098 | 6123 | 6149 | 6175 | 6200 | 6226 | 6251 | 6277 | 6303 | 6328 | 26 |
| 3.91 | 1.3 6354 | 6379 | 6405 | 6430 | 6456 | 6481 | 6507 | 6533 | 6558 | 6584 | 26 |
| 3.92 | 1.3 6609 | 6635 | 6660 | 6686 | 6711 | 6737 | 6762 | 6788 | 6813 | 6838 | 26–25 |
| 3.93 | 1.3 6864 | 6889 | 6915 | 6940 | 6966 | 6991 | 7016 | 7042 | 7067 | 7093 | 25 |
| 3.94 | 1.3 7118 | 7143 | 7169 | 7194 | 7220 | 7245 | 7270 | 7296 | 7321 | 7346 | 25 |
| 3.95 | 1.3 7372 | 7397 | 7422 | 7447 | 7473 | 7498 | 7523 | 7549 | 7574 | 7599 | 25 |
| 3.96 | 1.3 7624 | 7650 | 7675 | 7700 | 7725 | 7751 | 7776 | 7801 | 7826 | 7851 | 25 |
| 3.97 | 1.3 7877 | 7902 | 7927 | 7952 | 7977 | 8002 | 8028 | 8053 | 8078 | 8103 | 25 |
| 3.98 | 1.3 8128 | 8143 | 8178 | 8204 | 8229 | 8254 | 8279 | 8304 | 8329 | 8354 | 25 |
| 3.99 | 1.3 8379 | 8404 | 8429 | 8454 | 8479 | 8504 | 8529 | 8554 | 8579 | 8604 | 25 |
| 4.00 | 1.3 8629 | 8654 | 8679 | 8704 | 8729 | 8754 | 8779 | 8804 | 8829 | 8854 | 25 |

## 9. FIVE-PLACE NATURAL LOGARITHMS

| No. | 0 | 1 | 2 | 3 | 4 | 5 | 6 | 7 | 8 | 9 | D |
|---|---|---|---|---|---|---|---|---|---|---|---|
| 4.00 | 1.3 8629 | 8654 | 8679 | 8704 | 8729 | 8754 | 8779 | 8804 | 8829 | 8854 | 25 |
| 4.01 | 1.3 8879 | 8904 | 8929 | 8954 | 8979 | 9004 | 9029 | 9054 | 9078 | 9103 | 25 |
| 4.02 | 1.3 9128 | 9153 | 9178 | 9203 | 9228 | 9252 | 9277 | 9302 | 9327 | 9352 | 25 |
| 4.03 | 1.3 9377 | 9401 | 9426 | 9451 | 9476 | 9501 | 9525 | 9550 | 9575 | 9600 | 25 |
| 4.04 | 1.3 9624 | 9649 | 9674 | 9699 | 9723 | 9748 | 9773 | 9798 | 9822 | 9847 | 25 |
| 4.05 | 1.3 9872 | 9896 | 9921 | 9946 | 9970 | 9995 | *0020 | *0044 | *0069 | *0094 | 25 |
| 4.06 | 1.4 0118 | 0143 | 0168 | 0192 | 0217 | 0241 | 0266 | 0291 | 0315 | 0340 | 25 |
| 4.07 | 1.4 0364 | 0389 | 0413 | 0438 | 0463 | 0487 | 0512 | 0536 | 0561 | 0585 | 25 |
| 4.08 | 1.4 0610 | 0634 | 0659 | 0683 | 0708 | 0732 | 0757 | 0781 | 0806 | 0830 | 25-24 |
| 4.09 | 1.4 0854 | 0879 | 0903 | 0928 | 0952 | 0977 | 1001 | 1025 | 1050 | 1074 | 24 |
| 4.10 | 1.4 1099 | 1123 | 1147 | 1172 | 1196 | 1221 | 1245 | 1269 | 1294 | 1318 | 24 |
| 4.11 | 1.4 1342 | 1367 | 1391 | 1415 | 1440 | 1464 | 1488 | 1512 | 1537 | 1561 | 24 |
| 4.12 | 1.4 1585 | 1610 | 1634 | 1658 | 1682 | 1707 | 1731 | 1755 | 1779 | 1804 | 24 |
| 4.13 | 1.4 1828 | 1852 | 1876 | 1900 | 1925 | 1949 | 1973 | 1997 | 2021 | 2045 | 24 |
| 4.14 | 1.4 2070 | 2094 | 2118 | 2142 | 2166 | 2190 | 2214 | 2239 | 2263 | 2287 | 24 |
| 4.15 | 1.4 2311 | 2335 | 2359 | 2383 | 2407 | 2431 | 2455 | 2479 | 2503 | 2527 | 24 |
| 4.16 | 1.4 2552 | 2576 | 2600 | 2624 | 2648 | 2672 | 2696 | 2720 | 2744 | 2768 | 24 |
| 4.17 | 1.4 2792 | 2816 | 2840 | 2864 | 2887 | 2911 | 2935 | 2959 | 2983 | 3007 | 24 |
| 4.18 | 1.4 3031 | 3055 | 3079 | 3103 | 3127 | 3151 | 3175 | 3198 | 3222 | 3246 | 24 |
| 4.19 | 1.4 3270 | 3294 | 3318 | 3342 | 3365 | 3389 | 3413 | 3437 | 3461 | 3485 | 24 |
| 4.20 | 1.4 3508 | 3532 | 3556 | 3580 | 3604 | 3627 | 3651 | 3675 | 3699 | 3723 | 24 |
| 4.21 | 1.4 3746 | 3770 | 3794 | 3817 | 3841 | 3865 | 3889 | 3912 | 3936 | 3960 | 24 |
| 4.22 | 1.4 3984 | 4007 | 4031 | 4055 | 4078 | 4102 | 4126 | 4149 | 4173 | 4197 | 24 |
| 4.23 | 1.4 4220 | 4244 | 4267 | 4291 | 4315 | 4338 | 4362 | 4386 | 4409 | 4433 | 24 |
| 4.24 | 1.4 4456 | 4480 | 4503 | 4527 | 4551 | 4574 | 4598 | 4621 | 4645 | 4668 | 24 |
| 4.25 | 1.4 4692 | 4715 | 4739 | 4762 | 4786 | 4809 | 4833 | 4856 | 4880 | 4903 | 24-23 |
| 4.26 | 1.4 4927 | 4950 | 4974 | 4997 | 5021 | 5044 | 5068 | 5091 | 5115 | 5138 | 23 |
| 4.27 | 1.4 5161 | 5185 | 5208 | 5232 | 5255 | 5278 | 5302 | 5325 | 5349 | 5372 | 23 |
| 4.28 | 1.4 5395 | 5419 | 5442 | 5465 | 5489 | 5512 | 5535 | 5559 | 5582 | 5605 | 23 |
| 4.29 | 1.4 5629 | 5652 | 5675 | 5699 | 5722 | 5745 | 5768 | 5792 | 5815 | 5838 | 23 |
| 4.30 | 1.4 5862 | 5885 | 5908 | 5931 | 5954 | 5978 | 6001 | 6024 | 6047 | 6071 | 23 |
| 4.31 | 1.4 6094 | 6117 | 6140 | 6163 | 6187 | 6210 | 6233 | 6256 | 6279 | 6302 | 23 |
| 4.32 | 1.4 6326 | 6349 | 6372 | 6395 | 6418 | 6441 | 6464 | 6487 | 6511 | 6534 | 23 |
| 4.33 | 1.4 6557 | 6580 | 6603 | 6626 | 6649 | 6672 | 6695 | 6718 | 6741 | 6764 | 23 |
| 4.34 | 1.4 6787 | 6810 | 6834 | 6857 | 6880 | 6903 | 6926 | 6949 | 6972 | 6995 | 23 |
| 4.35 | 1.4 7018 | 7041 | 7064 | 7087 | 7109 | 7132 | 7155 | 7178 | 7201 | 7224 | 23 |
| 4.36 | 1.4 7247 | 7270 | 7293 | 7316 | 7339 | 7362 | 7385 | 7408 | 7431 | 7453 | 23 |
| 4.37 | 1.4 7476 | 7499 | 7522 | 7545 | 7568 | 7591 | 7614 | 7636 | 7659 | 7682 | 23 |
| 4.38 | 1.4 7705 | 7728 | 7751 | 7773 | 7796 | 7819 | 7842 | 7865 | 7887 | 7910 | 23 |
| 4.39 | 1.4 7933 | 7956 | 7978 | 8001 | 8024 | 8047 | 8070 | 8092 | 8115 | 8138 | 23 |
| 4.40 | 1.4 8160 | 8183 | 8206 | 8229 | 8251 | 8274 | 8297 | 8319 | 8342 | 8365 | 23 |
| 4.41 | 1.4 8387 | 8410 | 8433 | 8455 | 8478 | 8501 | 8523 | 8546 | 8569 | 8591 | 23 |
| 4.42 | 1.4 8614 | 8637 | 8659 | 8682 | 8704 | 8727 | 8750 | 8772 | 8795 | 8817 | 23 |
| 4.43 | 1.4 8840 | 8863 | 8885 | 8908 | 8930 | 8953 | 8975 | 8998 | 9020 | 9043 | 23 |
| 4.44 | 1.4 9065 | 9088 | 9110 | 9133 | 9155 | 9178 | 9200 | 9223 | 9245 | 9268 | 23 |
| 4.45. | 1.4 9290 | 9313 | 9335 | 9358 | 9380 | 9403 | 9425 | 9448 | 9470 | 9492 | 23-22 |
| 4.46 | 1.4 9515 | 9537 | 9560 | 9582 | 9605 | 9627 | 9649 | 9672 | 9694 | 9716 | 22 |
| 4.47 | 1.4 9739 | 9761 | 9784 | 9806 | 9828 | 9851 | 9873 | 9895 | 9918 | 9940 | 22 |
| 4.48 | 1.4 9962 | 9985 | *0007 | *0029 | *0052 | *0074 | *0096 | *0118 | *0141 | *0163 | 22 |
| 4.49 | 1.5 0185 | 0208 | 0230 | 0252 | 0274 | 0297 | 0319 | 0341 | 0363 | 0386 | 22 |
| 4.50 | 1.5 0408 | 0430 | 0452 | 0474 | 0497 | 0519 | 0541 | 0563 | 0585 | 0608 | 22 |

*Note change in first decimal place.

## 9. FIVE-PLACE NATURAL LOGARITHMS

| No. | 0 | 1 | 2 | 3 | 4 | 5 | 6 | 7 | 8 | 9 | D |
|---|---|---|---|---|---|---|---|---|---|---|---|
| **4.50** | 1.5 0408 | 0430 | 0452 | 0474 | 0497 | 0519 | 0541 | 0563 | 0585 | 0608 | 22 |
| 4.51 | 1.5 0630 | 0652 | 0674 | 0696 | 0718 | 0741 | 0763 | 0785 | 0807 | 0829 | 22 |
| 4.52 | 1.5 0851 | 0873 | 0895 | 0918 | 0940 | 0962 | 0984 | 1006 | 1028 | 1050 | 22 |
| 4.53 | 1.5 1072 | 1094 | 1116 | 1138 | 1160 | 1183 | 1205 | 1227 | 1249 | 1271 | 22 |
| 4.54 | 1.5 1293 | 1315 | 1337 | 1359 | 1381 | 1403 | 1425 | 1447 | 1469 | 1491 | 22 |
| 4.55 | 1.5 1513 | 1535 | 1557 | 1579 | 1601 | 1623 | 1645 | 1666 | 1688 | 1710 | 22 |
| 4.56 | 1.5 1732 | 1754 | 1776 | 1798 | 1820 | 1842 | 1864 | 1886 | 1908 | 1929 | 22 |
| 4.57 | 1.5 1951 | 1973 | 1995 | 2017 | 2039 | 2061 | 2083 | 2104 | 2126 | 2148 | 22 |
| 4.58 | 1.5 2170 | 2192 | 2214 | 2235 | 2257 | 2279 | 2301 | 2323 | 2344 | 2366 | 22 |
| 4.59 | 1.5 2388 | 2410 | 2432 | 2453 | 2475 | 2497 | 2519 | 2540 | 2562 | 2584 | 22 |
| **4.60** | 1.5 2606 | 2627 | 2649 | 2671 | 2693 | 2714 | 2736 | 2758 | 2779 | 2801 | 22 |
| 4.61 | 1.5 2823 | 2844 | 2866 | 2888 | 2910 | 2931 | 2953 | 2975 | 2996 | 3018 | 22 |
| 4.62 | 1.5 3039 | 3061 | 3083 | 3104 | 3126 | 3148 | 3169 | 3191 | 3212 | 3234 | 22 |
| 4.63 | 1.5 3256 | 3277 | 3299 | 3320 | 3342 | 3364 | 3385 | 3407 | 3428 | 3450 | 22 |
| 4.64 | 1.5 3471 | 3493 | 3515 | 3536 | 3558 | 3579 | 3601 | 3622 | 3644 | 3665 | 22 |
| 4.65 | 1.5 3687 | 3708 | 3730 | 3751 | 3773 | 3794 | 3816 | 3837 | 3859 | 3880 | 22-21 |
| 4.66 | 1.5 3902 | 3923 | 3944 | 3966 | 3987 | 4009 | 4030 | 4052 | 4073 | 4094 | 21 |
| 4.67 | 1.5 4116 | 4137 | 4159 | 4180 | 4202 | 4223 | 4244 | 4266 | 4287 | 4308 | 21 |
| 4.68 | 1.5 4330 | 4351 | 4373 | 4394 | 4415 | 4437 | 4458 | 4479 | 4501 | 4522 | 21 |
| 4.69 | 1.5 4543 | 4565 | 4586 | 4607 | 4629 | 4650 | 4671 | 4692 | 4714 | 4735 | 21 |
| **4.70** | 1.5 4756 | 4778 | 4799 | 4820 | 4841 | 4863 | 4884 | 4905 | 4926 | 4948 | 21 |
| 4.71 | 1.5 4969 | 4990 | 5011 | 5032 | 5054 | 5075 | 5096 | 5117 | 5138 | 5160 | 21 |
| 4.72 | 1.5 5181 | 5202 | 5223 | 5244 | 5266 | 5287 | 5308 | 5329 | 5350 | 5371 | 21 |
| 4.73 | 1.5 5393 | 5414 | 5435 | 5456 | 5477 | 5498 | 5519 | 5540 | 5562 | 5583 | 21 |
| 4.74 | 1.5 5604 | 5625 | 5646 | 5667 | 5688 | 5709 | 5730 | 5751 | 5772 | 5793 | 21 |
| 4.75 | 1.5 5814 | 5836 | 5857 | 5878 | 5899 | 5920 | 5941 | 5962 | 5983 | 6004 | 21 |
| 4.76 | 1.5 6025 | 6046 | 6067 | 6088 | 6109 | 6130 | 6151 | 6172 | 6193 | 6214 | 21 |
| 4.77 | 1.5 6235 | 6256 | 6277 | 6298 | 6318 | 6339 | 6360 | 6381 | 6402 | 6423 | 21 |
| 4.78 | 1.5 6444 | 6465 | 6486 | 6507 | 6528 | 6549 | 6569 | 6590 | 6611 | 6632 | 21 |
| 4.79 | 1.5 6653 | 6674 | 6695 | 6716 | 6737 | 6757 | 6778 | 6799 | 6820 | 6841 | 21 |
| **4.80** | 1.5 6862 | 6882 | 6903 | 6924 | 6945 | 6966 | 6987 | 7007 | 7028 | 7049 | 21 |
| 4.81 | 1.5 7070 | 7090 | 7111 | 7132 | 7153 | 7174 | 7194 | 7215 | 7236 | 7257 | 21 |
| 4.82 | 1.5 7277 | 7298 | 7319 | 7340 | 7360 | 7381 | 7402 | 7423 | 7443 | 7464 | 21 |
| 4.83 | 1.5 7485 | 7505 | 7526 | 7547 | 7567 | 7588 | 7609 | 7629 | 7650 | 7671 | 21 |
| 4.84 | 1.5 7691 | 7712 | 7733 | 7753 | 7774 | 7795 | 7815 | 7836 | 7857 | 7877 | 21 |
| 4.85 | 1.5 7898 | 7918 | 7939 | 7960 | 7980 | 8001 | 8022 | 8042 | 8063 | 8083 | 21 |
| 4.86 | 1.5 8104 | 8124 | 8145 | 8166 | 8186 | 8207 | 8227 | 8248 | 8268 | 8289 | 21 |
| 4.87 | 1.5 8309 | 8330 | 8350 | 8371 | 8391 | 8412 | 8433 | 8453 | 8474 | 8494 | 21-20 |
| 4.88 | 1.5 8515 | 8535 | 8555 | 8576 | 8596 | 8617 | 8637 | 8658 | 8678 | 8699 | 20 |
| 4.89 | 1.5 8719 | 8740 | 8760 | 8781 | 8801 | 8821 | 8842 | 8862 | 8883 | 8903 | 20 |
| **4.90** | 1.5 8924 | 8944 | 8964 | 8985 | 9005 | 9026 | 9046 | 9066 | 9087 | 9107 | 20 |
| 4.91 | 1.5 9127 | 9148 | 9168 | 9188 | 9209 | 9229 | 9250 | 9270 | 9290 | 9311 | 20 |
| 4.92 | 1.5 9331 | 9351 | 9371 | 9392 | 9412 | 9432 | 9453 | 9473 | 9493 | 9514 | 20 |
| 4.93 | 1.5 9534 | 9554 | 9574 | 9595 | 9615 | 9635 | 9656 | 9676 | 9696 | 9716 | 20 |
| 4.94 | 1.5 9737 | 9757 | 9777 | 9797 | 9817 | 9838 | 9858 | 9878 | 9898 | 9919 | 20 |
| 4.95 | 1.5 9939 | 9959 | 9979 | 9999 | *0020 | *0040 | *0060 | *0080 | *0100 | *0120 | 20 |
| 4.96 | 1.6 0141 | 0161 | 0181 | 0201 | 0221 | 0241 | 0261 | 0282 | 0302 | 0322 | 20 |
| 4.97 | 1.6 0342 | 0362 | 0382 | 0402 | 0422 | 0443 | 0463 | 0483 | 0503 | 0523 | 20 |
| 4.98 | 1.6 0543 | 0563 | 0583 | 0603 | 0623 | 0643 | 0663 | 0683 | 0704 | 0724 | 20 |
| 4.99 | 1.6 0744 | 0764 | 0784 | 0804 | 0824 | 0844 | 0864 | 0884 | 0904 | 0924 | 20 |
| **5.00** | 1.6 0944 | 0964 | 0984 | 1004 | 1024 | 1044 | 1064 | 1084 | 1104 | 1124 | 20 |

*Note change in first decimal place.

## 9. FIVE-PLACE NATURAL LOGARITHMS

| No. | 0 | 1 | 2 | 3 | 4 | 5 | 6 | 7 | 8 | 9 | D |
|---|---|---|---|---|---|---|---|---|---|---|---|
| 5.0 | 1.6 0944 | 1144 | 1343 | 1542 | 1741 | 1939 | 2137 | 2334 | 2531 | 2728 | 200–196 |
| 5.1 | 1.6 2924 | 3120 | 3315 | 3511 | 3705 | 3900 | 4094 | 4287 | 4481 | 4673 | 196–192 |
| 5.2 | 1.6 4866 | 5058 | 5250 | 5441 | 5632 | 5823 | 6013 | 6203 | 6393 | 6582 | 192–189 |
| 5.3 | 1.6 6771 | 6959 | 7147 | 7335 | 7523 | 7710 | 7896 | 8083 | 8269 | 8455 | 189–185 |
| 5.4 | 1.6 8640 | 8825 | 9010 | 9194 | 9378 | 9562 | 9745 | 9928 | *0111 | *0293 | 185–182 |
| 5.5 | 1.7 0475 | 0656 | 0838 | 1019 | 1199 | 1380 | 1560 | 1740 | 1919 | 2098 | 182–179 |
| 5.6 | 1.7 2277 | 2455 | 2633 | 2811 | 2988 | 3166 | 3342 | 3519 | 3695 | 3871 | 178–176 |
| 5.7 | 1.7 4047 | 4222 | 4397 | 4572 | 4746 | 4920 | 5094 | 5267 | 5440 | 5613 | 175–173 |
| 5.8 | 1.7 5786 | 5958 | 6130 | 6302 | 6473 | 6644 | 6815 | 6985 | 7156 | 7326 | 172–170 |
| 5.9 | 1.7 7495 | 7665 | 7834 | 8002 | 8171 | 8339 | 8507 | 8675 | 8842 | 9009 | 169–167 |
| 6.0 | 1.7 9176 | 9342 | 9509 | 9675 | 9840 | *0006 | *0171 | *0336 | *0500 | *0665 | 167–164 |
| 6.1 | 1.8 0829 | 0993 | 1156 | 1319 | 1482 | 1645 | 1808 | 1970 | 2132 | 2294 | 164–161 |
| 6.2 | 1.8 2455 | 2616 | 2777 | 2938 | 3098 | 3258 | 3418 | 3578 | 3737 | 3896 | 161–159 |
| 6.3 | 1.8 4055 | 4214 | 4372 | 4530 | 4688 | 4845 | 5003 | 5160 | 5317 | 5473 | 159–156 |
| 6.4 | 1.8 5630 | 5786 | 5942 | 6097 | 6253 | 6408 | 6563 | 6718 | 6872 | 7026 | 156–154 |
| 6.5 | 1.8 7180 | 7334 | 7487 | 7641 | 7794 | 7947 | 8099 | 8251 | 8403 | 8555 | 154–152 |
| 6.6 | 1.8 8707 | 8858 | 9010 | 9160 | 9311 | 9462 | 9612 | 9762 | 9912 | *0061 | 151–149 |
| 6.7 | 1.9 0211 | 0360 | 0509 | 0658 | 0806 | 0954 | 1102 | 1250 | 1398 | 1545 | 149–147 |
| 6.8 | 1.9 1692 | 1839 | 1986 | 2132 | 2279 | 2425 | 2571 | 2716 | 2862 | 3007 | 147–145 |
| 6.9 | 1.9 3152 | 3297 | 3442 | 3586 | 3730 | 3874 | 4018 | 4162 | 4305 | 4448 | 145–143 |
| 7.0 | 1.9 4591 | 4734 | 4876 | 5019 | 5161 | 5303 | 5445 | 5586 | 5727 | 5869 | 143–141 |
| 7.1 | 1.9 6009 | 6150 | 6291 | 6431 | 6571 | 6711 | 6851 | 6991 | 7130 | 7269 | 141–139 |
| 7.2 | 1.9 7408 | 7547 | 7685 | 7824 | 7962 | 8100 | 8238 | 8376 | 8513 | 8650 | 139–137 |
| 7.3 | 1.9 8787 | 8924 | 9061 | 9198 | 9334 | 9470 | 9606 | 9742 | 9877 | *0013 | 137–135 |
| 7.4 | 2.0 0148 | 0283 | 0418 | 0553 | 0687 | 0821 | 0956 | 1089 | 1223 | 1357 | 135–133 |
| 7.5 | 2.0 1490 | 1624 | 1757 | 1890 | 2022 | 2155 | 2287 | 2419 | 2551 | 2683 | 133–132 |
| 7.6 | 2.0 2815 | 2946 | 3078 | 3209 | 3340 | 3471 | 3601 | 3732 | 3862 | 3992 | 131–130 |
| 7.7 | 2.0 4122 | 4252 | 4381 | 4511 | 4640 | 4769 | 4898 | 5027 | 5156 | 5284 | 130–128 |
| 7.8 | 2.0 5412 | 5540 | 5668 | 5796 | 5924 | 6051 | 6179 | 6306 | 6433 | 6560 | 128–127 |
| 7.9 | 2.0 6686 | 6813 | 6939 | 7065 | 7191 | 7317 | 7443 | 7568 | 7694 | 7819 | 127–125 |
| 8.0 | 2.0 7944 | 8069 | 8194 | 8318 | 8443 | 8567 | 8691 | 8815 | 8939 | 9063 | 125–124 |
| 8.1 | 2.0 9186 | 9310 | 9433 | 9556 | 9679 | 9802 | 9924 | *0047 | *0169 | *0291 | 123–122 |
| 8.2 | 2.1 0413 | 0535 | 0657 | 0779 | 0900 | 1021 | 1142 | 1263 | 1384 | 1505 | 122–121 |
| 8.3 | 2.1 1626 | 1746 | 1866 | 1986 | 2106 | 2226 | 2346 | 2465 | 2585 | 2704 | 120–119 |
| 8.4 | 2.1 2823 | 2942 | 3061 | 3180 | 3298 | 3417 | 3535 | 3653 | 3771 | 3889 | 119–118 |
| 8.5 | 2.1 4007 | 4124 | 4242 | 4359 | 4476 | 4593 | 4710 | 4827 | 4943 | 5060 | 118–116 |
| 8.6 | 2.1 5176 | 5292 | 5409 | 5524 | 5640 | 5756 | 5871 | 5987 | 6102 | 6217 | 116–115 |
| 8.7 | 2.1 6332 | 6447 | 6562 | 6677 | 6791 | 6905 | 7020 | 7134 | 7248 | 7361 | 115–114 |
| 8.8 | 2.1 7475 | 7589 | 7702 | 7816 | 7929 | 8042 | 8155 | 8267 | 8380 | 8493 | 114–112 |
| 8.9 | 2.1 8605 | 8717 | 8830 | 8942 | 9054 | 9165 | 9277 | 9389 | 9500 | 9611 | 112–111 |
| 9.0 | 2.1 9722 | 9834 | 9944 | *0055 | *0166 | *0276 | *0387 | *0497 | *0607 | *0717 | 111–110 |
| 9.1 | 2.2 0827 | 0937 | 1047 | 1157 | 1266 | 1375 | 1485 | 1594 | 1703 | 1812 | 110–109 |
| 9.2 | 2.2 1920 | 2029 | 2138 | 2246 | 2354 | 2462 | 2570 | 2678 | 2786 | 2894 | 109–108 |
| 9.3 | 2.2 3001 | 3109 | 3216 | 3324 | 3431 | 3538 | 3645 | 3751 | 3858 | 3965 | 107–106 |
| 9.4 | 2.2 4071 | 4177 | 4284 | 4390 | 4496 | 4601 | 4707 | 4813 | 4918 | 5024 | 106–105 |
| 9.5 | 2.2 5129 | 5234 | 5339 | 5444 | 5549 | 5654 | 5759 | 5863 | 5968 | 6072 | 105–104 |
| 9.6 | 2.2 6176 | 6280 | 6384 | 6488 | 6592 | 6696 | 6799 | 6903 | 7006 | 7109 | 104–103 |
| 9.7 | 2.2 7213 | 7316 | 7419 | 7521 | 7624 | 7727 | 7829 | 7932 | 8034 | 8136 | 103–102 |
| 9.8 | 2.2 8238 | 8340 | 8442 | 8544 | 8646 | 8747 | 8849 | 8950 | 9051 | 9152 | 102–101 |
| 9.9 | 2.2 9253 | 9354 | 9455 | 9556 | 9657 | 9757 | 9858 | 9958 | *0058 | *0158 | 101–100 |
| 10.0 | 2.3 0259 | 0358 | 0458 | 0558 | 0658 | 0757 | 0857 | 0956 | 1055 | 1154 | 100–99 |

*Note change in first decimal place.

## 10. NATURAL LOGARITHMS OF NUMBERS FROM 0.01 TO 0.99

| No. | 0 | 1 | 2 | 3 | 4 | 5 | 6 | 7 | 8 | 9 |
|-----|-----|-----|-----|-----|-----|-----|-----|-----|-----|-----|
| 0.0 | | 5.395 | 6.088 | 6.493 | 6.781 | 7.004 | 7.187 | 7.341 | 7.474 | 7.592 |
| 0.1 | 7.697 | 7.793 | 7.880 | 7.960 | 8.034 | 8.103 | 8.167 | 8.228 | 8.285 | 8.339 |
| 0.2 | 8.391 | 8.439 | 8.486 | 8.530 | 8.573 | 8.614 | 8.653 | 8.691 | 8.727 | 8.762 |
| 0.3 | 8.796 | 8.829 | 8.861 | 8.891 | 8.921 | 8.950 | 8.978 | 9.006 | 9.032 | 9.058 |
| 0.4 | 9.084 | 9.108 | 9.132 | 9.156 | 9.179 | 9.201 | 9.223 | 9.245 | 9.266 | 9.287 |
| 0.5 | 9.307 | 9.327 | 9.346 | 9.365 | 9.384 | 9.402 | 9.420 | 9.438 | 9.455 | 9.472 |
| 0.6 | 9.489 | 9.506 | 9.522 | 9.538 | 9.554 | 9.569 | 9.584 | 9.600 | 9.614 | 9.629 |
| 0.7 | 9.643 | 9.658 | 9.671 | 9.685 | 9.699 | 9.712 | 9.726 | 9.739 | 9.752 | 9.764 |
| 0.8 | 9.777 | 9.789 | 9.802 | 9.814 | 9.826 | 9.837 | 9.849 | 9.861 | 9.872 | 9.883 |
| 0.9 | 9.895 | 9.906 | 9.917 | 9.927 | 9.938 | 9.949 | 9.959 | 9.970 | 9.980 | 9.990 |

Note. Subtract 10 from each entry.

## 11. NATURAL LOGARITHMS OF INTEGERS FROM 10 TO 209

| No. | 0 | 1 | 2 | 3 | 4 | 5 | 6 | 7 | 8 | 9 |
|-----|-----|-----|-----|-----|-----|-----|-----|-----|-----|-----|
| 1 | 2.3026 | 3979 | 4849 | 5649 | 6391 | 7080 | 7726 | 8332 | 8904 | 9444 |
| 2 | 2.9957 | *0445 | *0910 | *1355 | *1781 | *2189 | *2581 | *2958 | *3322 | *3673 |
| 3 | 3.4012 | 4340 | 4657 | 4965 | 5264 | 5553 | 5835 | 6109 | 6376 | 6636 |
| 4 | 3.6889 | 7136 | 7377 | 7612 | 7842 | 8067 | 8286 | .8501 | 8712 | 8918 |
| 5 | 3.9120 | 9318 | 9512 | 9703 | 9890 | *0073 | *0254 | *0431 | *0604 | *0775 |
| 6 | 4.0943 | 1109 | 1271 | 1431 | 1589 | 1744 | 1897 | 2047 | 2195 | 2341 |
| 7 | 4.2485 | 2627 | 2767 | 2905 | 3041 | 3175 | 3307 | 3438 | 3567 | 3694 |
| 8 | 4.3820 | 3944 | 4067 | 4188 | 4308 | 4427 | 4543 | 4659 | 4773 | 4886 |
| 9 | 4.4998 | 5109 | 5218 | 5326 | 5433 | 5539 | 5643 | 5747 | 5850 | 5951 |
| 10 | 4.6052 | 6151 | 6250 | 6347 | 6444 | 6540 | 6634 | 6728 | 6821 | 6913 |
| 11 | 4.7005 | 7095 | 7185 | 7274 | 7362 | 7449 | 7536 | 7622 | 7707 | 7791 |
| 12 | 4.7875 | 7958 | 8040 | 8122 | 8203 | 8283 | 8363 | 8442 | 8520 | 8598 |
| 13 | 4.8675 | 8752 | 8828 | 8903 | 8978 | 9053 | 9127 | 9200 | 9273 | 9345 |
| 14 | 4.9416 | 9488 | 9558 | 9628 | 9698 | 9767 | 9836 | 9904 | 9972 | *0039 |
| 15 | 5.0106 | 0173 | 0239 | 0304 | 0370 | 0434 | 0499 | 0562 | 0626 | 0689 |
| 16 | 5.0752 | 0814 | 0876 | 0938 | 0999 | 1059 | 1120 | 1180 | 1240 | 1299 |
| 17 | 5.1358 | 1417 | 1475 | 1533 | 1591 | 1648 | 1705 | 1762 | 1818 | 1874 |
| 18 | 5.1930 | 1985 | 2040 | 2095 | 2149 | 2204 | 2257 | 2311 | 2364 | 2417 |
| 19 | 5.2470 | 2523 | 2575 | 2627 | 2679 | 2730 | 2781 | 2832 | 2883 | 2933 |
| 20 | 5.2983 | 3033 | 3083 | 3132 | 3181 | 3230 | 3279 | 3327 | 3375 | 3423 |

*Note change in first figure.

## 12. FOUR-PLACE COMMON LOGARITHMS

| N | 0 | 1 | 2 | 3 | 4 | 5 | 6 | 7 | 8 | 9 | P.P. 1 2 3 4 5 |
|---|---|---|---|---|---|---|---|---|---|---|---|
| 10 | 0000 | 0043 | 0086 | 0128 | 0170 | 0212 | 0253 | 0294 | 0334 | 0374 | 4 8 12 17 21 |
| 11 | 0414 | 0453 | 0492 | 0531 | 0569 | 0607 | 0645 | 0682 | 0719 | 0755 | 4 8 11 15 19 |
| 12 | 0792 | 0828 | 0864 | 0899 | 0934 | 0969 | 1004 | 1038 | 1072 | 1106 | 3 7 10 14 17 |
| 13 | 1139 | 1173 | 1206 | 1239 | 1271 | 1303 | 1335 | 1367 | 1399 | 1430 | 3 6 10 13 16 |
| 14 | 1461 | 1492 | 1523 | 1553 | 1584 | 1614 | 1644 | 1673 | 1703 | 1732 | 3 6 9 12 15 |
| 15 | 1761 | 1790 | 1818 | 1847 | 1875 | 1903 | 1931 | 1959 | 1987 | 2014 | 3 6 8 11 14 |
| 16 | 2041 | 2068 | 2095 | 2122 | 2148 | 2175 | 2201 | 2227 | 2253 | 2279 | 3 5 8 11 13 |
| 17 | 2304 | 2330 | 2355 | 2380 | 2405 | 2430 | 2455 | 2480 | 2504 | 2529 | 2 5 7 10 12 |
| 18 | 2553 | 2577 | 2601 | 2625 | 2648 | 2672 | 2695 | 2718 | 2742 | 2765 | 2 5 7 9 12 |
| 19 | 2788 | 2810 | 2833 | 2856 | 2878 | 2900 | 2923 | 2945 | 2967 | 2989 | 2 4 7 9 11 |
| 20 | 3010 | 3032 | 3054 | 3075 | 3096 | 3118 | 3139 | 3160 | 3181 | 3201 | 2 4 6 8 11 |
| 21 | 3222 | 3243 | 3263 | 3284 | 3304 | 3324 | 3345 | 3365 | 3385 | 3404 | 2 4 6 8 10 |
| 22 | 3424 | 3444 | 3464 | 3483 | 3502 | 3522 | 3541 | 3560 | 3579 | 3598 | 2 4 6 8 10 |
| 23 | 3617 | 3636 | 3655 | 3674 | 3692 | 3711 | 3729 | 3747 | 3766 | 3784 | 2 4 5 7 9 |
| 24 | 3802 | 3820 | 3838 | 3856 | 3874 | 3892 | 3909 | 3927 | 3945 | 3962 | 2 4 5 7 9 |
| 25 | 3979 | 3997 | 4014 | 4031 | 4048 | 4065 | 4082 | 4099 | 4116 | 4133 | 2 3 5 7 9 |
| 26 | 4150 | 4166 | 4183 | 4200 | 4216 | 4232 | 4249 | 4265 | 4281 | 4298 | 2 3 5 7 8 |
| 27 | 4314 | 4330 | 4346 | 4362 | 4378 | 4393 | 4409 | 4425 | 4440 | 4456 | 2 3 5 6 8 |
| 28 | 4472 | 4487 | 4502 | 4518 | 4533 | 4548 | 4564 | 4579 | 4594 | 4609 | 2 3 5 6 8 |
| 29 | 4624 | 4639 | 4654 | 4669 | 4683 | 4698 | 4713 | 4728 | 4742 | 4757 | 1 3 4 6 7 |
| 30 | 4771 | 4786 | 4800 | 4814 | 4829 | 4843 | 4857 | 4871 | 4886 | 4900 | 1 3 4 6 7 |
| 31 | 4914 | 4928 | 4942 | 4955 | 4969 | 4983 | 4997 | 5011 | 5024 | 5038 | 1 3 4 6 7 |
| 32 | 5051 | 5065 | 5079 | 5092 | 5105 | 5119 | 5132 | 5145 | 5159 | 5172 | 1 3 4 5 7 |
| 33 | 5185 | 5198 | 5211 | 5224 | 5237 | 5250 | 5263 | 5276 | 5289 | 5302 | 1 3 4 5 6 |
| 34 | 5315 | 5328 | 5340 | 5353 | 5366 | 5378 | 5391 | 5403 | 5416 | 5428 | 1 3 4 5 6 |
| 35 | 5441 | 5453 | 5465 | 5478 | 5490 | 5502 | 5514 | 5527 | 5539 | 5551 | 1 2 4 5 6 |
| 36 | 5563 | 5575 | 5587 | 5599 | 5611 | 5623 | 5635 | 5647 | 5658 | 5670 | 1 2 4 5 6 |
| 37 | 5682 | 5694 | 5705 | 5717 | 5729 | 5740 | 5752 | 5763 | 5775 | 5786 | 1 2 3 5 6 |
| 38 | 5798 | 5809 | 5821 | 5832 | 5843 | 5855 | 5866 | 5877 | 5888 | 5899 | 1 2 3 5 6 |
| 39 | 5911 | 5922 | 5933 | 5944 | 5955 | 5966 | 5977 | 5988 | 5999 | 6010 | 1 2 3 4 6 |
| 40 | 6021 | 6031 | 6042 | 6053 | 6064 | 6075 | 6085 | 6096 | 6107 | 6117 | 1 2 3 4 5 |
| 41 | 6128 | 6138 | 6149 | 6160 | 6170 | 6180 | 6191 | 6201 | 6212 | 6222 | 1 2 3 4 5 |
| 42 | 6232 | 6243 | 6253 | 6263 | 6274 | 6284 | 6294 | 6304 | 6314 | 6325 | 1 2 3 4 5 |
| 43 | 6335 | 6345 | 6355 | 6365 | 6375 | 6385 | 6395 | 6405 | 6415 | 6425 | 1 2 3 4 5 |
| 44 | 6435 | 6444 | 6454 | 6464 | 6474 | 6484 | 6493 | 6503 | 6513 | 6522 | 1 2 3 4 5 |
| 45 | 6532 | 6542 | 6551 | 6561 | 6571 | 6580 | 6590 | 6599 | 6609 | 6618 | 1 2 3 4 5 |
| 46 | 6628 | 6637 | 6646 | 6656 | 6665 | 6675 | 6684 | 6693 | 6702 | 6712 | 1 2 3 4 5 |
| 47 | 6721 | 6730 | 6739 | 6749 | 6758 | 6767 | 6776 | 6785 | 6794 | 6803 | 1 2 3 4 5 |
| 48 | 6812 | 6821 | 6830 | 6839 | 6848 | 6857 | 6866 | 6875 | 6884 | 6893 | 1 2 3 4 4 |
| 49 | 6902 | 6911 | 6920 | 6928 | 6937 | 6946 | 6955 | 6964 | 6972 | 6981 | 1 2 3 4 4 |
| 50 | 6990 | 6998 | 7007 | 7016 | 7024 | 7033 | 7042 | 7050 | 7059 | 7067 | 1 2 3 3 4 |
| 51 | 7076 | 7084 | 7093 | 7101 | 7110 | 7118 | 7126 | 7135 | 7143 | 7152 | 1 2 3 3 4 |
| 52 | 7160 | 7168 | 7177 | 7185 | 7193 | 7202 | 7210 | 7218 | 7226 | 7235 | 1 2 2 3 4 |
| 53 | 7243 | 7251 | 7259 | 7267 | 7275 | 7284 | 7292 | 7300 | 7308 | 7316 | 1 2 2 3 4 |
| 54 | 7324 | 7332 | 7340 | 7348 | 7356 | 7364 | 7372 | 7380 | 7388 | 7396 | 1 2 2 3 4 |

## 12. FOUR-PLACE COMMON LOGARITHMS

| N | 0 | 1 | 2 | 3 | 4 | 5 | 6 | 7 | 8 | 9 | P.P. 1 | 2 | 3 | 4 | 5 |
|---|---|---|---|---|---|---|---|---|---|---|---|---|---|---|---|
| 55 | 7404 | 7412 | 7419 | 7427 | 7435 | 7443 | 7451 | 7459 | 7466 | 7474 | 1 | 2 | 2 | 3 | 4 |
| 56 | 7482 | 7490 | 7497 | 7505 | 7513 | 7520 | 7528 | 7536 | 7543 | 7551 | 1 | 2 | 2 | 3 | 4 |
| 57 | 7559 | 7566 | 7574 | 7582 | 7589 | 7597 | 7604 | 7612 | 7619 | 7627 | 1 | 2 | 2 | 3 | 4 |
| 58 | 7634 | 7642 | 7649 | 7657 | 7664 | 7672 | 7679 | 7686 | 7694 | 7701 | 1 | 1 | 2 | 3 | 4 |
| 59 | 7709 | 7716 | 7723 | 7731 | 7738 | 7745 | 7752 | 7760 | 7767 | 7774 | 1 | 1 | 2 | 3 | 4 |
| 60 | 7782 | 7789 | 7796 | 7803 | 7810 | 7818 | 7825 | 7832 | 7839 | 7846 | 1 | 1 | 2 | 3 | 4 |
| 61 | 7853 | 7860 | 7868 | 7875 | 7882 | 7889 | 7896 | 7903 | 7910 | 7917 | 1 | 1 | 2 | 3 | 4 |
| 62 | 7924 | 7931 | 7938 | 7945 | 7952 | 7959 | 7966 | 7973 | 7980 | 7987 | 1 | 1 | 2 | 3 | 3 |
| 63 | 7993 | 8000 | 8007 | 8014 | 8021 | 8028 | 8035 | 8041 | 8048 | 8055 | 1 | 1 | 2 | 3 | 3 |
| 64 | 8062 | 8069 | 8075 | 8082 | 8089 | 8096 | 8102 | 8109 | 8116 | 8122 | 1 | 1 | 2 | 3 | 3 |
| 65 | 8129 | 8136 | 8142 | 8149 | 8156 | 8162 | 8169 | 8176 | 8182 | 8189 | 1 | 1 | 2 | 3 | 3 |
| 66 | 8195 | 8202 | 8209 | 8215 | 8222 | 8228 | 8235 | 8241 | 8248 | 8254 | 1 | 1 | 2 | 3 | 3 |
| 67 | 8261 | 8267 | 8274 | 8280 | 8287 | 8293 | 8299 | 8306 | 8312 | 8319 | 1 | 1 | 2 | 3 | 3 |
| 68 | 8325 | 8331 | 8338 | 8344 | 8351 | 8357 | 8363 | 8370 | 8376 | 8382 | 1 | 1 | 2 | 3 | 3 |
| 69 | 8388 | 8395 | 8401 | 8407 | 8414 | 8420 | 8426 | 8432 | 8439 | 8445 | 1 | 1 | 2 | 3 | 3 |
| 70 | 8451 | 8457 | 8463 | 8470 | 8476 | 8482 | 8488 | 8494 | 8500 | 8506 | 1 | 1 | 2 | 2 | 3 |
| 71 | 8513 | 8519 | 8525 | 8531 | 8537 | 8543 | 8549 | 8555 | 8561 | 8567 | 1 | 1 | 2 | 2 | 3 |
| 72 | 8573 | 8579 | 8585 | 8591 | 8597 | 8603 | 8609 | 8615 | 8621 | 8627 | 1 | 1 | 2 | 2 | 3 |
| 73 | 8633 | 8639 | 8645 | 8651 | 8657 | 8663 | 8669 | 8675 | 8681 | 8686 | 1 | 1 | 2 | 2 | 3 |
| 74 | 8692 | 8698 | 8704 | 8710 | 8716 | 8722 | 8727 | 8733 | 8739 | 8745 | 1 | 1 | 2 | 2 | 3 |
| 75 | 8751 | 8756 | 8762 | 8768 | 8774 | 8779 | 8785 | 8791 | 8797 | 8802 | 1 | 1 | 2 | 2 | 3 |
| 76 | 8808 | 8814 | 8820 | 8825 | 8831 | 8837 | 8842 | 8848 | 8854 | 8859 | 1 | 1 | 2 | 2 | 3 |
| 77 | 8865 | 8871 | 8876 | 8882 | 8887 | 8893 | 8899 | 8904 | 8910 | 8915 | 1 | 1 | 2 | 2 | 3 |
| 78 | 8921 | 8927 | 8932 | 8938 | 8943 | 8949 | 8954 | 8960 | 8965 | 8971 | 1 | 1 | 2 | 2 | 3 |
| 79 | 8976 | 8982 | 8987 | 8993 | 8998 | 9004 | 9009 | 9015 | 9020 | 9025 | 1 | 1 | 2 | 2 | 3 |
| 80 | 9031 | 9036 | 9042 | 9047 | 9053 | 9058 | 9063 | 9069 | 9074 | 9079 | 1 | 1 | 2 | 2 | 3 |
| 81 | 9085 | 9090 | 9096 | 9101 | 9106 | 9112 | 9117 | 9122 | 9128 | 9133 | 1 | 1 | 2 | 2 | 3 |
| 82 | 9138 | 9143 | 9149 | 9154 | 9159 | 9165 | 9170 | 9175 | 9180 | 9186 | 1 | 1 | 2 | 2 | 3 |
| 83 | 9191 | 9196 | 9201 | 9206 | 9212 | 9217 | 9222 | 9227 | 9232 | 9238 | 1 | 1 | 2 | 2 | 3 |
| 84 | 9243 | 9248 | 9253 | 9258 | 9263 | 9269 | 9274 | 9279 | 9284 | 9289 | 1 | 1 | 2 | 2 | 3 |
| 85 | 9294 | 9299 | 9304 | 9309 | 9315 | 9320 | 9325 | 9330 | 9335 | 9340 | 1 | 1 | 2 | 2 | 3 |
| 86 | 9345 | 9350 | 9355 | 9360 | 9365 | 9370 | 9375 | 9380 | 9385 | 9390 | 1 | 1 | 2 | 2 | 3 |
| 87 | 9395 | 9400 | 9405 | 9410 | 9415 | 9420 | 9425 | 9430 | 9435 | 9440 | 0 | 1 | 1 | 2 | 2 |
| 88 | 9445 | 9450 | 9455 | 9460 | 9465 | 9469 | 9474 | 9479 | 9484 | 9489 | 0 | 1 | 1 | 2 | 2 |
| 89 | 9494 | 9499 | 9504 | 9509 | 9513 | 9518 | 9523 | 9528 | 9533 | 9538 | 0 | 1 | 1 | 2 | 2 |
| 90 | 9542 | 9547 | 9552 | 9557 | 9562 | 9566 | 9571 | 9576 | 9581 | 9586 | 0 | 1 | 1 | 2 | 2 |
| 91 | 9590 | 9595 | 9600 | 9605 | 9609 | 9614 | 9619 | 9624 | 9628 | 9633 | 0 | 1 | 1 | 2 | 2 |
| 92 | 9638 | 9643 | 9647 | 9652 | 9657 | 9661 | 9666 | 9671 | 9675 | 9680 | 0 | 1 | 1 | 2 | 2 |
| 93 | 9685 | 9689 | 9694 | 9699 | 9703 | 9708 | 9713 | 9717 | 9722 | 9727 | 0 | 1 | 1 | 2 | 2 |
| 94 | 9731 | 9736 | 9741 | 9745 | 9750 | 9754 | 9759 | 9763 | 9768 | 9773 | 0 | 1 | 1 | 2 | 2 |
| 95 | 9777 | 9782 | 9786 | 9791 | 9795 | 9800 | 9805 | 9809 | 9814 | 9818 | 0 | 1 | 1 | 2 | 2 |
| 96 | 9823 | 9827 | 9832 | 9836 | 9841 | 9845 | 9850 | 9854 | 9859 | 9863 | 0 | 1 | 1 | 2 | 2 |
| 97 | 9868 | 9872 | 9877 | 9881 | 9886 | 9890 | 9894 | 9899 | 9903 | 9908 | 0 | 1 | 1 | 2 | 2 |
| 98 | 9912 | 9917 | 9921 | 9926 | 9930 | 9934 | 9939 | 9943 | 9948 | 9952 | 0 | 1 | 1 | 2 | 2 |
| 99 | 9956 | 9961 | 9965 | 9969 | 9974 | 9978 | 9983 | 9987 | 9991 | 9996 | 0 | 1 | 1 | 2 | 2 |

## 12. FOUR-PLACE COMMON LOGARITHMS

| N | 0 | 1 | 2 | 3 | 4 | 5 | 6 | 7 | 8 | 9 | 10 |
|---|---|---|---|---|---|---|---|---|---|---|---|
| 100 | 0000 | 0004 | 0009 | 0013 | 0017 | 0022 | 0026 | 0030 | 0035 | 0039 | 0043 |
| 101 | 0043 | 0043 | 0052 | 0056 | 0060 | 0065 | 0069 | 0073 | 0077 | 0082 | 0086 |
| 102 | 0086 | 0090 | 0095 | 0099 | 0103 | 0107 | 0111 | 0116 | 0120 | 0124 | 0128 |
| 103 | 0128 | 0133 | 0137 | 0141 | 0145 | 0149 | 0154 | 0158 | 0162 | 0166 | 0170 |
| 104 | 0170 | 0175 | 0179 | 0183 | 0187 | 0191 | 0195 | 0199 | 0204 | 0208 | 0212 |
| 105 | 0212 | 0216 | 0220 | 0224 | 0228 | 0233 | 0237 | 0241 | 0245 | 0249 | 0253 |
| 106 | 0253 | 0257 | 0261 | 0265 | 0269 | 0273 | 0278 | 0282 | 0286 | 0290 | 0294 |
| 107 | 0294 | 0298 | 0302 | 0306 | 0310 | 0314 | 0318 | 0322 | 0326 | 0330 | 0334 |
| 108 | 0334 | 0338 | 0342 | 0346 | 0350 | 0354 | 0358 | 0362 | 0366 | 0370 | 0374 |
| 109 | 0374 | 0378 | 0382 | 0386 | 0390 | 0394 | 0398 | 0402 | 0406 | 0410 | 0414 |
| 110 | 0414 | 0418 | 0422 | 0426 | 0430 | 0434 | 0438 | 0441 | 0445 | 0449 | 0453 |
| 111 | 0453 | 0457 | 0461 | 0465 | 0469 | 0473 | 0477 | 0481 | 0484 | 0488 | 0492 |
| 112 | 0492 | 0496 | 0500 | 0504 | 0508 | 0512 | 0515 | 0519 | 0523 | 0527 | 0531 |
| 113 | 0531 | 0535 | 0538 | 0542 | 0546 | 0550 | 0554 | 0558 | 0561 | 0565 | 0569 |
| 114 | 0569 | 0573 | 0577 | 0580 | 0584 | 0588 | 0592 | 0596 | 0599 | 0603 | 0607 |
| 115 | 0607 | 0611 | 0615 | 0618 | 0622 | 0626 | 0630 | 0633 | 0637 | 0641 | 0645 |
| 116 | 0645 | 0648 | 0652 | 0656 | 0660 | 0663 | 0667 | 0671 | 0674 | 0678 | 0682 |
| 117 | 0682 | 0686 | 0689 | 0693 | 0697 | 0700 | 0704 | 0708 | 0711 | 0715 | 0719 |
| 118 | 0719 | 0722 | 0726 | 0730 | 0734 | 0737 | 0741 | 0745 | 0748 | 0752 | 0755 |
| 119 | 0755 | 0759 | 0763 | 0766 | 0770 | 0774 | 0777 | 0781 | 0785 | 0788 | 0792 |
| 120 | 0792 | 0795 | 0799 | 0803 | 0806 | 0810 | 0813 | 0817 | 0821 | 0824 | 0828 |
| 121 | 0828 | 0831 | 0835 | 0839 | 0842 | 0846 | 0849 | 0853 | 0856 | 0860 | 0864 |
| 122 | 0864 | 0867 | 0871 | 0874 | 0878 | 0881 | 0885 | 0888 | 0892 | 0896 | 0899 |
| 123 | 0899 | 0903 | 0906 | 0910 | 0913 | 0917 | 0920 | 0924 | 0927 | 0931 | 0934 |
| 124 | 0934 | 0938 | 0941 | 0945 | 0948 | 0952 | 0955 | 0959 | 0962 | 0966 | 0969 |
| 125 | 0969 | 0973 | 0976 | 0980 | 0983 | 0986 | 0990 | 0993 | 0997 | 1000 | 1004 |
| 126 | 1004 | 1007 | 1011 | 1014 | 1017 | 1021 | 1024 | 1028 | 1031 | 1035 | 1038 |
| 127 | 1038 | 1041 | 1045 | 1048 | 1052 | 1055 | 1059 | 1062 | 1065 | 1069 | 1072 |
| 128 | 1072 | 1075 | 1079 | 1082 | 1086 | 1089 | 1092 | 1096 | 1099 | 1103 | 1106 |
| 129 | 1106 | 1109 | 1113 | 1116 | 1119 | 1123 | 1126 | 1129 | 1133 | 1136 | 1139 |
| 130 | 1139 | 1143 | 1146 | 1149 | 1153 | 1156 | 1159 | 1163 | 1166 | 1169 | 1173 |
| 131 | 1173 | 1176 | 1179 | 1183 | 1186 | 1189 | 1193 | 1196 | 1199 | 1202 | 1206 |
| 132 | 1206 | 1209 | 1212 | 1216 | 1219 | 1222 | 1225 | 1229 | 1232 | 1235 | 1239 |
| 133 | 1239 | 1242 | 1245 | 1248 | 1252 | 1255 | 1258 | 1261 | 1265 | 1268 | 1271 |
| 134 | 1271 | 1274 | 1278 | 1281 | 1284 | 1287 | 1290 | 1294 | 1297 | 1300 | 1303 |
| 135 | 1303 | 1307 | 1310 | 1313 | 1316 | 1319 | 1323 | 1326 | 1329 | 1332 | 1335 |
| 136 | 1335 | 1339 | 1342 | 1345 | 1348 | 1351 | 1355 | 1358 | 1361 | 1364 | 1367 |
| 137 | 1367 | 1370 | 1374 | 1377 | 1380 | 1383 | 1386 | 1389 | 1392 | 1396 | 1399 |
| 138 | 1399 | 1402 | 1405 | 1408 | 1411 | 1414 | 1418 | 1421 | 1424 | 1427 | 1430 |
| 139 | 1430 | 1433 | 1436 | 1440 | 1443 | 1446 | 1449 | 1452 | 1455 | 1458 | 1461 |
| 140 | 1461 | 1464 | 1467 | 1471 | 1474 | 1477 | 1480 | 1483 | 1486 | 1489 | 1492 |
| 141 | 1492 | 1495 | 1498 | 1501 | 1504 | 1508 | 1511 | 1514 | 1517 | 1520 | 1523 |
| 142 | 1523 | 1526 | 1529 | 1532 | 1535 | 1538 | 1541 | 1544 | 1547 | 1550 | 1553 |
| 143 | 1553 | 1556 | 1559 | 1562 | 1565 | 1569 | 1572 | 1575 | 1578 | 1581 | 1584 |
| 144 | 1584 | 1587 | 1590 | 1593 | 1596 | 1599 | 1602 | 1605 | 1608 | 1611 | 1614 |
| 145 | 1614 | 1617 | 1620 | 1623 | 1626 | 1629 | 1632 | 1635 | 1638 | 1641 | 1644 |
| 146 | 1644 | 1647 | 1649 | 1652 | 1655 | 1658 | 1661 | 1664 | 1667 | 1670 | 1673 |
| 147 | 1673 | 1676 | 1679 | 1682 | 1685 | 1688 | 1691 | 1694 | 1697 | 1700 | 1703 |
| 148 | 1703 | 1706 | 1708 | 1711 | 1714 | 1717 | 1720 | 1723 | 1726 | 1729 | 1732 |
| 149 | 1732 | 1735 | 1738 | 1741 | 1744 | 1746 | 1749 | 1752 | 1755 | 1758 | 1761 |

## 12. FOUR-PLACE COMMON LOGARITHMS

| N | 0 | 1 | 2 | 3 | 4 | 5 | 6 | 7 | 8 | 9 | 10 |
|---|---|---|---|---|---|---|---|---|---|---|----|
| **150** | 1761 | 1764 | 1767 | 1770 | 1772 | 1775 | 1778 | 1781 | 1784 | 1787 | 1790 |
| 151 | 1790 | 1793 | 1796 | 1798 | 1801 | 1804 | 1807 | 1810 | 1813 | 1816 | 1818 |
| 152 | 1818 | 1821 | 1824 | 1827 | 1830 | 1833 | 1836 | 1838 | 1841 | 1844 | 1847 |
| 153 | 1847 | 1850 | 1853 | 1855 | 1858 | 1861 | 1864 | 1867 | 1870 | 1872 | 1875 |
| 154 | 1875 | 1878 | 1881 | 1884 | 1886 | 1889 | 1892 | 1895 | 1898 | 1901 | 1903 |
| **155** | 1903 | 1906 | 1909 | 1912 | 1915 | 1917 | 1920 | 1923 | 1926 | 1928 | 1931 |
| 156 | 1931 | 1934 | 1937 | 1940 | 1942 | 1945 | 1948 | 1951 | 1953 | 1956 | 1959 |
| 157 | 1959 | 1962 | 1965 | 1967 | 1970 | 1973 | 1976 | 1978 | 1981 | 1984 | 1987 |
| 158 | 1987 | 1989 | 1992 | 1995 | 1998 | 2000 | 2003 | 2006 | 2009 | 2011 | 2014 |
| 159 | 2014 | 2017 | 2019 | 2022 | 2025 | 2028 | 2030 | 2033 | 2036 | 2038 | 2041 |
| **160** | 2041 | 2044 | 2047 | 2049 | 2052 | 2055 | 2057 | 2060 | 2063 | 2066 | 2068 |
| 161 | 2068 | 2071 | 2074 | 2076 | 2079 | 2082 | 2084 | 2087 | 2090 | 2092 | 2095 |
| 162 | 2095 | 2098 | 2101 | 2103 | 2106 | 2109 | 2111 | 2114 | 2117 | 2119 | 2122 |
| 163 | 2122 | 2125 | 2127 | 2130 | 2133 | 2135 | 2138 | 2140 | 2143 | 2146 | 2148 |
| 164 | 2148 | 2151 | 2154 | 2156 | 2159 | 2162 | 2164 | 2167 | 2170 | 2172 | 2175 |
| **165** | 2175 | 2177 | 2180 | 2183 | 2185 | 2188 | 2191 | 2193 | 2196 | 2198 | 2201 |
| 166 | 2201 | 2204 | 2206 | 2209 | 2212 | 2214 | 2217 | 2219 | 2222 | 2225 | 2227 |
| 167 | 2227 | 2230 | 2232 | 2235 | 2238 | 2240 | 2243 | 2245 | 2248 | 2251 | 2253 |
| 168 | 2253 | 2256 | 2258 | 2261 | 2263 | 2266 | 2269 | 2271 | 2274 | 2276 | 2279 |
| 169 | 2279 | 2281 | 2284 | 2287 | 2289 | 2292 | 2294 | 2297 | 2299 | 2302 | 2304 |
| **170** | 2304 | 2307 | 2310 | 2312 | 2315 | 2317 | 2320 | 2322 | 2325 | 2327 | 2330 |
| 171 | 2330 | 2333 | 2335 | 2338 | 2340 | 2343 | 2345 | 2348 | 2350 | 2353 | 2355 |
| 172 | 2355 | 2358 | 2360 | 2363 | 2365 | 2368 | 2370 | 2373 | 2375 | 2378 | 2380 |
| 173 | 2380 | 2383 | 2385 | 2388 | 2390 | 2393 | 2395 | 2398 | 2400 | 2403 | 2405 |
| 174 | 2405 | 2408 | 2410 | 2413 | 2415 | 2418 | 2420 | 2423 | 2425 | 2428 | 2430 |
| **175** | 2430 | 2433 | 2435 | 2438 | 2440 | 2443 | 2445 | 2448 | 2450 | 2453 | 2455 |
| 176 | 2455 | 2458 | 2460 | 2463 | 2465 | 2467 | 2470 | 2472 | 2475 | 2477 | 2480 |
| 177 | 2480 | 2482 | 2485 | 2487 | 2490 | 2492 | 2494 | 2497 | 2499 | 2502 | 2504 |
| 178 | 2504 | 2507 | 2509 | 2512 | 2514 | 2516 | 2519 | 2521 | 2524 | 2526 | 2529 |
| 179 | 2529 | 2531 | 2533 | 2536 | 2538 | 2541 | 2543 | 2545 | 2548 | 2550 | 2553 |
| **180** | 2553 | 2555 | 2558 | 2560 | 2562 | 2565 | 2567 | 2570 | 2572 | 2574 | 2577 |
| 181 | 2577 | 2579 | 2582 | 2584 | 2586 | 2589 | 2591 | 2594 | 2596 | 2598 | 2601 |
| 182 | 2601 | 2603 | 2605 | 2608 | 2610 | 2613 | 2615 | 2617 | 2620 | 2622 | 2625 |
| 183 | 2625 | 2627 | 2629 | 2632 | 2634 | 2636 | 2639 | 2641 | 2643 | 2646 | 2648 |
| 184 | 2648 | 2651 | 2653 | 2655 | 2658 | 2660 | 2662 | 2665 | 2667 | 2669 | 2672 |
| **185** | 2672 | 2674 | 2676 | 2679 | 2681 | 2683 | 2686 | 2688 | 2690 | 2693 | 2695 |
| 186 | 2695 | 2697 | 2700 | 2702 | 2704 | 2707 | 2709 | 2711 | 2714 | 2716 | 2718 |
| 187 | 2718 | 2721 | 2723 | 2725 | 2728 | 2730 | 2732 | 2735 | 2737 | 2739 | 2742 |
| 188 | 2742 | 2744 | 2746 | 2749 | 2751 | 2753 | 2755 | 2758 | 2760 | 2762 | 2765 |
| 189 | 2765 | 2767 | 2769 | 2772 | 2774 | 2776 | 2778 | 2781 | 2783 | 2785 | 2788 |
| **190** | 2788 | 2790 | 2792 | 2794 | 2797 | 2799 | 2801 | 2804 | 2806 | 2808 | 2810 |
| 191 | 2810 | 2813 | 2815 | 2817 | 2819 | 2822 | 2824 | 2826 | 2828 | 2831 | 2833 |
| 192 | 2833 | 2835 | 2838 | 2840 | 2842 | 2844 | 2847 | 2849 | 2851 | 2853 | 2856 |
| 193 | 2856 | 2858 | 2860 | 2862 | 2865 | 2867 | 2869 | 2871 | 2874 | 2876 | 2878 |
| 194 | 2878 | 2880 | 2882 | 2885 | 2887 | 2889 | 2891 | 2894 | 2896 | 2898 | 2900 |
| **195** | 2900 | 2903 | 2905 | 2907 | 2909 | 2911 | 2914 | 2916 | 2918 | 2920 | 2923 |
| 196 | 2923 | 2925 | 2927 | 2929 | 2931 | 2934 | 2936 | 2938 | 2940 | 2942 | 2945 |
| 197 | 2945 | 2947 | 2949 | 2951 | 2953 | 2956 | 2958 | 2960 | 2962 | 2964 | 2967 |
| 198 | 2967 | 2969 | 2971 | 2973 | 2975 | 2978 | 2980 | 2982 | 2984 | 2986 | 2989 |
| 199 | 2989 | 2991 | 2993 | 2995 | 2997 | 2999 | 3002 | 3004 | 3006 | 3008 | 3010 |

## 13. NATURAL AND LOGARITHMIC TRIGONOMETRIC FUNCTIONS

| RADIANS | DEGREES | SIN | | COS | | TAN | | CTN | | DEGREES | RADIANS |
|---|---|---|---|---|---|---|---|---|---|---|---|
| | | Nat. | Log. | Nat. | Log. | Nat. | Log. | Nat. | Log. | | |
| 0.0000 | 0° 00′ | .0000 | ∞ | 1.0000 | 0.0000 | .0000 | ∞ | ∞ | ∞ | 90° 00′ | 1.5708 |
| 0.0029 | 10 | .0029 | 7.4637 | 1.0000 | .0000 | .0029 | 7.4637 | 343.77 | 2.5363 | 50 | 1.5679 |
| 0.0058 | 20 | .0058 | .7648 | 1.0000 | .0000 | .0058 | .7648 | 171.89 | .2352 | 40 | 1.5650 |
| 0.0087 | 30 | .0087 | .9408 | 1.0000 | .0000 | .0087 | .9409 | 114.59 | .0591 | 30 | 1.5621 |
| 0.0116 | 40 | .0116 | 8.0658 | .9999 | .0000 | .0116 | 8.0658 | 85.940 | 1.9342 | 20 | 1.5592 |
| 0.0145 | 50 | .0145 | .1627 | .9999 | .0000 | .0145 | .1627 | 68.750 | .8373 | 10 | 1.5563 |
| 0.0175 | 1° 00′ | .0175 | 8.2419 | .9998 | 9.9999 | .0175 | 8.2419 | 57.290 | 1.7581 | 89° 00′ | 1.5533 |
| 0.0204 | 10 | .0204 | .3088 | .9998 | .9999 | .0204 | .3089 | 49.104 | .6911 | 50 | 1.5504 |
| 0.0233 | 20 | .0233 | .3668 | .9997 | .9999 | .0233 | .3669 | 42.964 | .6331 | 40 | 1.5475 |
| 0.0262 | 30 | .0262 | .4179 | .9997 | .9999 | .0262 | .4181 | 38.188 | .5819 | 30 | 1.5446 |
| 0.0291 | 40 | .0291 | .4637 | .9996 | .9998 | .0291 | .4638 | 34.368 | .5362 | 20 | 1.5417 |
| 0.0320 | 50 | .0320 | .5050 | .9995 | .9998 | .0320 | .5053 | 31.242 | .4947 | 10 | 1.5388 |
| 0.0349 | 2° 00′ | .0349 | 8.5428 | .9994 | 9.9997 | .0349 | 8.5431 | 28.636 | 1.4569 | 88° 00′ | 1.5359 |
| 0.0378 | 10 | .0378 | .5776 | .9993 | .9997 | .0378 | .5779 | 26.432 | .4221 | 50 | 1.5330 |
| 0.0407 | 20 | .0407 | .6097 | .9992 | .9996 | .0407 | .6101 | 24.542 | .3899 | 40 | 1.5301 |
| 0.0436 | 30 | .0436 | .6397 | .9990 | .9996 | .0437 | .6401 | 22.904 | .3599 | 30 | 1.5272 |
| 0.0465 | 40 | .0465 | .6677 | .9989 | .9995 | .0466 | .6682 | 21.470 | .3318 | 20 | 1.5243 |
| 0.0495 | 50 | .0494 | .6940 | .9988 | .9995 | .0495 | .6945 | 20.206 | .3055 | 10 | 1.5213 |
| 0.0524 | 3° 00′ | .0523 | 8.7188 | .9986 | 9.9994 | .0524 | 8.7194 | 19.081 | 1.2806 | 87° 00′ | 1.5184 |
| 0.0553 | 10 | .0552 | .7423 | .9985 | .9993 | .0553 | .7429 | 18.075 | .2571 | 50 | 1.5155 |
| 0.0582 | 20 | .0581 | .7645 | .9983 | .9993 | .0582 | .7652 | 17.169 | .2348 | 40 | 1.5126 |
| 0.0611 | 30 | .0610 | .7857 | .9981 | .9992 | .0612 | .7865 | 16.350 | .2135 | 30 | 1.5097 |
| 0.0640 | 40 | .0640 | .8059 | .9980 | .9991 | .0641 | .8067 | 15.605 | .1933 | 20 | 1.5068 |
| 0.0669 | 50 | .0669 | .8251 | .9978 | .9990 | .0670 | .8261 | 14.924 | .1739 | 10 | 1.5039 |
| 0.0698 | 4° 00′ | .0698 | 8.8436 | .9976 | 9.9989 | .0699 | 8.8446 | 14.301 | 1.1554 | 86° 00′ | 1.5010 |
| 0.0727 | 10 | .0727 | .8613 | .9974 | .9989 | .0729 | .8624 | 13.727 | .1376 | 50 | 1.4981 |
| 0.0756 | 20 | .0756 | .8783 | .9971 | .9988 | .0758 | .8795 | 13.197 | .1205 | 40 | 1.4952 |
| 0.0785 | 30 | .0785 | .8946 | .9969 | .9987 | .0787 | .8960 | 12.706 | .1040 | 30 | 1.4923 |
| 0.0814 | 40 | .0814 | .9104 | .9967 | .9986 | .0816 | .9118 | 12.251 | .0882 | 20 | 1.4893 |
| 0.0844 | 50 | .0843 | .9256 | .9964 | .9985 | .0846 | .9272 | 11.826 | .0728 | 10 | 1.4864 |
| 0.0873 | 5° 00′ | .0872 | 8.9403 | .9962 | 9.9983 | .0875 | 8.9420 | 11.430 | 1.0580 | 85° 00′ | 1.4835 |
| 0.0902 | 10 | .0901 | .9545 | .9959 | .9982 | .0904 | .9563 | 11.059 | .0437 | 50 | 1.4806 |
| 0.0931 | 20 | .0929 | .9682 | .9957 | .9981 | .0934 | .9701 | 10.712 | .0299 | 40 | 1.4777 |
| 0.0960 | 30 | .0958 | .9816 | .9954 | .9980 | .0963 | .9836 | 10.385 | .0164 | 30 | 1.4748 |
| 0.0989 | 40 | .0987 | .9945 | .9951 | .9979 | .0992 | .9966 | 10.078 | .0034 | 20 | 1.4719 |
| 0.1018 | 50 | .1016 | 9.0070 | .9948 | .9977 | .1022 | 9.0093 | 9.7882 | 0.9907 | 10 | 1.4690 |
| 0.1047 | 6° 00′ | .1045 | 9.0192 | .9945 | 9.9976 | .1051 | 9.0216 | 9.5144 | 0.9784 | 84° 00′ | 1.4661 |
| 0.1076 | 10 | .1074 | .0311 | .9942 | .9975 | .1080 | .0336 | 9.2553 | .9664 | 50 | 1.4632 |
| 0.1105 | 20 | .1103 | .0426 | .9939 | .9973 | .1110 | .0453 | 9.0098 | .9547 | 40 | 1.4603 |
| 0.1134 | 30 | .1132 | .0539 | .9936 | .9972 | .1139 | .0567 | 8.7769 | .9433 | 30 | 1.4574 |
| 0.1164 | 40 | .1161 | .0648 | .9932 | .9971 | .1169 | .0678 | 8.5555 | .9322 | 20 | 1.4544 |
| 0.1193 | 50 | .1190 | .0755 | .9929 | .9969 | .1198 | .0786 | 8.3450 | .9214 | 10 | 1.4515 |
| 0.1222 | 7° 00′ | .1219 | 9.0859 | .9925 | 9.9968 | .1228 | 9.0891 | 8.1443 | 0.9109 | 83° 00′ | 1.4486 |
| 0.1251 | 10 | .1248 | .0961 | .9922 | .9966 | .1257 | .0995 | 7.9530 | .9005 | 50 | 1.4457 |
| 0.1280 | 20 | .1276 | .1060 | .9918 | .9964 | .1287 | .1096 | 7.7704 | .8904 | 40 | 1.4428 |
| 0.1309 | 30 | .1305 | .1157 | .9914 | .9963 | .1317 | .1194 | 7.5958 | .8806 | 30 | 1.4399 |
| 0.1338 | 40 | .1334 | .1252 | .9911 | .9961 | .1346 | .1291 | 7.4287 | .8709 | 20 | 1.4370 |
| 0.1367 | 50 | .1363 | .1345 | .9907 | .9959 | .1376 | .1385 | 7.2687 | .8615 | 10 | 1.4341 |
| 0.1396 | 8° 00′ | .1392 | 9.1436 | .9903 | 9.9958 | .1405 | 9.1478 | 7.1154 | 0.8522 | 82° 00′ | 1.4312 |
| | | Nat. | Log. | Nat. | Log. | Nat. | Log. | Nat. | Log. | | |
| | | COS | | SIN | | CTN | | TAN | | DEGREES | RADIANS |

# 13. NATURAL AND LOGARITHMIC TRIGONOMETRIC FUNCTIONS

| RADIANS | DEGREES | SIN | | COS | | TAN | | CTN | | | |
|---|---|---|---|---|---|---|---|---|---|---|---|
| | | Nat. | Log. | Nat. | Log. | Nat. | Log. | Nat. | Log. | | |
| 0.1396 | 8° 00′ | .1392 | 9.1436 | .9903 | 9.9958 | .1405 | 9.1478 | 7.1154 | 0.8522 | 82° 00′ | 1.4312 |
| 0.1425 | 10 | .1421 | .1525 | .9899 | .9956 | .1435 | .1569 | 6.9682 | .8431 | 50 | 1.4283 |
| 0.1454 | 20 | .1449 | .1612 | .9894 | .9954 | .1465 | .1658 | 6.8269 | .8342 | 40 | 1.4254 |
| 0.1484 | 30 | .1478 | .1697 | .9890 | .9952 | .1495 | .1745 | 6.6912 | .8255 | 30 | 1.4224 |
| 0.1513 | 40 | .1507 | .1781 | .9886 | .9950 | .1524 | .1831 | 6.5606 | .8169 | 20 | 1.4195 |
| 0.1542 | 50 | .1536 | .1863 | .9881 | .9948 | .1554 | .1915 | 6.4348 | .8085 | 10 | 1.4166 |
| 0.1571 | 9° 00′ | .1564 | 9.1943 | .9877 | 9.9946 | .1584 | 9.1997 | 6.3138 | 0.8003 | 81° 00′ | 1.4137 |
| 0.1600 | 10 | .1593 | .2022 | .9872 | .9944 | .1614 | .2078 | 6.1970 | .7922 | 50 | 1.4108 |
| 0.1629 | 20 | .1622 | .2100 | .9868 | .9942 | .1644 | .2158 | 6.0844 | .7842 | 40 | 1.4079 |
| 0.1658 | 30 | .1650 | .2176 | .9863 | .9940 | .1673 | .2236 | 5.9758 | .7764 | 30 | 1.4050 |
| 0.1687 | 40 | .1679 | .2251 | .9858 | .9938 | .1703 | .2313 | 5.8708 | .7687 | 20 | 1.4021 |
| 0.1716 | 50 | .1708 | .2324 | .9853 | .9936 | .1733 | .2389 | 5.7694 | .7611 | 10 | 1.3992 |
| 0.1745 | 10° 00′ | .1736 | 9.2397 | .9848 | 9.9934 | .1763 | 9.2463 | 5.6713 | 0.7537 | 80° 00′ | 1.3963 |
| 0.1774 | 10 | .1765 | .2468 | .9843 | .9931 | .1793 | .2536 | 5.5764 | .7464 | 50 | 1.3934 |
| 0.1804 | 20 | .1794 | .2538 | .9838 | .9929 | .1823 | .2609 | 5.4845 | .7391 | 40 | 1.3904 |
| 0.1833 | 30 | .1822 | .2606 | .9833 | .9927 | .1853 | .2680 | 5.3955 | .7320 | 30 | 1.3875 |
| 0.1862 | 40 | .1851 | .2674 | .9827 | .9924 | .1883 | .2750 | 5.3093 | .7250 | 20 | 1.3846 |
| 0.1891 | 50 | .1880 | .2740 | .9822 | .9922 | .1914 | .2819 | 5.2257 | .7181 | 10 | 1.3817 |
| 0.1920 | 11° 00′ | .1908 | 9.2806 | .9816 | 9.9919 | .1944 | 9.2887 | 5.1446 | 0.7113 | 79° 00′ | 1.3783 |
| 0.1949 | 10 | .1937 | .2870 | .9811 | .9917 | .1974 | .2953 | 5.0658 | .7047 | 50 | 1.3759 |
| 0.1978 | 20 | .1965 | .2934 | .9805 | .9914 | .2004 | .3020 | 4.9894 | .6980 | 40 | 1.3730 |
| 0.2007 | 30 | .1994 | .2997 | .9799 | .9912 | .2035 | .3085 | 4.9152 | .6915 | 30 | 1.3701 |
| 0.2036 | 40 | .2022 | .3058 | .9793 | .9909 | .2065 | .3149 | 4.8430 | .6851 | 20 | 1.3672 |
| 0.2065 | 50 | .2051 | .3119 | .9787 | .9907 | .2095 | .3212 | 4.7729 | .6788 | 10 | 1.3643 |
| 0.2094 | 12° 00′ | .2079 | 9.3179 | .9781 | 9.9904 | .2126 | 9.3275 | 4.7046 | 0.6725 | 78° 00′ | 1.3614 |
| 0.2123 | 10 | .2108 | .3238 | .9775 | .9901 | .2156 | .3336 | 4.6382 | .6664 | 50 | 1.3584 |
| 0.2153 | 20 | .2136 | .3296 | .9769 | .9899 | .2186 | .3397 | 4.5736 | .6603 | 40 | 1.3555 |
| 0.2182 | 30 | .2164 | .3353 | .9763 | .9896 | .2217 | .3458 | 4.5107 | .6542 | 30 | 1.3526 |
| 0.2211 | 40 | .2193 | .3410 | .9757 | .9893 | .2247 | .3517 | 4.4494 | .6483 | 20 | 1.3497 |
| 0.2240 | 50 | .2221 | .3466 | .9750 | .9890 | .2278 | .3576 | 4.3897 | .6424 | 10 | 1.3468 |
| 0.2269 | 13° 00′ | .2250 | 9.3521 | .9744 | 9.9887 | .2309 | 9.3634 | 4.3315 | 0.6366 | 77° 00′ | 1.3439 |
| 0.2298 | 10 | .2278 | .3575 | .9737 | .9884 | .2339 | .3691 | 4.2747 | .6309 | 50 | 1.3410 |
| 0.2327 | 20 | .2306 | .3629 | .9730 | .9881 | .2370 | .3748 | 4.2193 | .6252 | 40 | 1.3381 |
| 0.2356 | 30 | .2334 | .3682 | .9724 | .9878 | .2401 | .3804 | 4.1653 | .6196 | 30 | 1.3352 |
| 0.2385 | 40 | .2363 | .3734 | .9717 | .9875 | .2432 | .3859 | 4.1126 | .6141 | 20 | 1.3323 |
| 0.2414 | 50 | .2391 | .3786 | .9710 | .9872 | .2462 | .3914 | 4.0611 | .6086 | 10 | 1.3294 |
| 0.2443 | 14° 00′ | .2419 | 9.3837 | .9703 | 9.9869 | .2493 | 9.3968 | 4.0108 | 0.6032 | 76° 00′ | 1.3265 |
| 0.2473 | 10 | .2447 | .3887 | .9696 | .9866 | .2524 | .4021 | 3.9617 | .5979 | 50 | 1.3235 |
| 0.2502 | 20 | .2476 | .3937 | .9689 | .9863 | .2555 | .4074 | 3.9136 | .5926 | 40 | 1.3206 |
| 0.2531 | 30 | .2504 | .3986 | .9681 | .9859 | .2586 | .4127 | 3.8667 | .5873 | 30 | 1.3177 |
| 0.2560 | 40 | .2532 | .4035 | .9674 | .9856 | .2617 | .4178 | 3.8208 | .5822 | 20 | 1.3148 |
| 0.2589 | 50 | .2560 | .4083 | .9667 | .9853 | .2648 | .4230 | 3.7760 | .5770 | 10 | 1.3119 |
| 0.2618 | 15° 00′ | .2588 | 9.4130 | .9659 | 9.9849 | .2679 | 9.4281 | 3.7321 | 0.5719 | 75° 00′ | 1.3090 |
| 0.2647 | 10 | .2616 | .4177 | .9652 | .9846 | .2711 | .4331 | 3.6891 | .5669 | 50 | 1.3061 |
| 0.2676 | 20 | .2644 | .4223 | .9644 | .9843 | .2742 | .4381 | 3.6470 | .5619 | 40 | 1.3032 |
| 0.2705 | 30 | .2672 | .4269 | .9636 | .9839 | .2773 | .4430 | 3.6059 | .5570 | 30 | 1.3003 |
| 0.2734 | 40 | .2700 | .4314 | .9628 | .9836 | .2805 | .4479 | 3.5656 | .5521 | 20 | 1.2974 |
| 0.2763 | 50 | .2728 | .4359 | .9621 | .9832 | .2836 | .4527 | 3.5261 | .5473 | 10 | 1.2945 |
| 0.2793 | 16° 00′ | .2756 | 9.4403 | .9613 | 9.9828 | .2867 | 9.4575 | 3.4874 | 0.5425 | 74° 00′ | 1.2915 |
| | | Nat. | Log. | Nat. | Log. | Nat. | Log. | Nat. | Log. | | |
| | | COS | | SIN | | CTN | | TAN | | DEGREES | RADIANS |

## 13. NATURAL AND LOGARITHMIC TRIGONOMETRIC FUNCTIONS

| RADIANS | DEGREES | SIN Nat. | SIN Log. | COS Nat. | COS Log. | TAN Nat. | TAN Log. | CTN Nat. | CTN Log. | | |
|---|---|---|---|---|---|---|---|---|---|---|---|
| 0.2793 | 16° 00′ | .2756 | 9.4403 | .9613 | 9.9828 | .2867 | 9.4575 | 3.4874 | 0.5425 | 74° 00′ | 1.2915 |
| 0.2822 | 10 | .2784 | .4447 | .9605 | .9825 | .2899 | .4622 | 3.4495 | .5378 | 50 | 1.2886 |
| 0.2851 | 20 | .2812 | .4491 | .9596 | .9821 | .2931 | .4669 | 3.4124 | .5331 | 40 | 1.2857 |
| 0.2880 | 30 | .2840 | .4533 | .9588 | .9817 | .2962 | .4716 | 3.3759 | .5284 | 30 | 1.2828 |
| 0.2909 | 40 | .2868 | .4576 | .9580 | .9814 | .2994 | .4762 | 3.3402 | .5238 | 20 | 1.2799 |
| 0.2938 | 50 | .2896 | .4618 | .9572 | .9810 | .3026 | .4808 | 3.3052 | .5192 | 10 | 1.2770 |
| 0.2967 | 17° 00′ | .2924 | 9.4659 | .9563 | 9.9806 | .3057 | 9.4853 | 3.2709 | 0.5147 | 73° 00′ | 1.2741 |
| 0.2996 | 10 | .2952 | .4700 | .9555 | .9802 | .3089 | .4898 | 3.2371 | .5102 | 50 | 1.2712 |
| 0.3025 | 20 | .2979 | .4741 | .9546 | .9798 | .3121 | .4943 | 3.2041 | .5057 | 40 | 1.2683 |
| 0.3054 | 30 | .3007 | .4781 | .9537 | .9794 | .3153 | .4987 | 3.1716 | .5013 | 30 | 1.2654 |
| 0.3083 | 40 | .3035 | .4821 | .9528 | .9790 | .3185 | .5031 | 3.1397 | .4969 | 20 | 1.2625 |
| 0.3113 | 50 | .3062 | .4861 | .9520 | .9786 | .3217 | .5075 | 3.1084 | .4925 | 10 | 1.2595 |
| 0.3142 | 18° 00′ | .3090 | 9.4900 | .9511 | 9.9782 | .3249 | 9.5118 | 3.0777 | 0.4882 | 72° 00′ | 1.2566 |
| 0.3171 | 10 | .3118 | .4939 | .9502 | .9778 | .3281 | .5161 | 3.0475 | .4839 | 50 | 1.2537 |
| 0.3200 | 20 | .3145 | .4977 | .9492 | .9774 | .3314 | .5203 | 3.0178 | .4797 | 40 | 1.2508 |
| 0.3229 | 30 | .3173 | 5015 | .9483 | .9770 | .3346 | .5245 | 2.9887 | .4755 | 30 | 1.2479 |
| 0.3258 | 40 | .3201 | .5052 | .9474 | .9765 | .3378 | .5287 | 2.9600 | .4713 | 20 | 1.2450 |
| 0.3287 | 50 | .3228 | .5090 | .9465 | .9761 | .3411 | .5329 | 2.9319 | .4671 | 10 | 1.2421 |
| 0.3316 | 19° 00′ | .3256 | 9.5126 | .9455 | 9.9757 | .3443 | 9.5370 | 2.9042 | 0.4630 | 71° 00′ | 1.2392 |
| 0.3345 | 10 | .3283 | .5163 | .9446 | .9752 | .3476 | .5411 | 2.8770 | .4589 | 50 | 1.2363 |
| 0.3374 | 20 | .3311 | .5199 | .9436 | .9748 | .3508 | .5451 | 2.8502 | .4549 | 40 | 1.2334 |
| 0.3403 | 30 | .3338 | .5235 | .9426 | .9743 | .3541 | .5491 | 2.8239 | .4509 | 30 | 1.2305 |
| 0.3432 | 40 | .3365 | .5270 | .9417 | .9739 | .3574 | .5531 | 2.7980 | .4469 | 20 | 1.2275 |
| 0.3462 | 50 | .3393 | .5306 | .9407 | .9734 | .3607 | .5571 | 2.7725 | .4429 | 10 | 1.2246 |
| 0.3491 | 20° 00′ | .3420 | 9.5341 | .9397 | 9.9730 | .3640 | 9.5611 | 2.7475 | 0.4389 | 70° 00′ | 1.2217 |
| 0.3520 | 10 | .3448 | .5375 | .9387 | .9725 | .3673 | .5650 | 2.7228 | .4350 | 50 | 1.2188 |
| 0.3549 | 20 | .3475 | .5409 | .9377 | .9721 | .3706 | .5689 | 2.6985 | .4311 | 40 | 1.2159 |
| 0.3578 | 30 | .3502 | .5443 | .9367 | .9716 | .3739 | .5727 | 2.6746 | .4273 | 30 | 1.2130 |
| 0.3607 | 40 | .3529 | .5477 | .9356 | .9711 | .3772 | .5766 | 2.6511 | .4234 | 20 | 1.2101 |
| 0.3636 | 50 | .3557 | .5510 | .9346 | .9706 | .3805 | .5804 | 2.6279 | .4196 | 10 | 1.2072 |
| 0.3665 | 21° 00′ | .3584 | 9.5543 | .9336 | 9.9702 | .3839 | 9.5842 | 2.6051 | 0.4158 | 69° 00′ | 1.2043 |
| 0.3694 | 10 | .3611 | .5576 | .9325 | .9697 | .3872 | .5879 | 2.5826 | .4121 | 50 | 1.2014 |
| 0.3723 | 20 | .3638 | .5609 | .9315 | .9692 | .3906 | .5917 | 2.5605 | .4083 | 40 | 1.1985 |
| 0.3752 | 30 | .3665 | .5641 | .9304 | .9687 | .3939 | .5954 | 2.5386 | .4046 | 30 | 1.1956 |
| 0.3782 | 40 | .3692 | .5673 | .9293 | .9682 | .3973 | .5991 | 2.5172 | .4009 | 20 | 1.1926 |
| 0.3811 | 50 | .3719 | .5704 | .9283 | .9677 | .4006 | .6028 | 2.4960 | .3972 | 10 | 1.1897 |
| 0.3840 | 22° 00′ | .3746 | 9.5736 | .9272 | 9.9672 | .4040 | 9.6064 | 2.4751 | 0.3936 | 68° 00′ | 1.1868 |
| 0.3869 | 10 | .3773 | .5767 | .9261 | .9667 | .4074 | .6100 | 2.4545 | .3900 | 50 | 1.1839 |
| 0.3898 | 20 | .3800 | .5798 | .9250 | .9661 | .4108 | .6136 | 2.4342 | .3864 | 40 | 1.1810 |
| 0.3927 | 30 | .3827 | .5828 | .9239 | .9656 | .4142 | .6172 | 2.4142 | .3828 | 30 | 1.1781 |
| 0.3956 | 40 | .3854 | .5859 | .9228 | .9651 | .4176 | .6208 | 2.3945 | .3792 | 20 | 1.1752 |
| 0.3985 | 50 | .3881 | .5889 | .9216 | .9646 | .4210 | .6243 | 2.3750 | .3757 | 10 | 1.1723 |
| 0.4014 | 23° 00′ | .3907 | 9.5919 | .9205 | 9.9640 | .4245 | 9.6279 | 2.3559 | 0.3721 | 67° 00′ | 1.1694 |
| 0.4043 | 10 | .3934 | .5948 | .9194 | .9635 | .4279 | .6314 | 2.3369 | .3686 | 50 | 1.1665 |
| 0.4072 | 20 | .3961 | .5978 | .9182 | .9629 | .4314 | .6348 | 2.3183 | .3652 | 40 | 1.1636 |
| 0.4102 | 30 | .3987 | .6007 | .9171 | .9624 | .4348 | .6383 | 2.2998 | .3617 | 30 | 1.1606 |
| 0.4131 | 40 | .4014 | .6036 | .9159 | .9618 | .4383 | .6417 | 2.2817 | .3583 | 20 | 1.1577 |
| 0.4160 | 50 | .4041 | .6065 | .9147 | .9613 | .4417 | .6452 | 2.2637 | .3548 | 10 | 1.1548 |
| 0.4189 | 24° 00′ | .4067 | 9.6093 | .9135 | 9.9607 | .4452 | 9.6486 | 2.2460 | 0.3514 | 66° 00′ | 1.1519 |
| | | Nat. | Log. | Nat. | Log. | Nat. | Log. | Nat. | Log. | | |
| | | COS | | SIN | | CTN | | TAN | | DEGREES | RADIANS |

## 13. NATURAL AND LOGARITHMIC TRIGONOMETRIC FUNCTIONS

| RADIANS | DEGREES | SIN | | COS | | TAN | | CTN | | | |
|---|---|---|---|---|---|---|---|---|---|---|---|
| | | Nat. | Log. | Nat. | Log. | Nat. | Log. | Nat. | Log. | | |
| 0.4189 | 24° 00′ | .4067 | 9.6093 | .9135 | 9.9607 | .4452 | 9.6486 | 2.2460 | 0.3514 | 66° 00′ | 1.1519 |
| 0.4218 | 10 | .4094 | .6121 | .9124 | .9602 | .4487 | .6520 | 2.2286 | .3480 | 50 | 1.1490 |
| 0.4247 | 20 | .4120 | .6149 | .9112 | .9596 | .4522 | .6553 | 2.2113 | .3447 | 40 | 1.1461 |
| 0.4276 | 30 | .4147 | .6177 | .9100 | .9590 | .4557 | .6587 | 2.1943 | .3413 | 30 | 1.1432 |
| 0.4305 | 40 | .4173 | .6205 | .9088 | .9584 | .4592 | .6620 | 2.1775 | .3380 | 20 | 1.1403 |
| 0.4334 | 50 | .4200 | .6232 | .9075 | .9579 | .4628 | .6654 | 2.1609 | .3346 | 10 | 1.1374 |
| 0.4363 | 25° 00′ | .4226 | 9.6259 | .9063 | 9.9573 | .4663 | 9.6687 | 2.1445 | 0.3313 | 65° 00′ | 1.1345 |
| 0.4392 | 10 | .4253 | .6286 | .9051 | .9567 | .4699 | .6720 | 2.1283 | .3280 | 50 | 1.1316 |
| 0.4422 | 20 | .4279 | .6313 | .9038 | .9561 | .4734 | .6752 | 2.1123 | .3248 | 40 | 1.1286 |
| 0.4451 | 30 | .4305 | .6340 | .9026 | .9555 | .4770 | .6785 | 2.0965 | .3215 | 30 | 1.1257 |
| 0.4480 | 40 | .4331 | .6366 | .9013 | .9549 | .4806 | .6817 | 2.0809 | .3183 | 20 | 1.1228 |
| 0.4509 | 50 | .4358 | .6392 | .9001 | .9543 | .4841 | .6850 | 2.0655 | .3150 | 10 | 1.1199 |
| 0.4538 | 26° 00′ | .4384 | 9.6418 | .8988 | 9.9537 | .4877 | 9.6882 | 2.0503 | 0.3118 | 64° 00′ | 1.1170 |
| 0.4567 | 10 | .4410 | .6444 | .8975 | .9530 | .4913 | .6914 | 2.0353 | .3086 | 50 | 1.1141 |
| 0.4596 | 20 | .4436 | .6470 | .8962 | .9524 | .4950 | .6946 | 2.0204 | .3054 | 40 | 1.1112 |
| 0.4625 | 30 | .4462 | .6495 | .8949 | .9518 | .4986 | .6977 | 2.0057 | .3023 | 30 | 1.1083 |
| 0.4654 | 40 | .4488 | .6521 | .8936 | .9512 | .5022 | .7009 | 1.9912 | .2991 | 20 | 1.1054 |
| 0.4683 | 50 | .4514 | .6546 | .8923 | .9505 | .5059 | .7040 | 1.9768 | .2960 | 10 | 1.1025 |
| 0.4712 | 27° 00′ | .4540 | 9.6570 | .8910 | 9.9499 | .5095 | 9.7072 | 1.9626 | 0.2928 | 63° 00′ | 1.0996 |
| 0.4741 | 10 | .4566 | .6595 | .8897 | .9492 | .5132 | .7103 | 1.9486 | .2897 | 50 | 1.0966 |
| 0.4771 | 20 | .4592 | .6620 | .8884 | .9486 | .5169 | .7134 | 1.9347 | .2866 | 40 | 1.0937 |
| 0.4800 | 30 | .4617 | .6644 | .8870 | .9479 | .5206 | .7165 | 1.9210 | .2835 | 30 | 1.0908 |
| 0.4829 | 40 | .4643 | .6668 | .8857 | .9473 | .5243 | .7196 | 1.9074 | .2804 | 20 | 1.0879 |
| 0.4858 | 50 | .4669 | .6692 | .8843 | .9466 | .5280 | .7226 | 1.8940 | .2774 | 10 | 1.0850 |
| 0.4887 | 28° 00′ | .4695 | 9.6716 | .8829 | 9.9459 | .5317 | 9.7257 | 1.8807 | 0.2743 | 62° 00′ | 1.0821 |
| 0.4916 | 10 | .4720 | .6740 | .8816 | .9453 | .5354 | .7287 | 1.8676 | .2713 | 50 | 1.0792 |
| 0.4945 | 20 | .4746 | .6763 | .8802 | .9446 | .5392 | .7317 | 1.8546 | .2683 | 40 | 1.0763 |
| 0.4974 | 30 | .4772 | .6787 | .8788 | .9439 | .5430 | .7348 | 1.8418 | .2652 | 30 | 1.0734 |
| 0.5003 | 40 | .4797 | .6810 | .8774 | .9432 | .5467 | .7378 | 1.8291 | .2622 | 20 | 1.0705 |
| 0.5032 | 50 | .4823 | .6833 | .8760 | .9425 | .5505 | .7408 | 1.8165 | .2592 | 10 | 1.0676 |
| 0.5061 | 29° 00′ | .4848 | 9.6856 | .8746 | 9.9418 | .5543 | 9.7438 | 1.8040 | 0.2562 | 61° 00′ | 1.0647 |
| 0.5091 | 10 | .4874 | .6878 | .8732 | .9411 | .5581 | .7467 | 1.7917 | .2533 | 50 | 1.0617 |
| 0.5120 | 20 | .4899 | .6901 | .8718 | .9404 | .5619 | .7497 | 1.7796 | .2503 | 40 | 1.0588 |
| 0.5149 | 30 | .4924 | .6923 | .8704 | .9397 | .5658 | .7526 | 1.7675 | .2474 | 30 | 1.0559 |
| 0.5178 | 40 | .4950 | .6946 | .8689 | .9390 | .5696 | .7556 | 1.7556 | .2444 | 20 | 1.0530 |
| 0.5207 | 50 | .4975 | .6968 | .8675 | .9383 | .5735 | .7585 | 1.7437 | .2415 | 10 | 1.0501 |
| 0.5236 | 30° 00′ | .5000 | 9.6990 | .8660 | 9.9375 | .5774 | 9.7614 | 1.7321 | 0.2386 | 60° 00′ | 1.0472 |
| 0.5265 | 10 | .5025 | .7012 | .8646 | .9368 | .5812 | .7644 | 1.7205 | .2356 | 50 | 1.0443 |
| 0.5294 | 20 | .5050 | .7033 | .8631 | .9361 | .5851 | .7673 | 1.7090 | .2327 | 40 | 1.0414 |
| 0.5323 | 30 | .5075 | .7055 | .8616 | .9353 | .5890 | .7701 | 1.6977 | .2299 | 30 | 1.0385 |
| 0.5352 | 40 | .5100 | .7076 | .8601 | .9346 | .5930 | .7730 | 1.6864 | .2270 | 20 | 1.0356 |
| 0.5381 | 50 | .5125 | .7097 | .8587 | .9338 | .5969 | .7759 | 1.6753 | .2241 | 10 | 1.0327 |
| 0.5411 | 31° 00′ | .5150 | 9.7118 | .8572 | 9.9331 | .6009 | 9.7788 | 1.6643 | 0.2212 | 59° 00′ | 1.0297 |
| 0.5440 | 10 | .5175 | .7139 | .8557 | .9323 | .6048 | .7816 | 1.6534 | .2184 | 50 | 1.0268 |
| 0.5469 | 20 | .5200 | .7160 | .8542 | .9315 | .6088 | .7845 | 1.6426 | .2155 | 40 | 1.0239 |
| 0.5498 | 30 | .5225 | .7181 | .8526 | .9308 | .6128 | .7873 | 1.6319 | .2127 | 30 | 1.0210 |
| 0.5527 | 40 | .5250 | .7201 | .8511 | .9300 | .6168 | .7902 | 1.6212 | .2098 | 20 | 1.0181 |
| 0.5556 | 50 | .5275 | .7222 | .8496 | .9292 | .6208 | .7930 | 1.6107 | .2070 | 10 | 1.0152 |
| 0.5585 | 32° 00′ | .5299 | 9.7242 | .8480 | 9.9284 | .6249 | 9.7958 | 1.6003 | 0.2042 | 58° 00′ | 1.0123 |
| | | Nat. | Log. | Nat. | Log. | Nat. | Log. | Nat. | Log. | | |
| | | COS | | SIN | | CTN | | TAN | | DEGREES | RADIANS |

## 13. NATURAL AND LOGARITHMIC TRIGONOMETRIC FUNCTIONS

| RADIANS | DEGREES | SIN | | COS | | TAN | | CTN | | | |
|---|---|---|---|---|---|---|---|---|---|---|---|
| | | Nat. | Log. | Nat. | Log. | Nat. | Log. | Nat. | Log. | | |
| 0.5585 | 32° 00′ | .5299 | 9.7242 | .8480 | 9.9284 | .6249 | 9.7958 | 1.6003 | 0.2042 | 58° 00′ | 1.0123 |
| 0.5614 | 10 | .5324 | .7262 | .8465 | .9276 | .6289 | .7986 | 1.5900 | .2014 | 50 | 1.0094 |
| 0.5643 | 20 | .5348 | .7282 | .8450 | .9268 | .6330 | .8014 | 1.5798 | .1986 | 40 | 1.0065 |
| 0.5672 | 30 | .5373 | .7302 | .8434 | .9260 | .6371 | .8042 | 1.5697 | .1958 | 30 | 1.0036 |
| 0.5701 | 40 | .5398 | .7322 | .8418 | .9252 | .6412 | .8070 | 1.5597 | .1930 | 20 | 1.0007 |
| 0.5730 | 50 | .5422 | .7342 | .8403 | .9244 | .6453 | .8097 | 1.5497 | .1903 | 10 | 0.9977 |
| 0.5760 | 33° 00′ | .5446 | 9.7361 | .8387 | 9.9236 | .6494 | 9.8125 | 1.5399 | 0.1875 | 57° 00′ | 0.9948 |
| 0.5789 | 10 | .5471 | .7380 | .8371 | .9228 | .6536 | .8153 | 1.5301 | .1847 | 50 | 0.9919 |
| 0.5818 | 20 | .5495 | .7400 | .8355 | .9219 | .6577 | .8180 | 1.5204 | .1820 | 40 | 0.9890 |
| 0.5847 | 30 | .5519 | .7419 | .8339 | .9211 | .6619 | .8208 | 1.5108 | .1792 | 30 | 0.9861 |
| 0.5876 | 40 | .5544 | .7438 | .8323 | .9203 | .6661 | .8235 | 1.5013 | .1765 | 20 | 0.9832 |
| 0.5905 | 50 | .5568 | .7457 | .8307 | .9194 | .6703 | .8263 | 1.4919 | .1737 | 10 | 0.9803 |
| 0.5934 | 34° 00′ | .5592 | 9.7476 | .8290 | 9.9186 | .6745 | 9.8290 | 1.4826 | 0.1710 | 56° 00′ | 0.9774 |
| 0.5963 | 10 | .5616 | .7494 | .8274 | .9177 | .6787 | .8317 | 1.4733 | .1683 | 50 | 0.9745 |
| 0.5992 | 20 | .5640 | .7513 | .8258 | .9169 | .6830 | .8344 | 1.4641 | .1656 | 40 | 0.9716 |
| 0.6021 | 30 | .5664 | .7531 | .8241 | .9160 | .6873 | .8371 | 1.4550 | .1629 | 30 | 0.9687 |
| 0.6050 | 40 | .5688 | .7550 | .8225 | .9151 | .6916 | .8398 | 1.4460 | .1602 | 20 | 0.9657 |
| 0.6080 | 50 | .5712 | .7568 | .8208 | .9142 | .6959 | .8425 | 1.4370 | .1575 | 10 | 0.9628 |
| 0.6109 | 35° 00′ | .5736 | 9.7586 | .8192 | 9.9134 | .7002 | 9.8452 | 1.4281 | 0.1548 | 55° 00′ | 0.9599 |
| 0.6138 | 10 | .5760 | .7604 | .8175 | .9125 | .7046 | .8479 | 1.4193 | .1521 | 50 | 0.9570 |
| 0.6167 | 20 | .5783 | .7622 | .8158 | .9116 | .7089 | .8506 | 1.4106 | .1494 | 40 | 0.9541 |
| 0.6196 | 30 | .5807 | .7640 | .8141 | .9107 | .7133 | .8533 | 1.4019 | .1467 | 30 | 0.9512 |
| 0.6225 | 40 | .5831 | .7657 | .8124 | .9098 | .7177 | .8559 | 1.3934 | .1441 | 20 | 0.9483 |
| 0.6254 | 50 | .5854 | .7675 | .8107 | .9089 | .7221 | .8586 | 1.3848 | .1414 | 10 | 0.9454 |
| 0.6283 | 36° 00′ | .5878 | 9.7692 | .8090 | 9.9080 | .7265 | 9.8613 | 1.3764 | 0.1387 | 54° 00′ | 0.9425 |
| 0.6312 | 10 | .5901 | .7710 | .8073 | .9070 | .7310 | .8639 | 1.3680 | .1361 | 50 | 0.9396 |
| 0.6341 | 20 | .5925 | .7727 | .8056 | .9061 | .7355 | .8666 | 1.3597 | .1334 | 40 | 0.9367 |
| 0.6370 | 30 | .5948 | .7744 | .8039 | .9052 | .7400 | .8692 | 1.3514 | .1308 | 30 | 0.9338 |
| 0.6400 | 40 | .5972 | .7761 | .8021 | .9042 | .7445 | .8718 | 1.3432 | .1282 | 20 | 0.9308 |
| 0.6429 | 50 | .5995 | .7778 | .8004 | .9033 | .7490 | .8745 | 1.3351 | .1255 | 10 | p.9279 |
| 0.6458 | 37° 00′ | .6018 | 9.7795 | .7986 | 9.9023 | .7536 | 9.8771 | 1.3270 | 0.1229 | 53° 00′ | 0.9250 |
| 0.6487 | 10 | .6041 | .7811 | .7969 | .9014 | .7581 | .8797 | 1.3190 | .1203 | 50 | 0.9221 |
| 0.6516 | 20 | .6065 | .7828 | .7951 | .9004 | .7627 | .8824 | 1.3111 | .1176 | 40 | 0.9192 |
| 0.6545 | 30 | .6088 | .7844 | .7934 | .8995 | .7673 | .8850 | 1.3032 | .1150 | 30 | 0.9163 |
| 0.6574 | 40 | .6111 | .7861 | .7916 | .8985 | .7720 | .8876 | 1.2954 | .1124 | 20 | 0.9134 |
| 0.6603 | 50 | .6134 | .7877 | .7898 | .8975 | .7766 | .8902 | 1.2876 | .1098 | 10 | 0.9105 |
| 0.6632 | 38° 00′ | .6157 | 9.7893 | .7880 | 9.8965 | .7813 | 9.8928 | 1.2799 | 0.1072 | 52° 00′ | 0.9076 |
| 0.6661 | 10 | .6180 | .7910 | .7862 | .8955 | .7860 | .8954 | 1.2723 | .1046 | 50 | 0.9047 |
| 0.6690 | 20 | .6202 | .7926 | .7844 | .8945 | .7907 | .8980 | 1.2647 | .1020 | 40 | 0.9018 |
| 0.6720 | 30 | .6225 | .7941 | .7826 | .8935 | .7954 | .9006 | 1.2572 | .0994 | 30 | 0.8988 |
| 0.6749 | 40 | .6248 | .7957 | .7808 | .8925 | .8002 | .9032 | 1.2497 | .0968 | 20 | 0.8959 |
| 0.6778 | 50 | .6271 | .7973 | .7790 | .8915 | .8050 | .9058 | 1.2423 | .0942 | 10 | 0.8930 |
| 0.6807 | 39° 00′ | .6293 | 9.7989 | .7771 | 9.8905 | .8098 | 9.9084 | 1.2349 | 0.0916 | 51° 00′ | 0.8901 |
| 0.6836 | 10 | .6316 | .8004 | .7753 | .8895 | .8146 | .9110 | 1.2276 | .0890 | 50 | 0.8872 |
| 0.6865 | 20 | .6338 | .8020 | .7735 | .8884 | .8195 | .9135 | 1.2203 | .0865 | 40 | 0.8843 |
| 0.6894 | 30 | .6361 | .8035 | .7716 | .8874 | .8243 | .9161 | 1.2131 | .0839 | 30 | 0.8814 |
| 0.6923 | 40 | .6383 | .8050 | .7698 | .8864 | .8292 | .9187 | 1.2059 | .0813 | 20 | 0.8785 |
| 0.6952 | 50 | .6406 | .8066 | .7679 | .8853 | .8342 | .9212 | 1.1988 | .0788 | 10 | 0.8756 |
| 0.6981 | 40° 00′ | .6428 | 9.8081 | .7660 | 9.8843 | .8391 | 9.9238 | 1.1918 | 0.0762 | 50° 00′ | 0.8727 |
| | | Nat. | Log. | Nat. | Log. | Nat. | Log. | Nat. | Log. | | |

| | | COS | | SIN | | CTN | | TAN | | DEGREES | RADIANS |
|---|---|---|---|---|---|---|---|---|---|---|---|

# 13. NATURAL AND LOGARITHMIC TRIGONOMETRIC FUNCTIONS

| RADIANS | DEGREES | SIN Nat. | Log. | COS Nat. | Log. | TAN Nat. | Log. | CTN Nat. | Log. | | |
|---|---|---|---|---|---|---|---|---|---|---|---|
| 0.6981 | 40° 00′ | .6428 | 9.8081 | .7660 | 9.8843 | .8391 | 9.9238 | 1.1918 | 0.0762 | 50° 00′ | 0.8727 |
| 0.7010 | 10 | .6450 | .8096 | .7642 | .8832 | .8441 | .9264 | 1.1847 | .0736 | 50 | 0.8698 |
| 0.7039 | 20 | .6472 | .8111 | .7623 | .8821 | .8491 | .9289 | 1.1778 | .0711 | 40 | 0.8668 |
| 0.7069 | 30 | .6494 | .8125 | .7604 | .8810 | .8541 | .9315 | 1.1708 | .0685 | 30 | 0.8639 |
| 0.7098 | 40 | .6517 | .8140 | .7585 | .8800 | .8591 | .9341 | 1.1640 | .0659 | 20 | 0.8610 |
| 0.7127 | 50 | .6539 | .8155 | .7566 | .8789 | .8642 | .9366 | 1.1571 | .0634 | 10 | 0.8581 |
| 0.7156 | 41° 00′ | .6561 | 9.8169 | .7547 | 9.8778 | .8693 | 9.9392 | 1.1504 | 0.0608 | 49° 00′ | 0.8552 |
| 0.7185 | 10 | .6583 | .8184 | .7528 | .8767 | .8744 | .9417 | 1.1436 | .0583 | 50 | 0.8523 |
| 0.7214 | 20 | .6604 | .8198 | .7509 | .8756 | .8796 | .9443 | 1.1369 | .0557 | 40 | 0.8494 |
| 0.7243 | 30 | .6626 | .8213 | .7490 | .8745 | .8847 | .9468 | 1.1303 | .0532 | 30 | 0.8465 |
| 0.7272 | 40 | .6648 | .8227 | .7470 | .8733 | .8899 | .9494 | 1.1237 | .0506 | 20 | 0.8436 |
| 0.7301 | 50 | .6670 | .8241 | .7451 | .8722 | .8952 | .9519 | 1.1171 | .0481 | 10 | 0.8407 |
| 0.7330 | 42° 00′ | .6691 | 9.8255 | .7431 | 9.8711 | .9004 | 9.9544 | 1.1106 | 0.0456 | 48° 00′ | 0.8378 |
| 0.7359 | 10 | .6713 | .8269 | .7412 | .8699 | .9057 | .9570 | 1.1041 | .0430 | 50 | 0.8348 |
| 0.7389 | 20 | .6734 | .8283 | .7392 | .8688 | .9110 | .9595 | 1.0977 | .0405 | 40 | 0.8319 |
| 0.7418 | 30 | .6756 | .8297 | .7373 | .8676 | .9163 | .9621 | 1.0913 | .0379 | 30 | 0.8290 |
| 0.7447 | 40 | .6777 | .8311 | .7353 | .8665 | .9217 | .9646 | 1.0850 | .0354 | 20 | 0.8261 |
| 0.7476 | 50 | .6799 | .8324 | .7333 | .8653 | .9271 | .9671 | 1.0786 | .0329 | 10 | 0.8232 |
| 0.7505 | 43° 00′ | .6820 | 9.8338 | .7314 | 9.8641 | .9325 | 9.9697 | 1.0724 | 0.0303 | 47° 00′ | 0.8203 |
| 0.7534 | 10 | .6841 | .8351 | .7294 | .8629 | .9380 | .9722 | 1.0661 | .0278 | 50 | 0.8174 |
| 0.7563 | 20 | .6862 | .8365 | .7274 | .8618 | .9435 | .9747 | 1.0599 | .0253 | 40 | 0.8145 |
| 0.7592 | 30 | .6884 | .8378 | .7254 | .8606 | .9490 | .9772 | 1.0538 | .0228 | 30 | 0.8116 |
| 0.7621 | 40 | .6905 | .8391 | .7234 | .8594 | .9545 | .9798 | 1.0477 | .0202 | 20 | 0.8087 |
| 0.7650 | 50 | .6926 | .8405 | .7214 | .8582 | .9601 | .9823 | 1.0416 | .0177 | 10 | 0.8058 |
| 0.7679 | 44° 00′ | .6947 | 9.8418 | .7193 | 9.8569 | .9657 | 9.9848 | 1.0355 | 0.0152 | 46° 00′ | 0.8029 |
| 0.7709 | 10 | .6967 | .8431 | .7173 | .8557 | .9713 | .9874 | 1.0295 | .0126 | 50 | 0.7999 |
| 0.7738 | 20 | .6988 | .8444 | .7153 | .8545 | .9770 | .9899 | 1.0235 | .0101 | 40 | 0.7970 |
| 0.7767 | 30 | .7009 | .8457 | .7133 | .8532 | .9827 | .9924 | 1.0176 | .0076 | 30 | 0.7941 |
| 0.7796 | 40 | .7030 | .8469 | .7112 | .8520 | .9884 | .9949 | 1.0117 | .0051 | 20 | 0.7912 |
| 0.7825 | 50 | .7050 | .8482 | .7092 | .8507 | .9942 | .9975 | 1.0058 | .0025 | 10 | 0.7883 |
| 0.7854 | 45° 00′ | .7071 | 9.8495 | .7071 | 9.8495 | 1.0000 | 0.0000 | 1.0000 | 0.0000 | 45° 00′ | 0.7854 |
| | | Nat. | Log. | Nat. | Log. | Nat. | Log. | Nat. | Log. | | |
| | | COS | | SIN | | CTN | | TAN | | DEGREES | RADIANS |

## 14. EQUIVALENTS OF RADIANS iN DEGREES, MINUTES, SECONDS

| RADIANS | DEGREES | | RADIANS | DEGREES |
|---|---|---|---|---|
| 0.0001 | 0° 0′ 20″.6 or 0°.005730 | | 0.0600 | 3° 26′ 15″.9 or 3°.437747 |
| 0.0002 | 0° 0′ 41″.3 or 0°.011459 | | 0.0700 | 4° 0′ 38″.5 or 4°.010705 |
| 0.0003 | 0° 1′ 01″.9 or 0°.017189 | | 0.0800 | 4° 35′ 01″.2 or 4°.583662 |
| 0.0004 | 0° 1′ 22″.5 or 0°.022918 | | 0.0900 | 5° 9′ 23″.8 or 5°.156620 |
| 0.0005 | 0° 1′ 43″.1 or 0°.028648 | | 0.1000 | 5° 43′ 46″.5 or 5°.729578 |
| 0.0006 | 0° 2′ 03″.8 or 0°.034377 | | 0.2000 | 11° 27′ 33″.0 or 11°.459156 |
| 0.0007 | 0° 2′ 24″.4 or 0°.040107 | | 0.3000 | 17° 11′ 19″.4 or 17°.188734 |
| 0.0008 | 0° 2′ 45″.0 or 0°.045837 | | 0.4000 | 22° 55′ 05″.9 or 22°.918312 |
| 0.0009 | 0° 3′ 05″.6 or 0°.051566 | | 0.5000 | 28° 38′ 52″.4 or 28°.647890 |
| 0.0010 | 0° 3′ 26″.3 or 0°.057296 | | 0.6000 | 34° 22′ 38″.9 or 34°.377468 |
| 0.0020 | 0° 6′ 52″.5 or 0°.114592 | | 0.7000 | 40° 6′ 25″.4 or 40°.107046 |
| 0.0030 | 0° 10′ 18″.8 or 0°.171887 | | 0.8000 | 45° 50′ 11″.8 or 45°.836624 |
| 0.0040 | 0° 13′ 45″.1 or 0°.229183 | | 0.9000 | 51° 33′ 58″.3 or 51°.566202 |
| 0.0050 | 0° 17′ 11″.3 or 0°.286479 | | 1.0000 | 57° 17′ 44″.8 or 57°.295780 |
| 0.0060 | 0° 20′ 37″.6 or 0°.343775 | | 2.0000 | 114° 35′ 29″.6 or 114°.591559 |
| 0.0070 | 0° 24′ 03″.9 or 0°.401070 | | 3.0000 | 171° 53′ 14″.4 or 171°.887339 |
| 0.0080 | 0° 27′ 30″.1 or 0°.458366 | | 4.0000 | 229° 10′ 59″.2 or 229°.183118 |
| 0.0090 | 0° 30′ 56″.4 or 0°.515662 | | 5.0000 | 286° 28′ 44″.0 or 286°.478898 |
| 0.0100 | 0° 34′ 22″.6 or 0°.572958 | | 6.0000 | 343° 46′ 28″.8 or 343°.774677 |
| 0.0200 | 1° 8′ 45″.3 or 1°.145916 | | 7.0000 | 401° 4′ 13″.6 or 401°.070457 |
| 0.0300 | 1° 43′ 07″.9 or 1°.718873 | | 8.0000 | 458° 21′ 58″.4 or 458°.366236 |
| 0.0400 | 2° 17′ 30″.6 or 2°.291831 | | 9.0000 | 515° 39′ 43″.3 or 515°.662016 |
| 0.0500 | 2° 51′ 53″.2 or 2°.864789 | | 10.0000 | 572° 57′ 28″.1 or 572°.957795 |

## 15. EQUIVALENTS OF DEGREES AND MINUTES IN RADIANS

| | | | | | | | | | |
|---|---|---|---|---|---|---|---|---|---|
| 1′ | 0.0003 | 9′ | 0.0026 | 3° | 0.0524 | 20° | 0.3491 | 100° | 1.7453 |
| 2′ | 0.0006 | 10′ | 0.0029 | 4° | 0.0698 | 30° | 0.5236 | 110° | 1.9199 |
| 3′ | 0.0009 | 20′ | 0.0058 | 5° | 0.0873 | 40° | 0.6981 | 120° | 2.0944 |
| 4′ | 0.0012 | 30′ | 0.0087 | 6° | 0.1047 | 50° | 0.8727 | 130° | 2.2689 |
| 5′ | 0.0015 | 40′ | 0.0116 | 7° | 0.1222 | 60° | 1.0472 | 140° | 2.4435 |
| 6′ | 0.0017 | 50′ | 0.0145 | 8° | 0.1396 | 70° | 1.2217 | 150° | 2.6180 |
| 7′ | 0.0020 | 1° | 0.0175 | 9° | 0.1571 | 80° | 1.3963 | 160° | 2.7925 |
| 8′ | 0.0023 | 2° | 0.0349 | 10° | 0.1745 | 90° | 1.5708 | 170° | 2.9671 |

## 16. SQUARES, CUBES, ROOTS, RECIPROCALS

| N | N² | √N | √10N | N³ | ∛N | ∛10N | ∛100N | 1/N | N |
|---|---|---|---|---|---|---|---|---|---|
| **1.00** | 1 .0000 | 1.0 0000 | 3.1 6228 | 1.00 000 | 1.0 0000 | 2.1 5443 | 4.6 4159 | 1.0 0000 | **1.00** |
| 1.01 | .0201 | 0499 | 7805 | 1.03 030 | 0332 | 6159 | 5701 | .99 0099 | 1.01 |
| 1.02 | .0404 | 0995 | 3.1 9374 | 1.06 121 | 0662 | 6870 | 7233 | .98 0392 | 1.02 |
| 1.03 | .0609 | 1489 | 3.2 0936 | 1.09 273 | 0990 | 7577 | 4.6 8755 | .97 0874 | 1.03 |
| 1.04 | .0816 | 1980 | 2490 | 1.12 486 | 1316 | 8279 | 4.7 0267 | .96 1538 | 1.04 |
| 1.05 | .1025 | 2470 | 4037 | 1.15 762 | 1640 | 8976 | 1769 | .95 2381 | 1.05 |
| 1.06 | .1236 | 2956 | 5576 | 1.19 102 | 1961 | 2.1 9669 | 3262 | .94 3396 | 1.06 |
| 1.07 | .1449 | 3441 | 7109 | 1.22 504 | 2281 | 2.2 0358 | 4746 | .93 4579 | 1.07 |
| 1.08 | .1664 | 3923 | 3.2 8634 | 1.25 971 | 2599 | 1042 | 6220 | .92 5926 | 1.08 |
| 1.09 | .1881 | 4403 | 3.3 0151 | 1.29 503 | 2914 | 1722 | 7686 | .91 7431 | 1.09 |
| **1.10** | 1 .2100 | 1.0 4881 | 3.3 1662 | 1.33 100 | 1.0 3228 | 2.2 2398 | 4.7 9142 | .90 9091 | **1.10** |
| 1.11 | .2321 | 5357 | 3167 | 1.36 763 | 3540 | 3070 | 4.8 0590 | .90 0901 | 1.11 |
| 1.12 | .2544 | 5830 | 4664 | 1.40 493 | 3850 | 3738 | 2028 | .89 2857 | 1.12 |
| 1.13 | .2769 | 6301 | 6155 | 1.44 290 | 4158 | 4402 | 3459 | .88 4956 | 1.13 |
| 1.14 | .2996 | 6771 | 7639 | 1.48 154 | 4464 | 5062 | 4881 | .87 7193 | 1.14 |
| 1.15 | .3225 | 7238 | 3.3 9116 | 1.52 078 | 4769 | 5718 | 6294 | .86 9565 | 1.15 |
| 1.16 | .3456 | 7703 | 3.4 0588 | 1.56 090 | 5072 | 6370 | 7700 | .86 2069 | 1.16 |
| 1.17 | .3689 | 8167 | 2053 | 1.60 161 | 5373 | 7019 | 4.8 9097 | .85 4701 | 1.17 |
| 1.18 | .3924 | 8628 | 3511 | 1.64 303 | 5672 | 7664 | 4.9 0487 | .84 7458 | 1.18 |
| 1.19 | .4161 | 9087 | 4964 | 1.68 516 | 5970 | 8305 | 1868 | .84 0336 | 1.19 |
| **1.20** | 1 .4400 | 1.0 9545 | 3.4 6410 | 1.72 800 | 1.0 6266 | 2.2 8943 | 4.9 3242 | .83 3333 | **1.20** |
| 1.21 | .4641 | 1.1 0000 | 7851 | 1.77 156 | 6560 | 2.2 9577 | 4609 | .82 6446 | 1.21 |
| 1.22 | .4884 | 0454 | 3.4 9285 | 1.81 585 | 6853 | 2.3 0208 | 5968 | .81 9672 | 1.22 |
| 1.23 | .5129 | 0905 | 3.5 0714 | 1.86 087 | 7144 | 0835 | 7319 | .81 3008 | 1.23 |
| 1.24 | .5376 | 1355 | 2136 | 1.90 662 | 7434 | 1459 | 4.9 8663 | .80 6452 | 1.24 |
| 1.25 | .5625 | 1803 | 3553 | 1.95 312 | 7722 | 2079 | 5.0 0000 | .80 0000 | 1.25 |
| 1.26 | .5876 | 2250 | 4965 | 2.00 038 | 8008 | 2697 | 1330 | .79 3651 | 1.26 |
| 1.27 | .6129 | 2694 | 6371 | 2.04 838 | 8293 | 3311 | 2653 | .78 7402 | 1.27 |
| 1.28 | .6384 | 3137 | 7771 | 2.09 715 | 8577 | 3921 | 3968 | .78 1250 | 1.28 |
| 1.29 | .6641 | 3578 | 3.5 9166 | 2.14 669 | 8859 | 4529 | 5277 | .77 5194 | 1.29 |
| **1.30** | 1 .6900 | 1.1 4018 | 3.6 0555 | 2.19 700 | 1.0 9139 | 2.3 5133 | 5.0 6580 | .76 9231 | **1.30** |
| 1.31 | .7161 | 4455 | 1939 | 2.24 809 | 9418 | 5735 | 7875 | .76 3359 | 1.31 |
| 1.32 | .7424 | 4891 | 3318 | 2.29 997 | 9696 | 6333 | 5.0 9164 | .75 7576 | 1.32 |
| 1.33 | .7689 | 5326 | 4692 | 2.35 264 | 1.0 9972 | 6928 | 5.1 0447 | .75 1880 | 1.33 |
| 1.34 | .7956 | 5758 | 6060 | 2.40 610 | 1.1 0247 | 7521 | 1723 | .74 6269 | 1.34 |
| 1.35 | .8225 | 6190 | 7423 | 2.46 038 | 0521 | 8110 | 2993 | .74 0741 | 1.35 |
| 1.36 | .8496 | 6619 | 3.6 8782 | 2.51 546 | 0793 | 8697 | 4256 | .73 5294 | 1.36 |
| 1.37 | .8769 | 7047 | 3.7 0135 | 2.57 135 | 1064 | 9280 | 5514 | .72 9927 | 1.37 |
| 1.38 | .9044 | 7473 | 1484 | 2.62 807 | 1334 | 2.3 9861 | 6765 | .72 4638 | 1.38 |
| 1.39 | .9321 | 7898 | 2827 | 2.68 562 | 1602 | 2.4 0439 | 8010 | .71 9424 | 1.39 |
| **1.40** | 1 .9600 | 1.1 8322 | 3.7 4166 | 2.74 400 | 1.1 1869 | 2.4 1014 | 5.1 9249 | .71 4286 | **1.40** |
| 1.41 | 1 .9881 | 8743 | 5500 | 2.80 322 | 2135 | 1587 | 5.2 0483 | .70 9220 | 1.41 |
| 1.42 | 2 .0164 | 9164 | 6829 | 2.86 329 | 2399 | 2156 | 1710 | .70 4225 | 1.42 |
| 1.43 | .0449 | 1.1 9583 | 8153 | 2.92 421 | 2662 | 2724 | 2932 | .69 9301 | 1.43 |
| 1.44 | .0736 | 1.2 0000 | 3.7 9473 | 2.98 598 | 2924 | 3288 | 4148 | .69 4444 | 1.44 |
| 1.45 | .1025 | 0416 | 3.8 0789 | 3.04 862 | 3185 | 3850 | 5359 | .68 9655 | 1.45 |
| 1.46 | .1316 | 0830 | 2099 | 3.11 214 | 3445 | 4409 | 6564 | .68 4932 | 1.46 |
| 1.47 | .1609 | 1244 | 3406 | 3.17 652 | 3703 | 4966 | 7763 | .68 0272 | 1.47 |
| 1.48 | .1904 | 1655 | 4708 | 3.24 179 | 3960 | 5520 | 5.2 8957 | .67 5676 | 1.48 |
| 1.49 | .2201 | 2066 | 6005 | 3.30 795 | 4216 | 6072 | 5.3 0146 | .67 1141 | 1.49 |
| **1.50** | 2 .2500 | 1.2 2474 | 3.8 7298 | 3.37 500 | 1.1 4471 | 2.4 6621 | 5.3 1329 | .66 6667 | **1.50** |

## 16. SQUARES, CUBES, ROOTS, RECIPROCALS

| N | N² | √N | √10N | N³ | $\sqrt[3]{N}$ | $\sqrt[3]{10N}$ | $\sqrt[3]{100N}$ | 1/N | N |
|---|---|---|---|---|---|---|---|---|---|
| **1.50** | 2 .2500 | 1.2 2474 | 3.8 7298 | 3.37 500 | 1.1 4471 | 2.4 6621 | 5.3 1329 | .66 6667 | **1.50** |
| 1.51 | .2801 | 2882 | 8587 | 3.44 295 | 4725 | 7168 | 2507 | .66 2252 | 1.51 |
| 1.52 | .3104 | 3288 | 3.8 9872 | 3.51 181 | 4978 | 7712 | 3680 | .65 7895 | 1.52 |
| 1.53 | .3409 | 3693 | 3.9 1152 | 3.58 158 | 5230 | 8255 | 4848 | .65 3595 | 1.53 |
| 1.54 | .3716 | 4097 | 2428 | 3.65 226 | 5480 | 8794 | 6011 | .64 9351 | 1.54 |
| 1.55 | .4025 | 4499 | 3700 | 3.72 388 | 5729 | 9332 | 7168 | .64 5161 | 1.55 |
| 1.56 | .4336 | 4900 | 4968 | 3.79 642 | 5978 | 2.4 9867 | 8321 | .64 1026 | 1.56 |
| 1.57 | .4649 | 5300 | 6232 | 3.86 989 | 6225 | 2.5 0399 | 5.3 9469 | .63 6943 | 1.57 |
| 1.58 | .4964 | 5698 | 7492 | 3.94 431 | 6471 | 0930 | 5.4 0612 | .63 2911 | 1.58 |
| 1.59 | .5281 | 6095 | 3.9 8748 | 4.01 968 | 6717 | 1458 | 1750 | .62 8931 | 1.59 |
| **1.60** | 2 .5600 | 1.2 6491 | 4.0 0000 | 4.09 600 | 1.1 6961 | 2.5 1984 | 5.4 2884 | .62 5000 | **1.60** |
| 1.61 | .5921 | 6886 | 1248 | 4.17 328 | 7204 | 2508 | 4012 | .62 1118 | 1.61 |
| 1.62 | .6244 | 7279 | 2492 | 4.25 153 | 7446 | 3030 | 5136 | .61 7284 | 1.62 |
| 1.63 | .6569 | 7671 | 3733 | 4.33 075 | 7687 | 3549 | 6256 | .61 3497 | 1.63 |
| 1.64 | .6896 | 8062 | 4969 | 4.41 094 | 7927 | 4067 | 7370 | .60 9756 | 1.64 |
| 1.65 | .7225 | 8452 | 6202 | 4.49 212 | 8167 | 4582 | 8481 | .60 6061 | 1.65 |
| 1.66 | .7556 | 8841 | 7431 | 4.57 430 | 8405 | 5095 | 5.4 9586 | .60 2410 | 1.66 |
| 1.67 | .7889 | 9228 | 8656 | 4.65 746 | 8642 | 5607 | 5.5 0688 | .59 8802 | 1.67 |
| 1.68 | .8224 | 1.2 9615 | 4.0 9878 | 4.74 163 | 8878 | 6116 | 1785 | .59 5238 | 1.68 |
| 1.69 | .8561 | 1.3 0000 | 4.1 1096 | 4.82 681 | 9114 | 6623 | 2877 | 59 1716 | 1.69 |
| **1.70** | 2 .8900 | 1.3 0384 | 4.1 2311 | 4.91 300 | 1.1 9348 | 2.5 7128 | 5.3 3966 | .58 8235 | **1.70** |
| 1.71 | .9241 | 0767 | 3521 | 5.00 021 | 9582 | 7631 | 5050 | .58 4795 | 1.71 |
| 1.72 | .9584 | 1149 | 4729 | 5.08 845 | 1.1 9815 | 8133 | 6130 | .58 1395 | 1.72 |
| 1.73 | 2 .9929 | 1529 | 5933 | 5.17 772 | 1.2 0046 | 8632 | 7205 | .57 8035 | 1.73 |
| 1.74 | 3 .0276 | 1909 | 7133 | 5.26 802 | 0277 | 9129 | 8277 | .57 4713 | 1.74 |
| 1.75 | .0625 | 2288 | 8330 | 5.35 938 | 0507 | 2.5 9625 | 5.5 9344 | .57 1429 | 1.75 |
| 1.76 | .0976 | 2665 | 4.1 9524 | 5.45 178 | 0736 | 2.6 0118 | 5.6 0408 | .56 8182 | 1.76 |
| 1.77 | .1329 | 3041 | 4.2 0714 | 5.54 523 | 0964 | 0610 | 1467 | .56 4972 | 1.77 |
| 1.78 | .1684 | 3417 | 1900 | 5.63 975 | 1192 | 1100 | 2523 | .56 1798 | 1.78 |
| 1.79 | .2041 | 3791 | 3084 | 5.73 534 | 1418 | 1588 | 3574 | .55 8659 | 1.79 |
| **1.80** | 3 .2400 | 1.3 4164 | 4.2 4264 | 5.83 200 | 1.2 1644 | 2.6 2074 | 5.6 4622 | .55 5556 | **1.80** |
| 1.81 | .2761 | 4536 | 5441 | 5.92 974 | 1869 | 2559 | 5665 | .55 2486 | 1.81 |
| 1.82 | .3124 | 4907 | 6615 | 6.02 857 | 2093 | 3041 | 6705 | .54 9451 | 1.82 |
| 1.83 | .3489 | 5277 | 7785 | 6.12 849 | 2316 | 3522 | 7741 | .54 6448 | 1.83 |
| 1.84 | .3856 | 5647 | 4.2 8952 | 6.22 950 | 2539 | 4001 | 8773 | .54 3478 | 1.84 |
| 1.85 | .4225 | 6015 | 4.3 0116 | 6.33 162 | 2760 | 4479 | 5.6 9802 | .54 0541 | 1.85 |
| 1.86 | .4596 | 6382 | 1277 | 6.43 486 | 2981 | 4954 | 5.7 0827 | .53 7634 | 1.86 |
| 1.87 | .4969 | 6748 | 2435 | 6.53 920 | 3201 | 5428 | 1848 | .53 4759 | 1.87 |
| 1.88 | .5344 | 7113 | 3590 | 6.64 467 | 3420 | 5901 | 2865 | .53 1915 | 1.88 |
| 1.89 | .5721 | 7477 | 4741 | 6.75 127 | 3639 | 6371 | 3879 | .52 9101 | 1.89 |
| **1.90** | 3 .6100 | 1.3 7840 | 4.3 5890 | 6.85 900 | 1.2 3856 | 2.6 6840 | 5.7 4890 | .52 6316 | **1.90** |
| 1.91 | .6481 | 8203 | 7035 | 6.96 787 | 4073 | 7307 | 5897 | .52 3560 | 1.91 |
| 1.92 | .6864 | 8564 | 8178 | 7.07 789 | 4289 | 7773 | 6900 | .52 0833 | 1.92 |
| 1.93 | .7249 | 8924 | 4.3 9318 | 7.18 906 | 4505 | 8237 | 7900 | .51 8135 | 1.93 |
| 1.94 | .7636 | 9284 | 4.4 0454 | 7.30 138 | 4719 | 8700 | 8896 | .51 5464 | 1.94 |
| 1.95 | .8025 | 1.3 9642 | 1588 | 7.41 488 | 4933 | 9161 | 5.7 9889 | .51 2821 | 1.95 |
| 1.96 | .8416 | 1.4 0000 | 2719 | 7.52 954 | 5146 | 2.6 9620 | 5.8 0879 | .51 0204 | 1.96 |
| 1.97 | .8809 | 0357 | 3847 | 7.64 537 | 5359 | 2.7 0078 | 1865 | .50 7614 | 1.97 |
| 1.98 | .9204 | 0712 | 4972 | 7.76 239 | 5571 | 0534 | 2848 | .50 5051 | 1.98 |
| 1.99 | 3 .9601 | 1067 | 6094 | 7.88 060 | 5782 | 0989 | 3827 | .50 2513 | 1.99 |
| **2.00** | 4 .0000 | 1.4 1421 | 4.4 7214 | 8.00 000 | 1.2 5992 | 2.7 1442 | 5.8 4804 | .50 0000 | **2.00** |

## 16. SQUARES, CUBES, ROOTS, RECIPROCALS

| N | N² | √N | √10N | N³ | ∛N | ∛10N | ∛100N | 1/N | N |
|---|---|---|---|---|---|---|---|---|---|
| 2.00 | 4 .0000 | 1.4 1421 | 4.4 7214 | 8.00 000 | 1.2 5992 | 2.7 1442 | 5.8 4804 | .50 0000 | 2.00 |
| 2.01 | .0401 | 1774 | 8330 | 8.12 060 | 6202 | 1893 | 5777 | .49 7512 | 2.01 |
| 2.02 | .0804 | 2127 | 4.4 9444 | 8.24 241 | 6411 | 2344 | 6746 | .49 5050 | 2.02 |
| 2.03 | .1209 | 2478 | 4.5 0555 | 8.36 543 | 6619 | 2792 | 7713 | .49 2611 | 2.03 |
| 2.04 | .1616 | 2829 | 1664 | 8.48 966 | 6827 | 3239 | 8677 | .49 0196 | 2.04 |
| 2.05 | .2025 | 3178 | 2769 | 8.61 512 | 7033 | 3685 | 5.8 9637 | .48 7805 | 2.05 |
| 2.06 | .2436 | 3527 | 3872 | 8.74 182 | 7240 | 4129 | 5.9 0594 | .48 5437 | 2.06 |
| 2.07 | .2849 | 3875 | 4973 | 8.86 974 | 7445 | 4572 | 1548 | .48 3092 | 2.07 |
| 2.08 | .3264 | 4222 | 6070 | 8.99 891 | 7650 | 5014 | 2499 | .48 0769 | 2.08 |
| 2.09 | .3681 | 4568 | 7165 | 9.12 933 | 7854 | 5454 | 3447 | .47 8469 | 2.09 |
| 2.10 | 4 .4100 | 1.4 4914 | 4.5 8258 | 9.26 100 | 1.2 8058 | 2.7 5892 | 5.9 4392 | .47 6190 | 2.10 |
| 2.11 | .4521 | 5258 | 4.5 9347 | 9.39 393 | 8261 | 6330 | 5334 | .47 3934 | 2.11 |
| 2.12 | .4944 | 5602 | 4.6 0435 | 9.52 813 | 8463 | 6766 | 6273 | .47 1698 | 2.12 |
| 2.13 | .5369 | 5945 | 1519 | 9.66 360 | 8665 | 7200 | 7209 | .46 9484 | 2.13 |
| 2.14 | .5796 | 6287 | 2601 | 9.80 034 | 8866 | 7633 | 8142 | .46 7290 | 2.14 |
| 2.15 | .6225 | 6629 | 3681 | 9.93 838 | 9066 | 8065 | 5.9 9073 | .46 5116 | 2.15 |
| 2.16 | .6656 | 6969 | 4758 | 10 .0777 | 9266 | 8495 | 6.0 0000 | .46 2963 | 2.16 |
| 2.17 | .7089 | 7309 | 5833 | 10. 2183 | 9465 | 8924 | 0925 | .46 0829 | 2.17 |
| 2.18 | .7524 | 7648 | 6905 | 10. 3602 | 9664 | 9352 | 1846 | .45 8716 | 2.18 |
| 2.19 | .7961 | 7986 | 7974 | 10. 5035 | 1.2 9862 | 2.7 9779 | 2765 | .45 6621 | 2.19 |
| 2.20 | 4 .8400 | 1.4 8324 | 4.6 9042 | 10. 6480 | 1.3 0059 | 2.8 0204 | 6.0 3681 | .45 4545 | 2.20 |
| 2.21 | .8841 | 8661 | 4.7 0106 | 10. 7939 | 0256 | 0628 | 4594 | .45 2489 | 2.21 |
| 2.22 | .9284 | 8997 | 1169 | 10. 9410 | 0452 | 1050 | 5505 | .45 0450 | 2.22 |
| 2.23 | 4 .9729 | 9332 | 2229 | 11 .0896 | 0648 | 1472 | 6413 | .44 8430 | 2.23 |
| 2.24 | 5 .0176 | 1.4 9666 | 3286 | 11 .2394 | 0843 | 1892 | 7318 | .44 6429 | 2.24 |
| 2.25 | .0625 | 1.5 0000 | 4342 | 11 .3906 | 1037 | 2311 | 8220 | .44 4444 | 2.25 |
| 2.26 | .1076 | 0333 | 5395 | 11 .5432 | 1231 | 2728 | 6.0 9120 | .44 2478 | 2.26 |
| 2.27 | .1529 | 0665 | 6445 | 11 .6971 | 1424 | 3145 | 6.1 0017 | .44 0529 | 2.27 |
| 2.28 | .1984 | 0997 | 7493 | 11 .8524 | 1617 | 3560 | 0911 | .43 8596 | 2.28 |
| 2.29 | .2441 | 1327 | 8539 | 12 .0090 | 1809 | 2974 | 1803 | .43 6681 | 2.29 |
| 2.30 | 5 .2900 | 1.5 1658 | 4.7 9583 | 12 .1670 | 1.3 2001 | 2.8 4387 | 6.1 2693 | .43 4783 | 2.30 |
| 2.31 | .3361 | 1987 | 4.8 0625 | 12 .3264 | 2192 | 4798 | 3579 | .43 2900 | 2.31 |
| 2.32 | .3824 | 2315 | 1664 | 12 .4872 | 2382 | 5209 | 4463 | .43 1034 | 2.32 |
| 2.33 | .4289 | 2643 | 2701 | 12 .6493 | 2572 | 5618 | 5345 | .42 9185 | 2.33 |
| 2.34 | .4756 | 2971 | 3735 | 12 .8129 | 2761 | 6026 | 6224 | .42 7350 | 2.34 |
| 2.35 | .5225 | 3297 | 4768 | 12 .9779 | 2950 | 6433 | 7101 | .42 5532 | 2.35 |
| 2.36 | .5696 | 3623 | 5798 | 13. 1443 | 3139 | 6838 | 7975 | .42 3729 | 2.36 |
| 2.37 | .6169 | 3948 | 6826 | 13. 3121 | 3326 | 7243 | 8846 | .42 1941 | 2.37 |
| 2.38 | .6644 | 4272 | 7852 | 13. 4813 | 3514 | 7646 | 6.1 9715 | .42 0168 | 2.38 |
| 2.39 | .7121 | 4596 | 8876 | 13. 6519 | 3700 | 8049 | 6.2 0582 | .41 8410 | 2.39 |
| 2.40 | 5 .7600 | 1.5 4919 | 4.8 9898 | 13. 8240 | 1.3 3887 | 2.8 8450 | 6.2 1447 | .41 6667 | 2.40 |
| 2.41 | .8081 | 5242 | 4.9 0918 | 13. 9975 | 4072 | 8850 | 2308 | .41 4938 | 2.41 |
| 2.42 | .8564 | 5563 | 1935 | 14 .1725 | 4257 | 9249 | 3168 | .41 3223 | 2.42 |
| 2.43 | .9049 | 5885 | 2950 | 14 .3489 | 4442 | 2.8 9647 | 4025 | .41 1523 | 2.43 |
| 2.44 | 5 .9536 | 6205 | 3964 | 14 .5268 | 4626 | 2.9 0044 | 4880 | .40 9836 | 2.44 |
| 2.45 | 6 .0025 | 6525 | 4975 | 14 .7061 | 4810 | 0439 | 5732 | .40 8163 | 2.45 |
| 2.46 | .0516 | 6844 | 5984 | 14 .8869 | 4993 | 0834 | 6583 | .40 6504 | 2.46 |
| 2.47 | .1009 | 7162 | 6991 | 15 .0692 | 5176 | 1227 | 7431 | .40 4858 | 2.47 |
| 2.48 | .1504 | 7480 | 7996 | 15 .2530 | 5358 | 1620 | 8276 | .40 3226 | 2.48 |
| 2.49 | .2001 | 7797 | 4.9 8999 | 15 .4382 | 5540 | 2011 | 9119 | .40 1606 | 2.49 |
| 2.50 | 6 .2500 | 1.5 8114 | 5.0 0000 | 15 .6250 | 1.3 5721 | 2.9 2402 | 6.2 9961 | .40 0000 | 2.50 |

## 16. SQUARES, CUBES, ROOTS, RECIPROCALS

| N | N² | √N | √10N | N³ | ³√N | ³√10N | ³√100N | 1/N | N |
|---|---|---|---|---|---|---|---|---|---|
| **2.50** | 6 .2500 | 1.5 8114 | 5.0 0000 | 15 .6250 | 1.3 5721 | 2.9 2402 | 6.2 9961 | .40 0000 | **2.50** |
| 2.51 | .3001 | 8430 | 0999 | 15 .8133 | 5902 | 2791 | 6.3 0799 | .39 8406 | 2.51 |
| 2.52 | .3504 | 8745 | 1996 | 16 .0030 | 6082 | 3179 | 1636 | .39 6825 | 2.52 |
| 2.53 | .4009 | 9060 | 2991 | 16 .1943 | 6262 | 3567 | 2470 | .39 5257 | 2.53 |
| 2.54 | .4516 | 9374 | 3984 | 16 .3871 | 6441 | 3953 | 3303 | .39 3701 | 2.54 |
| 2.55 | .5025 | 1.5 9687 | 4975 | 16 .5814 | 6620 | 4338 | 4133 | .39 2157 | 2.55 |
| 2.56 | .5536 | 1.6 0000 | 5964 | 16 .7772 | 6798 | 4723 | 4960 | .39 0625 | 2.56 |
| 2.57 | .6049 | 0312 | 6952 | 16 .9746 | 6976 | 5106 | 5786 | .38 9105 | 2.57 |
| 2.58 | .6564 | 0624 | 7937 | 17 .1735 | 7153 | 5488 | 6610 | .38 7597 | 2.58 |
| 2.59 | .7081 | 0935 | 8920 | 17 .3740 | 7330 | 5869 | 7431 | .38 6100 | 2.59 |
| **2.60** | 6 .7600 | 1.6 1245 | 5.0 9902 | 17 .5760 | 1.3 7507 | 2.9 6250 | 6.3 8250 | .38 4615 | **2 60** |
| 2.61 | .8121 | 1555 | 5.1 0882 | 17 .7796 | 7683 | 6629 | 9068 | .38 3142 | 2.61 |
| 2.62 | .8644 | 1864 | 1859 | 17 .9847 | 7859 | 7007 | 6.3 9883 | .38 1679 | 2.62 |
| 2.63 | .9169 | 2173 | 2835 | 18 .1914 | · 8034 | 7385 | 6.4 0696 | .38 0228 | 2.63 |
| 2.64 | 6 .9696 | 2481 | 3809 | 18 .3997 | 8208 | 7761 | 1507 | .37 8788 | 2.64 |
| 2.65 | 7 .0225 | 2788 | 4782 | 18 .6096 | 8383 | 8137 | 2316 | .37 7358 | 2.65 |
| 2.66 | .0756 | 3095 | 5752 | 18 .8211 | 8557 | 8511 | 3123 | .37 5940 | 2.66 |
| 2.67 | .1289 | 3401 | 6720 | 19 .0342 | 8730 | 8885 | 3928 | .37 4532 | 2.67 |
| 2.68 | .1824 | 3707 | 7687 | 19 .2488 | 8903 | 9257 | 4731 | .37 3134 | 2.68 |
| 2.69 | .2361 | 4012 | 8652 | 19 .4651 | 9076 | 2.9 9629 | 5531 | .37 1747 | 2.69 |
| **2.70** | 7 .2900 | 1.6 4317 | 5.1 9615 | 19 .6830 | 1.3 9248 | 3.0 0000 | 6.4 6330 | .37 0370 | **2.70** |
| 2.71 | .3441 | 4621 | 5.2 0577 | 19 .9025 | 9419 | 0370 | 7127 | .36 9004 | 2.71 |
| 2.72 | .3984 | 4924 | 1536 | 20 .1236 | 9591 | 0739 | 7922 | .36 7647 | 2.72 |
| 2.73 | .4529 | 5227 | 2494 | 20 .3464 | 9761 | 1107 | 8715 | .36 6300 | 2.73 |
| 2.74 | .5076 | 5529 | 3450 | 20 .5708 | 1.3 9932 | 1474 | 6.4 9507 | .36 4964 | 2.74 |
| 2.75 | .5625 | 5831 | 4404 | 20 .7969 | 1.4 0102 | 1841 | 6.5 0296 | .36 3636 | 2.75 |
| 2.76 | .6176 | 6132 | 5357 | 21 .0246 | 0272 | 2206 | 1083 | .36 2319 | 2.76 |
| 2.77 | .6729 | 6433 | 6308 | 21 .2539 | 0441 | 2571 | 1868 | .36 1011 | 2.77 |
| 2.78 | .7284 | 6733 | 7257 | 21 .4850 | 0610 | 2934 | 2652 | .35 9712 | 2.78 |
| 2.79 | .7841 | 7033 | 8205 | 21 .7176 | 0778 | 3297 | 3434 | .35 8423 | 2.79 |
| **2.80** | 7 .8400 | 1.6 7332 | 5.2 9150 | 21 .9520 | 1.4 0946 | 3.0 3659 | 6.5 4213 | .35 7143 | **2.80** |
| 2.81 | .8961 | 7631 | 5.3 0094 | 22 .1880 | 1114 | 4020 | 4991 | .35 5872 | 2.81 |
| 2.82 | 7 .9524 | 7929 | 1037 | 22 .4258 | 1281 | 4380 | 5767 | .35 4610 | 2.82 |
| 2.83 | 8 .0089 | 8226 | 1977 | 22 .6652 | 1448 | 4740 | 6541 | .35 3357 | 2.83 |
| 2.84 | .0656 | 8523 | 2917 | 22 .9063 | 1614 | 5098 | 7314 | .35 2113 | 2.84 |
| 2.85 | .1225 | 8819 | 3854 | 23 .1491 | 1780 | 5456 | 8084 | .35 0877 | 2.85 |
| 2.86 | .1796 | 9115 | 4790 | 23 .3937 | 1946 | 5813 | 8853 | .34 9650 | 2.86 |
| 2.87 | .2369 | 9411 | 5724 | 23 .6399 | 2111 | 6169 | 6.5 9620 | .34 8432 | 2.87 |
| 2.88 | .2944 | 1.6 9706 | 6656 | 23 .8879 | 2276 | 6524 | 6.6 0385 | .34 7222 | 2.88 |
| 2.89 | .3521 | 1.7 0000 | 7587 | 24 .1376 | 2440 | 6878 | 1149 | .34 6021 | 2.89 |
| **2.90** | 8 .4100 | 1.7 0294 | 5.3 8516 | 24 .3890 | 1.4 2604 | 3.0 7232 | 6.6 1911 | .34 4828 | **2.90** |
| 2.91 | .4681 | 0587 | 5.3 9444 | 24 .6422 | 2768 | 7584 | 2671 | .34 3643 | 2.91 |
| 2.92 | .5264 | 0880 | 5.4 0370 | 24 .8971 | 2931 | 7936 | 3429 | .34 2466 | 2.92 |
| 2.93 | .5849 | 1172 | 1295 | 25 .1538 | 3094 | 8287 | 4185 | .34 1297 | 2.93 |
| 2.94 | .6436 | 1464 | 2218 | 25 .4122 | 3257 | 8638 | 4940 | .34 0136 | 2.94 |
| 2.95 | .7025 | 1756 | 3139 | 25 .6724 | 3419 | 8987 | 5693 | .33 8983 | 2.95 |
| 2.96 | .7616 | 2047 | 4059 | 25 .9343 | 3581 | 9336 | 6444 | .33 7838 | 2.96 |
| 2.97 | .8209 | 2337 | 4977 | 26 .1981 | 3743 | 3.0 9684 | 7194 | .33 6700 | 2.97 |
| 2.98 | .8804 | 2627 | 5894 | 26 .4636 | 3904 | 3.1 0031 | 7942 | .33 5570 | 2.98 |
| 2.99 | 8 .9401 | 2916 | 6809 | 26 .7309 | 4065 | 0378 | 8688 | .33 4448 | 2.99 |
| **3.00** | 9 .0000 | 1.7 3205 | 5.4 7723 | 27 .0000 | 1.4 4225 | 3.1 0723 | 6.6 9433 | .33 3333 | **3.00** |

## 16. SQUARES, CUBES, ROOTS, RECIPROCALS

| N | N² | √N | √10N | N³ | ∛N | ∛10N | ∛100N | 1/N | N |
|---|---|---|---|---|---|---|---|---|---|
| **3.00** | 9 .0000 | 1.7 3205 | 5.4 7723 | 27 .0000 | 1.4 4225 | 3.1 0723 | 6.6 9433 | .33 3333 | **3.00** |
| 3.01 | .0601 | 3494 | 8635 | 27 .2709 | 4385 | 1068 | 6.7 0176 | 2226 | 3.01 |
| 3.02 | .1204 | 3781 | 5.4 9545 | 27 .5436 | 4545 | 1412 | 0917 | 1126 | 3.02 |
| 3.03 | .1809 | 4069 | 5.5 0454 | 27 .8181 | 4704 | 1756 | 1657 | .33 0033 | 3.03 |
| 3.04 | .2416 | 4356 | 1362 | 28 .0945 | 4863 | 2098 | 2395 | .32 8947 | 3.04 |
| 3.05 | .3025 | 4642 | 2268 | 28 .3726 | 5022 | 2440 | 3132 | 7869 | 3.05 |
| 3.06 | .3636 | 4929 | 3173 | 28 .6526 | 5180 | 2781 | 3866 | 6797 | 3.06 |
| 3.07 | .4249 | 5214 | 4076 | 28 .9344 | 5338 | 3121 | 4600 | 5733 | 3.07 |
| 3.08 | .4864 | 5499 | 4977 | 29 .2181 | 5496 | 3461 | 5331 | 4675 | 3.08 |
| 3.09 | .5481 | 5784 | 5878 | 29 .5036 | 5653 | 3800 | 6061 | 3625 | 3.09 |
| **3.10** | 9 .6100 | 1.7 6068 | 5.5 6776 | 29 .7910 | 1.4 5810 | 3.1 4138 | 6.7 6790 | .32 2581 | **3.10** |
| 3.11 | .6721 | 6352 | 7674 | 30 .0802 | 5967 | 4475 | 7517 | 1543 | 3.11 |
| 3.12 | .7344 | 6635 | 8570 | 30 .3713 | 6123 | 4812 | 8242 | .32 0513 | 3.12 |
| 3.13 | .7969 | 6918 | 5.5 9464 | 30 .6643 | 6279 | 5148 | 8966 | .31 9489 | 3.13 |
| 3.14 | .8596 | 7200 | 5.6 0357 | 30 .9591 | 6434 | 5483 | 6.7 9688 | 8471 | 3.14 |
| 3.15 | .9225 | 7482 | 1249 | 31 .2559 | 6590 | 5818 | 6.8 0409 | 7460 | 3.15 |
| 3.16 | 9 .9856 | 7764 | 2139 | 31 .5545 | 6745 | 6152 | 1128 | 6456 | 3.16 |
| 3.17 | 10 .0489 | 8045 | 3028 | 31 .8550 | 6899 | 6485 | 1846 | 5457 | 3.17 |
| 3.18 | .1124 | 8326 | 3915 | 32 .1574 | 7054 | 6817 | 2562 | 4465 | 3.18 |
| 3.19 | .1761 | 8606 | 4801 | 32 .4618 | 7208 | 7149 | 3277 | 3480 | 3.19 |
| **3.20** | 10 .2400 | 1.7 8885 | 5.6 5685 | 32 .7680 | 1.4 7361 | 3.1 7480 | 6.8 3990 | .31 2500 | **3.20** |
| 3.21 | .3041 | 9165 | 6569 | 33 .0762 | 7515 | 7811 | 4702 | 1526 | 3.21 |
| 3.22 | .3684 | 9444 | 7450 | 33 .3862 | 7668 | 8140 | 5412 | .31 0559 | 3.22 |
| 3.23 | .4329 | 1.7 9722 | 8331 | 33 .6983 | 7820 | 8469 | 6121 | .30 9598 | 3.23 |
| 3.24 | .4976 | 1.8 0000 | 5.6 9210 | 34 .0122 | 7973 | 8798 | 6829 | 8642 | 3.24 |
| 3.25 | .5625 | 0278 | 5.7 0088 | 34 .3281 | 8125 | 9125 | 7534 | 7692 | 3.25 |
| 3.26 | .6276 | 0555 | 0964 | 34 .6460 | 8277 | 9452 | 8239 | 6748 | 3.26 |
| 3.27 | .6929 | 0831 | 1839 | 34 .9658 | 8428 | 3.1 9778 | 8942 | 5810 | 3.27 |
| 3.28 | .7584 | 1108 | 2713 | 35 .2876 | 8579 | 3.2 0104 | 6.8 9643 | 4878 | 3.28 |
| 3.29 | .8241 | 1384 | 3585 | 35 .6113 | 8730 | 0429 | 6.9 0344 | 3951 | 3.29 |
| **3.30** | 10 .8900 | 1.8 1659 | 5.7 4456 | 35 .9370 | 1.4 8881 | 3.2 0753 | 6.9 1042 | .30 3030 | **3.30** |
| 3.31 | 10 .9561 | 1934 | 5326 | 36 .2647 | 9031 | 1077 | 1740 | 2115 | 3.31 |
| 3.32 | 11 .0224 | 2209 | 6194 | 36 .5944 | 9181 | 1400 | 2436 | 1205 | 3.32 |
| 3.33 | .0889 | 2483 | 7062 | 36 .9260 | 9330 | 1722 | 3130 | .30 0300 | 3.33 |
| 3.34 | .1556 | 2757 | 7927 | 37 .2597 | 9480 | 2044 | 3823 | .29 9401 | 3.34 |
| 3.35 | .2225 | 3030 | 8792 | 37 .5954 | 9629 | 2365 | 4515 | 8507 | 3.35 |
| 3.36 | .2896 | 3303 | 5.7 9655 | 37 .9331 | 9777 | 2686 | 5205 | 7619 | 3.36 |
| 3.37 | .3569 | 3576 | 5.8 0517 | 38 .2728 | 1.4 9926 | 3006 | 5894 | 6736 | 3.37 |
| 3.38 | .4244 | 3848 | 1378 | 38 .6145 | 1.5 0074 | 3325 | 6582 | 5858 | 3.38 |
| 3.39 | .4921 | 4120 | 2237 | 38 .9582 | 0222 | 3643 | 7268 | 4985 | 3.39 |
| **3.40** | 11 .5600 | 1.8 4391 | 5.8 3095 | 39 .3040 | 1.5 0369 | 3.2 3961 | 6.9 7953 | .29 4118 | **3.40** |
| 3.41 | .6281 | 4662 | 3952 | 39 .6518 | 0517 | 4278 | 8637 | 3255 | 3.41 |
| 3.42 | .6964 | 4932 | 4808 | 40 .0017 | 0664 | 4595 | 6.9 9319 | 2398 | 3.42 |
| 3.43 | .7649 | 5203 | 5662 | 40 .3536 | 0810 | 4911 | 7.0 0000 | 1545 | 3.43 |
| 3.44 | .8336 | 5472 | 6515 | 40 .7076 | 0957 | 5227 | 0680 | .29 0698 | 3.44 |
| 3.45 | .9025 | 5742 | 7367 | 41 .0636 | 1103 | 5542 | 1358 | .28 9855 | 3.45 |
| 3.46 | 11 .9716 | 6011 | 8218 | 41 .4217 | 1249 | 5856 | 2035 | 9017 | 3.46 |
| 3.47 | 12 .0409 | 6279 | 9067 | 41 .7819 | 1394 | 6169 | 2711 | 8184 | 3.47 |
| 3.48 | .1104 | 6548 | 5.8 9915 | 42 .1442 | 1540 | 6482 | 3385 | 7356 | 3.48 |
| 3.49 | .1801 | 6815 | 5.9 0762 | 42 .5085 | 1685 | 6795 | 4058 | 6533 | 3.49 |
| **3.50** | 12 .2500 | 1.8 7083 | 5.9 1608 | 42 .8750 | 1.5 1829 | 3.2 7107 | 7.0 4730 | .28 5714 | **3.50** |

## 16. SQUARES, CUBES, ROOTS, RECIPROCALS

| N | N² | √N | √10N | N³ | ∛N | ∛10N | ∛100N | 1/N | N |
|---|----|----|------|-----|-----|------|-------|-----|---|
| **3.50** | 12 .2500 | 1.8 7083 | 5.9 1608 | 42 .8750 | 1.5 1829 | 3.2 7107 | 7.0 4730 | .28 5714 | **3.50** |
| 3.51 | .3201 | 7350 | 2453 | 43 .2436 | 1974 | 7418 | 5400 | 4900 | 3.51 |
| 3.52 | .3904 | 7617 | 3296 | 43 .6142 | 2118 | 7729 | 6070 | 4091 | 3.52 |
| 3.53 | .4609 | 7883 | 4138 | 43 .9870 | 2262 | 8039 | 6738 | 3286 | 3.53 |
| 3.54 | .5316 | 8149 | 4979 | 44 .3619 | 2406 | 8348 | 7404 | 2486 | 3.54 |
| 3.55 | .6025 | 8414 | 5819 | 44 .7389 | 2549 | 8657 | 8070 | 1690 | 3.55 |
| 3.56 | .6736 | 8680 | 6657 | 45 .1180 | 2692 | 8965 | 8734 | 0899 | 3.56 |
| 3.57 | .7449 | 8944 | 7495 | 45 .4993 | 2835 | 9273 | 7.0 9397 | .28 0112 | 3.57 |
| 3.58 | .8164 | 9209 | 8331 | 45 .8827 | 2978 | 9580 | 7.1 0059 | .27 9330 | 3.58 |
| 3.59 | .8881 | 9473 | 5.9 9166 | 46 .2683 | 3120 | 3.2 9887 | 0719 | 8552 | 3.59 |
| **3.60** | 12 .9600 | 1.8 9737 | 6.0 0000 | 46 .6560 | 1.5 3262 | 3.3 0193 | 7.1 1379 | .27 7778 | **3.60** |
| 3.61 | 13 .0321 | 1.9 0000 | 0833 | 47 .0459 | 3404 | 0498 | 2037 | 7008 | 3.61 |
| 3.62 | .1044 | 0263 | 1664 | 47 .4379 | 3545 | 0803 | 2694 | 6243 | 3.62 |
| 3.63 | .1769 | 0526 | 2495 | 47 .8321 | 3686 | 1107 | 3349 | 5482 | 3.63 |
| 3.64 | .2496 | 0788 | 3324 | 48 .2285 | 3827 | 1411 | 4004 | 4725 | 3.64 |
| 3.65 | .3225 | 1050 | 4152 | 48 .6271 | 3968 | 1714 | 4657 | 3973 | 3.65 |
| 3.66 | .3956 | 1311 | 4979 | 49 .0279 | 4109 | 2017 | 5309 | 3224 | 3.66 |
| 3.67 | .4689 | 1572 | 5805 | 49 .4309 | 4249 | 2319 | 5960 | 2480 | 3.67 |
| 3.68 | .5424 | 1833 | 6630 | 49 .8360 | 4389 | 2621 | 6610 | 1739 | 3.68 |
| 3.69 | .6161 | 2094 | 7454 | 50 .2434 | 4529 | 2922 | 7258 | 1003 | 3.69 |
| **3.70** | 13 .6900 | 1.9 2354 | 6.0 8276 | 50 .6530 | 1.5 4668 | 3.3 3222 | 7.1 7905 | .27 0270 | **3.70** |
| 3.71 | .7641 | 2614 | 9098 | 51 .0648 | 4807 | 3522 | 8552 | .26 9542 | 3.71 |
| 3.72 | .8384 | 2873 | 6.0 9918 | 51 .4788 | 4946 | 3822 | 9197 | 8817 | 3.72 |
| 3.73 | .9129 | 3132 | 6.1 0737 | 51 .8951 | 5085 | 4120 | 7.1 9840 | 8097 | 3.73 |
| 3.74 | 13 .9876 | 3391 | 1555 | 52 .3136 | 5223 | 4419 | 7.2 0483 | 7380 | 3.74 |
| 3.75 | 14 .0625 | 3649 | 2372 | 52 .7344 | 5362 | 4716 | 1125 | 6667 | 3.75 |
| 3.76 | .1376 | 3907 | 3188 | 53 .1574 | 5500 | 5014 | 1765 | 5957 | 3.76 |
| 3.77 | .2129 | 4165 | 4003 | 53 .5826 | 5637 | 5310 | 2405 | 5252 | 3.77 |
| 3.78 | .2884 | 4422 | 4817 | 54 .0102 | 5775 | 5607 | 3043 | 4550 | 3.78 |
| 3.79 | .3641 | 4679 | 5630 | 54 .4399 | 5912 | 5902 | 3680 | 3852 | 3.79 |
| **3.80** | 14 .4400 | 1.9 4936 | 6.1 6441 | 54 .8720 | 1.5 6049 | 3.3 6198 | 7.2 4316 | .26 3158 | **3.80** |
| 3.81 | .5161 | 5192 | 7252 | 55 .3063 | 6186 | 6492 | 4950 | 2467 | 3.81 |
| 3.82 | .5924 | 5448 | 8061 | 55 .7430 | 6322 | 6786 | 5584 | 1780 | 3.82 |
| 3.83 | .6689 | 5704 | 8870 | 56 .1819 | 6459 | 7080 | 6217 | 1097 | 3.83 |
| 3.84 | .7456 | 5959 | 6.1 9677 | 56 .6231 | 6595 | 7373 | 6848 | .26 0417 | 3.84 |
| 3.85 | .8225 | 6214 | 6.2 0484 | 57 .0666 | 6731 | 7666 | 7479 | .25 9740 | 3.85 |
| 3.86 | .8996 | 6469 | 1289 | 57 .5125 | 6866 | 7958 | 8108 | 9067 | 3.86 |
| 3.87 | 14 .9769 | 6723 | 2093 | 57 .9606 | 7001 | 8249 | 8736 | 8398 | 3.87 |
| 3.88 | 15 .0544 | 6977 | 2896 | 58 .4111 | 7137 | 8540 | 9363 | 7732 | 3.88 |
| 3.89 | .1321 | 7231 | 3699 | 58 .8639 | 7271 | 8831 | 7.2 9989 | 7069 | 3.89 |
| **3.90** | 15 .2100 | 1.9 7484 | 6.2 4500 | 59 .3190 | 1.5 7406 | 3.3 9121 | 7.3 0614 | .25 6410 | **3.90** |
| 3.91 | .2881 | 7737 | 5300 | 59 .7765 | 7541 | 9411 | 1238 | 5754 | 3.91 |
| 3.92 | .3664 | 7990 | 6099 | 60 .2363 | 7675 | 9700 | 1861 | 5102 | 3.92 |
| 3.93 | .4449 | 8242 | 6897 | 60 .6985 | 7809 | 3.3 9988 | 2483 | 4453 | 3.93 |
| 3.94 | .5236 | 8494 | 7694 | 61 .1630 | 7942 | 3.4 0277 | 3104 | 3807 | 3.94 |
| 3.95 | .6025 | 8746 | 8490 | 61 .6299 | 8076 | 0564 | 3723 | 3165 | 3.95 |
| 3.96 | .6816 | 8997 | 6.2 9285 | 62 .0991 | 8209 | 0851 | 4342 | 2525 | 3.96 |
| 3.97 | .7609 | 9249 | 6.3 0079 | 62 .5708 | 8342 | 1138 | 4960 | 1889 | 3.97 |
| 3.98 | .8404 | 9499 | 0872 | 63 .0448 | 8475 | 1424 | 5576 | 1256 | 3.98 |
| 3.99 | 15 .9201 | 1.9 9750 | 1664 | 63 .5212 | 8608 | 1710 | 6192 | 0627 | 3.99 |
| **4.00** | 16 .0000 | 2.0 0000 | 6.3 2456 | 64 .0000 | 1.5 8740 | 3.4 1995 | 7.3 6806 | .25 0000 | **4.00** |

## 16. SQUARES, CUBES, ROOTS, RECIPROCALS

| N | N² | √N | √10N | N³ | ³√N | ³√10N | ³√100N | 1/N | N |
|---|---|---|---|---|---|---|---|---|---|
| **4.00** | 16 .0000 | 2.0 0000 | 6.3 2456 | 64 .0000 | 1.5 8740 | 3.4 1995 | 73. 6806 | .25 0000 | **4.00** |
| 4.01 | .0801 | 0250 | 3246 | 64 .4812 | 8872 | 2280 | 7420 | .24 9377 | 4.01 |
| 4.02 | .1604 | 0499 | 4035 | 64 .9648 | 9004 | 2564 | 8032 | 8756 | 4.02 |
| 4.03 | .2409 | 0749 | 4823 | 65 .4508 | 9136 | 2848 | 8644 | 8139 | 4.03 |
| 4.04 | .3216 | 0998 | 5610 | 65 .9393 | 9267 | 3131 | 9254 | 7525 | 4.04 |
| 4.05 | .4025 | 1246 | 6396 | 66 .4301 | 9399 | 3414 | 7.3 9864 | 6914 | 4.05 |
| 4.06 | .4836 | 1494 | 7181 | 66 .9234 | 9530 | 3697 | 7.4 0472 | 6305 | 4.06 |
| 4.07 | .5649 | 1742 | 7966 | 67 .4191 | 9661 | 3979 | 1080 | 5700 | 4.07 |
| 4.08 | .6464 | 1990 | 8749 | 67 .9173 | 9791 | 4260 | 1686 | 5098 | 4.08 |
| 4.09 | .7281 | 2237 | 6.3 9531 | 68 .4179 | 1.5 9922 | 4541 | 2291 | 4499 | 4.09 |
| **4.10** | 16 .8100 | 2.0 2485 | 6.4 0312 | 68 .9210 | 1.6 0052 | 3.4 4822 | 7.4 2896 | .24 3902 | **4.10** |
| 4.11 | .8921 | 2731 | 1093 | 69 .4265 | 0182 | 5102 | 3499 | 3309 | 4.11 |
| 4.12 | 16 .9744 | 2978 | 1872 | 69 .9345 | 0312 | 5381 | 4102 | 2718 | 4.12 |
| 4.13 | 17 .0569 | 3224 | 2651 | 70 .4450 | 0441 | 5661 | 4703 | 2131 | 4.13 |
| 4.14 | .1396 | 3470 | 3428 | 70 .9579 | 0571 | 5939 | 5304 | 1546 | 4.14 |
| 4.15 | .2225 | 3715 | 4205 | 71 .4734 | 0700 | 6218 | 5904 | 0964 | 4.15 |
| 4.16 | .3056 | 3961 | 4981 | 71 .9913 | 0829 | 6496 | 6502 | .24 0385 | 4.16 |
| 4.17 | .3889 | 4206 | 5755 | 72 .5117 | 0958 | 6773 | 7100 | .23 9808 | 4.17 |
| 4.18 | .4724 | 4450 | 6529 | 73 .0346 | 1086 | 7050 | 7697 | 9234 | 4.18 |
| 4.19 | .5561 | 4695 | 7302 | 73 .5601 | 1215 | 7327 | 8292 | 8663 | 4.19 |
| **4.20** | 17 .6400 | 2.0 4939 | 6.4 8074 | 74 .0880 | 1.6 1343 | 3.4 7603 | 7.4 8887 | .23 8095 | **4.20** |
| 4.21 | .7241 | 5183 | 8845 | 74 .6185 | 1471 | 7878 | 7.4 9481 | 7530 | 4.21 |
| 4.22 | .8084 | 5426 | 6.4 9615 | 75 .1514 | 1599 | 8154 | 7.5 0074 | 6967 | 4.22 |
| 4.23 | .8929 | 5670 | 6.5 0385 | 75 .6870 | 1726 | 8428 | 0666 | 6407 | 4.23 |
| 4.24 | 17 .9776 | 5913 | 1153 | 76 .2250 | 1853 | 8703 | 1257 | 5849 | 4.24 |
| 4.25 | 18 .0625 | 6155 | 1920 | 76 .7656 | 1981 | 8977 | 1847 | 5294 | 4.25 |
| 4.26 | .1476 | 6398 | 2687 | 77 .3088 | 2108 | 9250 | 2437 | 4742 | 4.26 |
| 4.27 | .2329 | 6640 | 3452 | 77 .8545 | 2234 | 9523 | 3025 | 4192 | 4.27 |
| 4.28 | .3184 | 6882 | 4217 | 78 .4028 | 2361 | 3.4 9796 | 3612 | 3645 | 4.28 |
| 4.29 | .4041 | 7123 | 4981 | 78 .9536 | 2487 | 3.5 0068 | 4199 | 3100 | 4.29 |
| **4.30** | 18 .4900 | 2.0 7364 | 6.5 5744 | 79 .5070 | 1.6 2613 | 3.5 0340 | 7.5 4784 | .23 2558 | **4.30** |
| 4.31 | .5761 | 7605 | 6506 | 80 .0630 | 2739 | 0611 | 5369 | 2019 | 4.31 |
| 4.32 | .6624 | 7846 | 7267 | 80 .6216 | 2865 | 0882 | 5953 | 1481 | 4.32 |
| 4.33 | .7489 | 8087 | 8027 | 81 .1827 | 2991 | 1153 | 6535 | 0947 | 4.33 |
| 4.34 | .8356 | 8327 | 8787 | 81 .7465 | 3116 | 1423 | 7117 | .23 0415 | 4.34 |
| 4.35 | 18 .9225 | 8567 | 6.5 9545 | 82 .3129 | 3241 | 1692 | 7698 | .22 9885 | 4.35 |
| 4.36 | 19 .0096 | 8806 | 6.6 0303 | 82 .8819 | 3366 | 1962 | 8279 | 9358 | 4.36 |
| 4.37 | .0969 | 9045 | 1060 | 83 .4535 | 3491 | 2231 | 8858 | 8833 | 4.37 |
| 4.38 | .1844 | 9284 | 1816 | 84 .0277 | 3616 | 2499 | 7.5 9436 | 8311 | 4.38 |
| 4.39 | .2721 | 9523 | 2571 | 84 .6045 | 3740 | 2767 | 7.6 0014 | 7790 | 4.39 |
| **4.40** | 19 .3600 | 2.0 9762 | 6.6 3325 | 85 .1840 | 1.6 3864 | 3.5 3035 | 7.6 0590 | .22 7273 | **4.40** |
| 4.41 | .4481 | 2.1 0000 | 4078 | 85 .7661 | 3988 | 3302 | 1166 | 6757 | 4.41 |
| 4.42 | .5364 | 0238 | 4831 | 86 .3509 | 4112 | 3569 | 1741 | 6244 | 4.42 |
| 4.43 | .6249 | 0476 | 5582 | 86 .9383 | 4236 | 3835 | 2315 | 5734 | 4.43 |
| 4.44 | .7136 | 0713 | 6333 | 87 .5284 | 4359 | 4101 | 2888 | 5225 | 4.44 |
| 4.45 | .8025 | 0950 | 7083 | 88 .1211 | 4483 | 4367 | 3461 | 4719 | 4.45 |
| 4.46 | .8916 | 1187 | 7832 | 88 .7165 | 4606 | 4632 | 4032 | 4215 | 4.46 |
| 4.47 | 19 .9809 | 1424 | 8581 | 89 .3146 | 4729 | 4897 | 4603 | 3714 | 4.47 |
| 4.48 | 20 .0704 | 1660 | 6.6 9328 | 89 .9154 | 4851 | 5162 | 5172 | 3214 | 4.48 |
| 4.49 | .1601 | 1896 | 6.7 0075 | 90 .5188 | 4974 | 5426 | 5741 | 2717 | 4.49 |
| **4.50** | 20 .2500 | 2.1 2132 | 6.7 0820 | 91 .1250 | 1.6 5096 | 3.5 5689 | 7.6 6309 | .22 2222 | **4.50** |

## 16. SQUARES, CUBES, ROOTS, RECIPROCALS

| N | N² | √N | √10N | N³ | ∛N | ∛10N | ∛100N | 1/N | N |
|---|---|---|---|---|---|---|---|---|---|
| 4.50 | 20 .2500 | 2.1 2132 | 6.7 0820 | 91 .1250 | 1.6 5096 | 3.5 5689 | 7.6 6309 | .22 2222 | 4.50 |
| 4.51 | .3401 | 2368 | 1565 | 91 .7339 | 5219 | 5953 | 6877 | 1729 | 4.51 |
| 4.52 | .4304 | 2603 | 2309 | 92 .3454 | 5341 | 6215 | 7443 | 1239 | 4.52 |
| 4.53 | .5209 | 2838 | 3053 | 92 .9597 | 5462 | 6478 | 8009 | 0751 | 4.53 |
| 4.54 | .6116 | 3073 | 3795 | 93 .5767 | 5584 | 6740 | 8573 | .22 0264 | 4.54 |
| 4.55 | .7025 | 3307 | 4537 | 94 .1964 | 5706 | 7002 | 9137 | .21 9780 | 4.55 |
| 4.56 | .7936 | 3542 | 5278 | 94 .8188 | 5827 | 7263 | 7.6 9700 | 9298 | 4.56 |
| 4.57 | .8849 | 3776 | 6018 | 95 .4440 | 5948 | 7524 | 7.7 0262 | 8818 | 4.57 |
| 4.58 | 20 .9764 | 4009 | 6757 | 96 .0719 | 6069 | 7785 | 0824 | 8341 | 4.58 |
| 4.59 | 21 .0681 | 4243 | 7495 | 96 .7026 | 6190 | 8045 | 1384 | 7865 | 4.59 |
| 4.60 | 21 .1600 | 2.1 4476 | 6.7 8233 | 97 .3360 | 1.6 6310 | 3.5 8305 | 7.7 1944 | .21 7391 | 4.60 |
| 4.61 | .2521 | 4709 | 8970 | 97 .9722 | 6431 | 8564 | 2503 | 6920 | 4.61 |
| 4.62 | .3444 | 4942 | 6.7 9706 | 98 .6111 | 6551 | 8823 | 3061 | 6450 | 4.62 |
| 4.63 | .4369 | 5174 | 6.8 0441 | 99 .2528 | 6671 | 9082 | 3619 | 5983 | 4.63 |
| 4.64 | .5296 | 5407 | 1175 | 99 .8973 | 6791 | 9340 | 4175 | 5517 | 4.64 |
| 4.65 | .6225 | 5639 | 1909 | 100 .545 | 6911 | 9598 | 4731 | 5054 | 4.65 |
| 4.66 | .7156 | 5870 | 2642 | 101 .195 | 7030 | 3.5 9856 | 5286 | 4592 | 4.66 |
| 4.67 | .8089 | 6102 | 3374 | 101 .848 | 7150 | 3.6 0113 | 5840 | 4133 | 4.67 |
| 4.68 | .9024 | 6333 | 4105 | 102 .503 | 7269 | 0370 | 6394 | 3675 | 4.68 |
| 4.69 | 21 .9961 | 6564 | 4836 | 103 .162 | 7388 | 0626 | 6946 | 3220 | 4.69 |
| 4.70 | 22 .0900 | 2.1 6795 | 6.8 5565 | 103 .823 | 1.6 7507 | 3.6 0883 | 7.7 7498 | .21 2766 | 4.70 |
| 4.71 | .1841 | 7025 | 6294 | 104 .487 | 7626 | 1138 | 8049 | 2314 | 4.71 |
| 4.72 | .2784 | 7256 | 7023 | 105 .154 | 7744 | 1394 | 8599 | 1864 | 4.72 |
| 4.73 | .3729 | 7486 | 7750 | 105 .824 | 7863 | 1649 | 9149 | 1416 | 4.73 |
| 4.74 | .4676 | 7715 | 8477 | 106 .496 | 7981 | 1903 | 7.7 9697 | 0970 | 4.74 |
| 4.75 | .5625 | 7945 | 9202 | 107 .172 | 8099 | 2158 | 7.8 0245 | 0526 | 4.75 |
| 4.76 | .6576 | 8174 | 6.8 9928 | 107 .850 | 8217 | 2412 | 0793 | .21 0084 | 4.76 |
| 4.77 | .7529 | 8403 | 6.9 0652 | 108 .531 | 8334 | 2665 | 1339 | .20 9644 | 4.77 |
| 4.78 | .8484 | 8632 | 1375 | 109 .215 | 8452 | 2919 | 1885 | 9205 | 4.78 |
| 4.79 | 22 .9441 | 8861 | 2098 | 109 .902 | 8569 | 3172 | 2429 | 8768 | 4.79 |
| 4.80 | 23 .0400 | 2.1 9089 | 6.9 2820 | 110 .592 | 1.6 8687 | 3.6 3424 | 7.8 2974 | .20 8333 | 4.80 |
| 4.81 | .1361 | 9317 | 3542 | 111 .285 | 8804 | 3676 | 3517 | 7900 | 4.81 |
| 4.82 | .2324 | 9545 | 4262 | 111 .980 | 8920 | 3928 | 4059 | 7469 | 4.82 |
| 4.83 | .3289 | 2.1 9773 | 4982 | 112 .679 | 9037 | 4180 | 4601 | 7039 | 4.83 |
| 4.84 | .4256 | 2.2 0000 | 5701 | 113 .380 | 9154 | 4431 | 5142 | 6612 | 4.84 |
| 4.85 | .5225 | 0227 | 6419 | 114 .084 | 9270 | 4682 | 5683 | 6186 | 4.85 |
| 4.86 | .6196 | 0454 | 7137 | 114 .791 | 9386 | 4932 | 6222 | 5761 | 4.86 |
| 4.87 | .7169 | 0681 | 7854 | 115 .501 | 9503 | 5182 | 6761 | 5339 | 4.87 |
| 4.88 | .8144 | 0907 | 8570 | 116 .214 | 9619 | 5432 | 7299 | 4918 | 4.88 |
| 4.89 | 23 .9121 | 1133 | 6.9 9285 | 116 .930 | 9734 | 5681 | 7837 | 4499 | 4.89 |
| 4.90 | 24 .0100 | 2.2 1359 | 7.0 0000 | 117 .649 | 1.6 9850 | 3.6 5931 | 7.8 8374 | .20 4082 | 4.90 |
| 4.91 | .1081 | 1585 | 0714 | 118 .371 | 1.6 9965 | 6179 | 8909 | 3666 | 4.91 |
| 4.92 | .2064 | 1811 | 1427 | 119 .095 | 1.7 0081 | 6428 | 9445 | 3252 | 4.92 |
| 4.93 | .3049 | 2036 | 2140 | 119 .823 | 0196 | 6676 | 7.8 9979 | 2840 | 4.93 |
| 4.94 | .4036 | 2261 | 2851 | 120 .554 | 0311 | 6924 | 7.9 0513 | 2429 | 4.94 |
| 4.95 | .5025 | 2486 | 3562 | 121 .287 | 0426 | 7171 | 1046 | 2020 | 4.95 |
| 4.96 | .6016 | 2711 | 4273 | 122 .024 | 0540 | 7418 | 1578 | 1613 | 4.96 |
| 4.97 | .7009 | 2935 | 4982 | 122 .763 | 0655 | 7665 | 2110 | 1207 | 4.97 |
| 4.98 | .8004 | 3159 | 5691 | 123 .506 | 0769 | 7911 | 2641 | 0803 | 4.98 |
| 4.99 | 24 .9001 | 3383 | 6399 | 124 .251 | 0884 | 8157 | 3171 | 0401 | 4.99 |
| 5.00 | 25 .0000 | 2.2 3607 | 7.0 7107 | 125 .000 | 1.7 0998 | 3.6 8403 | 7.9 3701 | .20 0000 | 5.00 |

## 16. SQUARES, CUBES, ROOTS, RECIPROCALS

| N | N² | √N | √10N | N³ | ∛N | ∛10N | ∛100N | 1/N | N |
|---|---|---|---|---|---|---|---|---|---|
| **5.00** | 25 .0000 | 2.2 3607 | 7.0 7107 | 125 .000 | 1.7 0998 | 3.6 8403 | 7.9 3701 | .20 0000 | **5.00** |
| 5.01 | .1001 | 3830 | 7814 | 125 .752 | 1112 | 8649 | 4229 | .19 9601 | 5.01 |
| 5.02 | .2004 | 4054 | 8520 | 126 .506 | 1225 | 8894 | 4757 | 9203 | 5.02 |
| 5.03 | .3009 | 4277 | 9225 | 127 .264 | 1339 | 9138 | 5285 | 8807 | 5.03 |
| 5.04 | .4016 | 4499 | 7.0 9930 | 128 .024 | 1452 | 9383 | 5811 | 8413 | 5.04 |
| 5.05 | .5025 | 4722 | 7.1 0634 | 128 .788 | 1566 | 9627 | 6337 | 8020 | 5.05 |
| 5.06 | .6036 | 4944 | 1337 | 129 .554 | 1679 | 3.6 9871 | 6863 | 7628 | 5.06 |
| 5.07 | .7049 | 5167 | 2039 | 130 .324 | 1792 | 3.7 0114 | 7387 | 7239 | 5.07 |
| 5.08 | .8064 | 5389 | 2741 | 131 .097 | 1905 | 0358 | 7911 | 6850 | 5.08 |
| 5.09 | 25 .9081 | 5610 | 3442 | 131 .872 | 2017 | 0600 | 8434 | 6464 | 5.09 |
| **5.10** | 26 .0100 | 2.2 5832 | 7.1 4143 | 132 .651 | 1.7 2130 | 3.7 0843 | 7.9 8957 | .19 6078 | **5.10** |
| 5.11 | .1121 | 6053 | 4843 | 133 .433 | 2242 | 1085 | 7.9 9479 | 5695 | 5.11 |
| 5.12 | .2144 | 6274 | 5542 | 134 .218 | 2355 | 1327 | 8.0 0000 | 5312 | 5.12 |
| 5.13 | .3169 | 6495 | 6240 | 135 .006 | 2467 | 1569 | 0520 | 4932 | 5.13 |
| 5.14 | .4196 | 6716 | 6938 | 135 .797 | 2579 | 1810 | 1040 | 4553 | 5.14 |
| 5.15 | .5225 | 6936 | 7635 | 136 .591 | 2691 | 2051 | 1559 | 4175 | 5.15 |
| 5.16 | .6256 | 7156 | 8331 | 137 .388 | 2802 | 2292 | 2078 | 3798 | 5.16 |
| 5.17 | .7289 | 7376 | 9027 | 138 .188 | 2914 | 2532 | 2596 | 3424 | 5.17 |
| 5.18 | .8324 | 7596 | 7.1 9722 | 138 .992 | 3025 | 2772 | 3113 | 3050 | 5.18 |
| 5.19 | 26 .9361 | 7816 | 7.2 0417 | 139 .798 | 3137 | 3012 | 3629 | 2678 | 5.19 |
| **5.20** | 27 .0400 | 2.2 8035 | 7.2 1110 | 140 .608 | 1.7 3248 | 3.7 3251 | 8.0 4145 | .19 2308 | **5.20** |
| 5.21 | .1441 | 8254 | 1803 | 141 .421 | 3359 | 3490 | 4660 | 1939 | 5.21 |
| 5.22 | .2484 | 8473 | 2496 | 142 .237 | 3470 | 3729 | 5175 | 1571 | 5.22 |
| 5.23 | .3529 | 8692 | 3187 | 143 .056 | 3580 | 3968 | 5689 | 1205 | 5.23 |
| 5.24 | .4576 | 8910 | 3878 | 143 .878 | 3691 | 4206 | 6202 | 0840 | 5.24 |
| 5.25 | .5625 | 9129 | 4569 | 144 .703 | 3801 | 4444 | 6714 | 0476 | 5.25 |
| 5.26 | .6676 | 9347 | 5259 | 145 .532 | 3912 | 4681 | 7226 | .19 0114 | 5.26 |
| 5.27 | .7729 | 9565 | 5948 | 146 .363 | 4022 | 4919 | 7737 | .18 9753 | 5.27 |
| 5.28 | .8784 | 2.2 9783 | 6636 | 147 .198 | 4132 | 5155 | 8248 | 9394 | 5.28 |
| 5.29 | 27 .9841 | 2.3 0000 | 7324 | 148 .036 | 4242 | 5392 | 8758 | 9036 | 5.29 |
| **5.30** | 28 .0900 | 2.3 0217 | 7.2 8011 | 148 .877 | 1.7 4351 | 3.7 5629 | 8.0 9267 | .18 8679 | **5.30** |
| 5.31 | .1961 | 0434 | 8697 | 149 .721 | 4461 | 5865 | 8.0 9776 | 8324 | 5.31 |
| 5.32 | .3024 | 0651 | 7.2 9383 | 150 .569 | 4570 | 6100 | 8.1 0284 | 7970 | 5.32 |
| 5.33 | .4089 | 0868 | 7.3 0068 | 151 .419 | 4680 | 6336 | 0791 | 7617 | 5.33 |
| 5.34 | .5156 | 1084 | 0753 | 152 .273 | 4789 | 6571 | 1298 | 7266 | 5.34 |
| 5.35 | .6225 | 1301 | 1437 | 153 .130 | 4898 | 6806 | 1804 | 6916 | 5.35 |
| 5.36 | .7296 | 1517 | 2120 | 153 .991 | 5007 | 7041 | 2310 | 6567 | 5.36 |
| 5.37 | .8369 | 1733 | 2803 | 154 .854 | 5116 | 7275 | 2814 | 6220 | 5.37 |
| 5.38 | 28 .9444 | 1948 | 3485 | 155 .721 | 5224 | 7509 | 3319 | 5874 | 5.38 |
| 5.39 | 29 .0521 | 2164 | 4166 | 156 .591 | 5333 | 7743 | 3822 | 5529 | 5.39 |
| **5.40** | 29 .1600 | 2.3 2379 | 7.3 4847 | 157 .464 | 1.7 5441 | 3.7 7976 | 8.1 4325 | .18 5185 | **5.40** |
| 5.41 | .2681 | 2594 | 5527 | 158 .340 | 5549 | 8209 | 4828 | 4843 | 5.41 |
| 5.42 | .3764 | 2809 | 6206 | 159 .220 | 5657 | 8442 | 5329 | 4502 | 5.42 |
| 5.43 | .4849 | 3024 | 6885 | 160 .103 | 5765 | 8675 | 5831 | 4162 | 5.43 |
| 5.44 | .5936 | 3238 | 7564 | 160 .989 | 5873 | 8907 | 6331 | 3824 | 5.44 |
| 5.45 | .7025 | 3452 | 8241 | 161 .879 | 5981 | 9139 | 6831 | 3486 | 5.45 |
| 5.46 | .8116 | 3666 | 8918 | 162 .771 | 6088 | 9371 | 7330 | 3150 | 5.46 |
| 5.47 | 29 .9209 | 3880 | 7.3 9594 | 163 .667 | 6196 | 9603 | 7829 | 2815 | 5.47 |
| 5.48 | 30 .0304 | 4094 | 7.4 0270 | 164 .567 | 6303 | 3.7 9834 | 8327 | 2482 | 5.48 |
| 5.49 | .1401 | 4307 | 0945 | 165 .469 | 6410 | 3.8 0065 | 8824 | 2149 | 5.49 |
| **5.50** | 30 .2500 | 2.3 4521 | 7.4 1620 | 166 .375 | 1.7 6517 | 3.8 0295 | 8.1 9321 | .18 1818 | **5.50** |

## 16. SQUARES, CUBES, ROOTS, RECIPROCALS

| N | $N^2$ | $\sqrt{N}$ | $\sqrt{10N}$ | $N^3$ | $\sqrt[3]{N}$ | $\sqrt[3]{10N}$ | $\sqrt[3]{100N}$ | $1/N$ | N |
|---|---|---|---|---|---|---|---|---|---|
| **5.50** | 30 .2500 | 2.3 4521 | 7.4 1620 | 166 .375 | 1.7 6517 | 3.8 0295 | 8.1 9321 | .18 1818 | **5.50** |
| 5.51 | .3601 | 4734 | 2294 | 167 .284 | 6624 | 0526 | 8.1 9818 | 1488 | 5.51 |
| 5.52 | .4704 | 4947 | 2967 | 168 .197 | 6731 | 0756 | 8.2 0313 | 1159 | 5.52 |
| 5.53 | .5809 | 5160 | 3640 | 169 .112 | 6838 | 0985 | 0808 | 0832 | 5.53 |
| 5.54 | .6916 | 5372 | 4312 | 170 .031 | 6944 | 1215 | 1303 | 0505 | 5.54 |
| 5.55 | .8025 | 5584 | 4983 | 170 .954 | 7051 | 1444 | 1797 | .18 0180 | 5.55 |
| 5.56 | 30 .9136 | 5797 | 5654 | 171 .880 | 7157 | 1673 | 2290 | .17 9856 | 5.56 |
| 5.57 | 31 .0249 | 6008 | 6324 | 172 .809 | 7263 | 1902 | 2783 | 9533 | 5.57 |
| 5.58 | .1364 | 6220 | 6994 | 173 .741 | 7369 | 2130 | 3275 | 9211 | 5.58 |
| 5.59 | · .2481 | 6432 | 7663 | 174 .677 | 7475 | 2358 | 3766 | 8891 | 5.59 |
| **5.60** | 31 .3600 | 2.3 6643 | 7.4 8331 | 175 .616 | 1.7 7581 | 3.8 2586 | 8.2 4257 | .17 8571 | **5.60** |
| 5.61 | .4721 | 6854 | 8999 | 176 .558 | 7686 | 2814 | 4747 | 8253 | 5.61 |
| 5.62 | .5844 | 7065 | 7.4 9667 | 177 .504 | 7792 | 3041 | 5237 | 7936 | 5.62 |
| 5.63 | .6969 | 7276 | 7.5 0333 | 178 .454 | 7897 | 3268 | 5726 | 7620 | 5.63 |
| 5.64 | .8096 | 7487 | 0999 | 179 .406 | 8003 | 3495 | 6215 | 7305 | 5.64 |
| 5.65 | 31 .9225 | 7697 | 1665 | 180 .362 | 8108 | 3722 | 6703 | 6991 | 5.65 |
| 5.66 | 32 .0356 | 7908 | 2330 | 181 .321 | 8213 | 3948 | 7190 | 6678 | 5.66 |
| 5.67 | .1489 | 8118 | 2994 | 182 .284 | 8318 | 4174 | 7677 | 6367 | 5.67 |
| 5.68 | .2624 | 8328 | 3658 | 183 .250 | 8422 | 4399 | 8164 | 6056 | 5.68 |
| 5.69 | .3761 | 8537 | 4321 | 184 .220 | 8527 | 4625 | 8649 | 5747 | 5.69 |
| **5.70** | 32 .4900 | 2.3 8747 | 7.5 4983 | 185 .193 | 1.7 8632 | 3.8 4850 | 8.2 9134 | .17 5439 | **5.70** |
| 5.71 | .6041 | 8956 | 5645 | 186 .169 | 8736 | 5075 | 8.2 9619 | 5131 | 5.71 |
| 5.72 | .7184 | 9165 | 6307 | 187 .149 | 8840 | 5300 | 8.3 0103 | 4825 | 5.72 |
| 5.73 | .8329 | 9374 | 6968 | 188 .133 | 8944 | 5524 | 0587 | 4520 | 5.73 |
| 5.74 | 32 .9476 | 9583 | 7628 | 189 .119 | 9048 | 5748 | 1069 | 4216 | 5.74 |
| 5.75 | 33 .0625 | 2.3 9792 | 8288 | 190 .109 | 9153 | 5972 | 1552 | 3913 | 5.75 |
| 5.76 | .1776 | 2.4 0000 | 8947 | 191 .103 | 9256 | 6196 | 2034 | 3611 | 5.76 |
| 5.77 | .2929 | 0208 | 7.5 9605 | 192 .100 | 9360 | 6419 | 2515 | 3310 | 5.77 |
| 5.78 | .4084 | 0416 | 7.6 0263 | 193 .101 | 9463 | 6642 | 2995 | 3010 | 5.78 |
| 5.79 | .5241 | 0624 | 0920 | 194 .105 | 9567 | 6865 | 3476 | 2712 | 5.79 |
| **5.80** | 33 .6400 | 2.4 0832 | 7.6 1577 | 195 .112 | 1.7 9670 | 3.8 7088 | 8.3 3955 | .17 2414 | **5.80** |
| 5.81 | .7561 | 1039 | 2234 | 196 .123 | 9773 | 7310 | 4434 | 2117 | 5.81 |
| 5.82 | .8724 | 1247 | 2889 | 197 .137 | 9876 | 7532 | 4913 | 1821 | 5.82 |
| 5.83 | 33 .9889 | 1454 | 3544 | 198 .155 | 1.7 9979 | 7754 | 5390 | 1527 | 5.83 |
| 5.84 | 34 .1056 | 1661 | 4199 | 199 .177 | 1.8 0082 | 7975 | 5868 | 1233 | 5.84 |
| 5.85 | .2225 | 1868 | 4853 | 200 .202 | 0185 | 8197 | 6345 | 0940 | 5.85 |
| 5.86 | .3396 | 2074 | 5506 | 201 .230 | 0288 | 8418 | 6821 | 0648 | 5.86 |
| 5.87 | .4569 | 2281 | 6159 | 202 .262 | 0390 | 8639 | 7297 | 0358 | 5.87 |
| 5.88 | .5744 | 2487 | 6812 | 203 .297 | 0492 | 8859 | 7772 | .17 0068 | 5.88 |
| 5.89 | .6921 | 2693 | 7463 | 204 .336 | 0595 | 9080 | 8247 | .16 9779 | 5.89 |
| **5.90** | 34 .8100 | 2.4 2899 | 7.6 8115 | 205 .379 | 1.8 0697 | 3.8 9300 | 8.3 8721 | .16 9492 | **5.90** |
| 5.91 | 34 .9281 | 3105 | 8765 | 206 .425 | 0799 | 9519 | 9194 | 9205 | 5.91 |
| 5.92 | 35 .0464 | 3311 | 7.6 9415 | 207 .475 | 0901 | 9739 | 8.3 9667 | 8919 | 5.92 |
| 5.93 | .1649 | 3516 | 7.7 0065 | 208 .528 | 1003 | 3.8 9958 | 8.4 0140 | 8634 | 5.93 |
| 5.94 | .2836 | 3721 | 0714 | 209 .585 | 1104 | 3.9 0177 | 0612 | 8350 | 5.94 |
| 5.95 | .4025 | 3926 | 1362 | 210 .645 | 1206 | 0396 | 1083 | 8067 | 5.95 |
| 5.96 | .5216 | 4131 | 2010 | 211 .709 | 1307 | 0615 | 1554 | 7785 | 5.96 |
| 5.97 | .6409 | 4336 | 2658 | 212 .776 | 1409 | 0833 | 2025 | 7504 | 5.97 |
| 5.98 | .7604 | 4540 | 3305 | 213 .847 | 1510 | 1051 | 2494 | 7224 | 5.98 |
| 5.99 | 35 .8801 | 4745 | 3951 | 214 .922 | 1611 | 1269 | 2964 | 6945 | 5.99 |
| **6.00** | 36 .0000 | 2.4 4949 | 7.7 4597 | 216 .000 | 1.8 1712 | 3.9 1487 | 8.4 3433 | .16 6667 | **6.00** |

## 16. SQUARES, CUBES, ROOTS, RECIPROCALS

| N | N² | √N | √10N | N³ | ∛N | ∛10N | ∛100N | 1/N | N |
|---|---|---|---|---|---|---|---|---|---|
| **6.00** | 36 .0000 | 2.4 4949 | 7.7 4597 | 216 .000 | 1.8 1712 | 3.9 1487 | 8.4 3433 | .16 6667 | **6.00** |
| 6.01 | .1201 | 5153 | 5242 | 217 .082 | 1813 | 1704 | 3901 | 6389 | 6.01 |
| 6.02 | .2404 | 5357 | 5887 | 218 .167 | 1914 | 1921 | 4369 | 6113 | 6.02 |
| 6.03 | .3609 | 5561 | 6531 | 219 .256 | 2014 | 2138 | 4836 | 5837 | 6.03 |
| 6.04 | .4816 | 5764 | 7174 | 220 .349 | 2115 | 2355 | 5303 | 5563 | 6.04 |
| 6.05 | .6025 | 5967 | 7817 | 221 .445 | 2215 | 2571 | 5769 | 5289 | 6.05 |
| 6.06 | .7236 | 6171 | 8460 | 222 .545 | 2316 | 2787 | 6235 | 5017 | 6.06 |
| 6.07 | .8449 | 6374 | 9102 | 223 .649 | 2416 | 3003 | 6700 | 4745 | 6.07 |
| 6.08 | 36 .9664 | 6577 | 7.7 9744 | 224 .756 | 2516 | 3219 | 7165 | 4474 | 6.08 |
| 6.09 | 37 .0881 | 6779 | 7.8 0385 | 225 .867 | 2616 | 3434 | 7629 | 4204 | 6.09 |
| **6.10** | 37 .2100 | 2.4 6982 | 7.8 1025 | 226 .981 | 1.8 2716 | 3.9 3650 | 8.4 8093 | .16 3934 | **6.10** |
| 6.11 | .3321 | 7184 | 1665 | 228 .099 | 2816 | 3865 | 8556 | 3666 | 6.11 |
| 6.12 | .4544 | 7386 | 2304 | 229 .221 | 2915 | 4079 | 9018 | 3399 | 6.12 |
| 6.13 | .5769 | 7588 | 2943 | 230 .346 | 3015 | 4294 | 9481 | 3132 | 6.13 |
| 6.14 | .6996 | 7790 | 3582 | 231 .476 | 3115 | 4508 | 8.4 9942 | 2866 | 6.14 |
| 6.15 | .8225 | 7992 | 4219 | 232 .608 | 3214 | 4722 | 8.5 0403 | 2602 | 6.15 |
| 6.16 | 37 .9456 | 8193 | 4857 | 233 .745 | 3313 | 4936 | 0864 | 2338 | 6.16 |
| 6.17 | 38 .0689 | 8395 | 5493 | 234 .885 | 3412 | 5150 | 1324 | 2075 | 6.17 |
| 6.18 | .1924 | 8596 | 6130 | 236 .029 | 3511 | 5363 | 1784 | 1812 | 6.18 |
| 6.19 | .3161 | 8797 | 6766 | 237 .177 | 3610 | 5576 | 2243 | 1551 | 6.19 |
| **6.20** | 38 .4400 | 2.4 8998 | 7.8 7401 | 238 .328 | 1.8 3709 | 3.9 5789 | 8.5 2702 | .16 1290 | **6.20** |
| 6.21 | .5641 | 9199 | 8036 | 239 .483 | 3808 | 6002 | 3160 | 1031 | 6.21 |
| 6.22 | .6884 | 9399 | 8670 | 240 .642 | 3906 | 6214 | 3618 | 0772 | 6.22 |
| 6.23 | .8129 | 9600 | 9303 | 241 .804 | 4005 | 6427 | 4075 | 0514 | 6.23 |
| 6.24 | 38 .9376 | 2.4 9800 | 7.8 9937 | 242 .971 | 4103 | 6638 | 4532 | 0256 | 6.24 |
| 6.25 | 39 .0625 | 2.5 0000 | 7.9 0569 | 244 .141 | 4202 | 6850 | 4988 | .16 0000 | 6.25 |
| 6.26 | .1876 | 0200 | 1202 | 245 .314 | 4300 | 7062 | 5444 | .15 9744 | 6.26 |
| 6.27 | .3129 | 0400 | 1833 | 246 .492 | 4398 | 7273 | 5899 | 9490 | 6.27 |
| 6.28 | .4384 | 0599 | 2465 | 247 .673 | 4496 | 7484 | 6354 | 9236 | 6.28 |
| 6.29 | .5641 | 0799 | 3095 | 248 .858 | 4594 | 7695 | 6808 | 8983 | 6.29 |
| **6.30** | 39 .6900 | 2.5 0998 | 7.9 3725 | 250 .047 | 1.8 4691 | 3.9 7906 | 8.5 7262 | .15 8730 | **6.30** |
| 6.31 | .8161 | 1197 | 4355 | 251 .240 | 4789 | 8116 | 7715 | 8479 | 6.31 |
| 6.32 | 39 .9424 | 1396 | 4984 | 252 .436 | 4887 | 8326 | 8168 | 8228 | 6.32 |
| 6.33 | 40 .0689 | 1595 | 5613 | 253 .636 | 4984 | 8536 | 8620 | 7978 | 6.33 |
| 6.34 | .1956 | 1794 | 6241 | 254 .840 | 5082 | 8746 | 9072 | 7729 | 6.34 |
| 6.35 | .3225 | 1992 | 6869 | 256 .048 | 5179 | 8956 | 9524 | 7480 | 6.35 |
| 6.36 | .4496 | 2190 | 7496 | 257 .259 | 5276 | 9165 | 8.5 9975 | 7233 | 6.36 |
| 6.37 | .5769 | 2389 | 8123 | 258 .475 | 5373 | 9374 | 8.6 0425 | 6986 | 6.37 |
| 6.38 | .7044 | 2587 | 8749 | 259 .694 | 5470 | 9583 | 0875 | 6740 | 6.38 |
| 6.39 | .8321 | 2784 | 7.9 9375 | 260 .917 | 5567 | 3.9 9792 | 1325 | 6495 | 6.39 |
| **6.40** | 40 .9600 | 2.5 2982 | 8.0 0000 | 262 .144 | 1.8 5664 | 4.0 0000 | 8.6 1774 | .15 6250 | **6.40** |
| 6.41 | 41 .0881 | 3180 | 0625 | 263 .375 | 5760 | 0208 | 2222 | 6006 | 6.41 |
| 6.42 | .2164 | 3377 | 1249 | 264 .609 | 5857 | 0416 | 2671 | 5763 | 6.42 |
| 6.43 | .3449 | 3574 | 1873 | 265 .848 | 5953 | 0624 | 3118 | 5521 | 6.43 |
| 6.44 | .4736 | 3772 | 2496 | 267 .090 | 6050 | 0832 | 3566 | 5280 | 6.44 |
| 6.45 | .6025 | 3969 | 3119 | 268 .336 | 6146 | 1039 | 4012 | 5039 | 6.45 |
| 6.46 | .7316 | 4165 | 3741 | 269 .586 | 6242 | 1246 | 4459 | 4799 | 6.46 |
| 6.47 | .8609 | 4362 | 4363 | 270 .840 | 6338 | 1453 | 4904 | 4560 | 6.47 |
| 6.48 | 41 .9904 | 4558 | 4984 | 272 .098 | 6434 | 1660 | 5350 | 4321 | 6.48 |
| 6.49 | 42 .1201 | 4755 | 5605 | 273 .359 | 6530 | 1866 | 5795 | 4083 | 6.49 |
| **6.50** | 42 .2500 | 2.5 4951 | 8.0 6226 | 274 .625 | 1.8 6626 | 4.0 2073 | 8.6 6239 | .15 3846 | **6.50** |

## 16. SQUARES, CUBES, ROOTS, RECIPROCALS

| N | N² | √N | √10N | N³ | ∛N | ∛10N | ∛100N | 1/N | N |
|---|---|---|---|---|---|---|---|---|---|
| **6.50** | 42 .2500 | 2.5 4951 | 8.0 6226 | 274 .625 | 1.8 6626 | 4.0 2073 | 8.6 6239 | .15 3846 | **6.50** |
| 6.51 | .3801 | 5147 | 6846 | 275 .894 | 6721 | 2279 | 6683 | 3610 | 6.51 |
| 6.52 | .5104 | 5343 | 7465 | 277 .168 | 6817 | 2485 | 7127 | 3374 | 6.52 |
| 6.53 | .6409 | 5539 | 8084 | 278 .445 | 6912 | 2690 | 7570 | 3139 | 6.53 |
| 6.54 | .7716 | 5734 | 8703 | 279 .726 | 7008 | 2896 | 8012 | 2905 | 6.54 |
| 6.55 | 42 .9025 | 5930 | 9321 | 281 .011 | 7103 | 3101 | 8455 | 2672 | 6.55 |
| 6.56 | 43 .0336 | 6125 | 8.0 9938 | 282 .300 | 7198 | 3306 | 8896 | 2439 | 6.56 |
| 6.57 | .1649 | 6320 | 8.1 0555 | 283 .593 | 7293 | 3511 | 9338 | 2207 | 6.57 |
| 6.58 | .2964 | 6515 | 1172 | 284 .890 | 7388 | 3715 | 8.6 9778 | 1976 | 6.58 |
| 6.59 | .4281 | 6710 | 1788 | 286 .191 | 7483 | 3920 | 8.7 0219 | 1745 | 6.59 |
| **6.60** | 43 .5600 | 2.5 6905 | 8.1 2404 | 287 .496 | 1.8 7578 | 4.0 4124 | 8.7 0659 | .15 1515 | **6.60** |
| 6.61 | .6921 | 7099 | 3019 | 288 .805 | 7672 | 4328 | 1098 | 1286 | 6.61 |
| 6.62 | .8244 | 7294 | 3634 | 290 .118 | 7767 | 4532 | 1537 | 1057 | 6.62 |
| 6.63 | 43 .9569 | 7488 | 4248 | 291 .434 | 7862 | 4735 | 1976 | 0830 | 6.63 |
| 6.64 | 44 .0896 | 7682 | 4862 | 292 .755 | 7956 | 4939 | 2414 | 0602 | 6.64 |
| 6.65 | .2225 | 7876 | 5475 | 294 .080 | 8050 | 5142 | 2852 | 0376 | 6.65 |
| 6.66 | .3556 | 8070 | 6088 | 295 .408 | 8144 | 5345 | 3289 | .15 0150 | 6.66 |
| 6.67 | .4889 | 8263 | 6701 | 296 .741 | 8239 | 5548 | 3726 | .14 9925 | 6.67 |
| 6.68 | .6224 | 8457 | 7313 | 298 .078 | 8333 | 5750 | 4162 | 9701 | 6.68 |
| 6.69 | .7561 | 8650 | 7924 | 299 .418 | 8427 | 5953 | 4598 | 9477 | 6.69 |
| **6.70** | 44 .8900 | 2.5 8844 | 8.1 8535 | 300 .763 | 1.8 8520 | 4.0 6155 | 8.7 5034 | .14 9254 | **6.70** |
| 6.71 | 45 .0241 | 9037 | 9146 | 302 .112 | 8614 | 6357 | 5469 | 9031 | 6.71 |
| 6.72 | .1584 | 9230 | 8.1 9756 | 303 .464 | 8708 | 6559 | 5904 | 8810 | 6.72 |
| 6.73 | .2929 | 9422 | 8.2 0366 | 304 .821 | 8801 | 6760 | 6338 | 8588 | 6.73 |
| 6.74 | .4276 | 9615 | 0975 | 306 .182 | 8895 | 6961 | 6772 | 8368 | 6.74 |
| 6.75 | .5625 | 2.5 9808 | 1584 | 307 .547 | 8988 | 7163 | 7205 | 8148 | 6.75 |
| 6.76 | .6976 | 2.6 0000 | 2192 | 308 .916 | 9081 | 7364 | 7638 | 7929 | 6.76 |
| 6.77 | .8329 | 0192 | 2800 | 310 .289 | 9175 | 7564 | 8071 | 7710 | 6.77 |
| 6.78 | 45 .9684 | 0384 | 3408 | 311 .666 | 9268 | 7765 | 8503 | 7493 | 6.78 |
| 6.79 | 46 .1041 | 0576 | 4015 | 313 .047 | 9361 | 7965 | 8935 | 7275 | 6.79 |
| **6.80** | 46 .2400 | 2.6 0768 | 8.2 4621 | 314 .432 | 1.8 9454 | 4.0 8166 | 8.7 9366 | .14 7059 | **6.80** |
| 6.81 | .3761 | 0960 | 5227 | 315 .821 | 9546 | 8365 | 8.7 9797 | 6843 | 6.81 |
| 6.82 | .5124 | 1151 | 5833 | 317 .215 | 9639 | 8565 | 8.8 0227 | 6628 | 6.82 |
| 6.83 | .6489 | 1343 | 6438 | 318 .612 | 9732 | 8765 | 0657 | 6413 | 6.83 |
| 6.84 | .7856 | 1534 | 7043 | 320 .014 | 9824 | 8964 | 1087 | 6199 | 6.84 |
| 6.85 | 46 .9225 | 1725 | 7647 | 321 .419 | 1.8 9917 | 9163 | 1516 | 5985 | 6.85 |
| 6.86 | 47 .0596 | 1916 | 8251 | 322 .829 | 1.9 0009 | 9362 | 1945 | 5773 | 6.86 |
| 6.87 | .1969 | 2107 | 8855 | 324 .243 | 0102 | 9561 | 2373 | 5560 | 6.87 |
| 6.88 | .3344 | 2298 | 8.2 9458 | 325 .661 | 0194 | 9760 | 2801 | 5349 | 6.88 |
| 6.89 | .4721 | 2488 | 8.3 0060 | 327 .083 | 0286 | 4.0 9958 | 3228 | 5138 | 6.89 |
| **6.90** | 47 .6100 | 2.6 2679 | 8.3 0662 | 328 .509 | 1.9 0378 | 4.1 0157 | 8.8 3656 | .14 4928 | **6.90** |
| 6.91 | .7481 | · 2869 | 1264 | 329 .939 | 0470 | 0355 | 4082 | 4718 | 6.91 |
| 6.92 | 47 .8864 | 3059 | 1865 | 331 .374 | 0562 | 0552 | 4509 | 4509 | 6.92 |
| 6.93 | 48 .0249 | 3249 | 2466 | 332 .813 | 0653 | 0750 | 4934 | 4300 | 6.93 |
| 6.94 | .1636 | 3439 | 3067 | 334 .255 | 0745 | 0948 | 5360 | 4092 | 6.94 |
| 6.95 | .3025 | 3629 | 3667 | 335 .702 | 0837 | 1145 | 5785 | 3885 | 6.95 |
| 6.96 | .4416 | 3818 | 4266 | 337 .154 | 0928 | 1342 | 6210 | 3678 | 6.96 |
| 6.97 | .5809 | 4008 | 4865 | 338 .609 | 1019 | 1539 | 6634 | 3472 | 6.97 |
| 6.98 | .7204 | 4197 | 5464 | 340 .068 | 1111 | 1736 | 7058 | 3266 | 6.98 |
| 6.99 | 48 .8601 | 4386 | 6062 | 341 .532 | 1202 | 1932 | 7481 | 3062 | 6.99 |
| **7.00** | 49 .0000 | 2.6 4575 | 8.3 6660 | 343 .000 | 1.9 1293 | 4.1 2129 | 8.8 7904 | .14 2857 | **7.00** |

## 16. SQUARES, CUBES, ROOTS, RECIPROCALS

| N | $N^2$ | $\sqrt{N}$ | $\sqrt{10N}$ | $N^3$ | $\sqrt[3]{N}$ | $\sqrt[3]{10N}$ | $\sqrt[3]{100N}$ | $1/N$ | N |
|---|---|---|---|---|---|---|---|---|---|
| **7.00** | 49 .0000 | 2.6 4575 | 8.3 6660 | 343 .000 | 1.9 1293 | 4.1 2129 | 8.8 7904 | .14 2857 | **7.00** |
| 7.01 | .1401 | 4764 | 7257 | 344 .472 | 1384 | 2325 | 8327 | 2653 | 7.01 |
| 7.02 | .2804 | 4953 | 7854 | 345 .948 | 1475 | 2521 | 8749 | 2450 | 7.02 |
| 7.03 | .4209 | 5141 | 8451 | 347 .429 | 1566 | 2716 | 9171 | 2248 | 7.03 |
| 7.04 | .5616 | 5330 | 9047 | 348 .914 | 1657 | 2912 | 8.8 9592 | 2045 | 7.04 |
| 7.05 | .7025 | 5518 | 8.3 9643 | 350 .403 | 1747 | 3107 | 8.9 0013 | 1844 | 7.05 |
| 7.06 | .8436 | 5707 | 8.4 0238 | 351 .896 | 1838 | 3303 | 0434 | 1643 | 7.06 |
| 7.07 | 49 .9849 | 5895 | 0833 | 353 .393 | 1929 | 3498 | 0854 | 1443 | 7.07 |
| 7.08 | 50 .1264 | 6083 | 1427 | 354 .895 | 2019 | 3693 | 1274 | 1243 | 7.08 |
| 7.09 | .2681 | 6271 | 2021 | 356 .401 | 2109 | 3887 | 1693 | 1044 | 7.09 |
| **7.10** | 50 .4100 | 2.6 6458 | 8.4 2615 | 357 .911 | 1.9 2200 | 4.1 4082 | 8.9 2112 | .14 0845 | **7.10** |
| 7.11 | .5521 | 6646 | 3208 | 359 .425 | 2290 | 4276 | 2531 | 0647 | 7.11 |
| 7.12 | .6944 | 6833 | 3801 | 360 .944 | 2380 | 4470 | 2949 | 0449 | 7.12 |
| 7.13 | .8369 | 7021 | 4393 | 362 .467 | 2470 | 4664 | 3367 | 0252 | 7.13 |
| 7.14 | 50 .9796 | 7208 | 4985 | 363 .994 | 2560 | 4858 | 3784 | .14 0056 | 7.14 |
| 7.15 | 51 .1225 | 7395 | 5577 | 365 .526 | 2650 | 5052 | 4201 | .13 9860 | 7.15 |
| 7.16 | .2656 | 7582 | 6168 | 367 .062 | 2740 | 5245 | 4618 | 9665 | 7.16 |
| 7.17 | .4089 | 7769 | 6759 | 368 .602 | 2829 | 5438 | 5034 | 9470 | 7.17 |
| 7.18 | .5524 | 7955 | 7349 | 370 .146 | 2919 | 5631 | 5450 | 9276 | 7.18 |
| 7.19 | .6961 | 8142 | 7939 | 371 .695 | 3008 | 5824 | 5866 | 9082 | 7.19 |
| **7.20** | 51 .8400 | 2.6 8328 | 8.4 8528 | 373 .248 | 1.9 3098 | 4.1 6017 | 8.9 6281 | .13 8889 | **7.20** |
| 7.21 | 51 .9841 | 8514 | 9117 | 374 .805 | 3187 | 6209 | 6696 | 8696 | 7.21 |
| 7.22 | 52 .1284 | 8701 | 8.4 9706 | 376 .367 | 3277 | 6402 | 7110 | 8504 | 7.22 |
| 7.23 | .2729 | 8887 | 8.5 0294 | 377 .933 | 3366 | 6594 | 7524 | 8313 | 7.23 |
| 7.24 | .4176 | 9072 | 0882 | 379 .503 | 3455 | 6786 | 7938 | 8122 | 7.24 |
| 7.25 | .5625 | 9258 | 1469 | 381 .078 | 3544 | 6978 | 835 | 7931 | 7.25 |
| 7.26 | .7076 | 9444 | 2056 | 382 .657 | 3633 | 7169 | 87 | 7741 | 7.26 |
| 7.27 | .8529 | 9629 | 2643 | 384 .241 | 3722 | 7361 | 91 .6 | 7552 | 7.27 |
| 7.28 | 52 .9984 | 2.6 9815 | 3229 | 385 .828 | 3810 | 7552 | 8.9 9588 | 7363 | 7.28 |
| 7.29 | 53 .1441 | 2.7 0000 | 3815 | 387 .420 | 3899 | 7743 | 9.0 0000 | 7174 | 7.29 |
| **7.30** | 53 .2900 | 2.7 0185 | 8.5 4400 | 389 .017 | 1.9 3988 | 4.1 7934 | 9.0 0411 | .13 6986 | **7.30** |
| 7.31 | .4361 | 0370 | 4985 | 390 .618 | 4076 | 8125 | 0822 | 6799 | 7.31 |
| 7.32 | .5824 | 0555 | 5570 | 392 .223 | 4165 | 8315 | 1233 | 6612 | 7.32 |
| 7.33 | .7289 | 0740 | 6154 | 393 .833 | 4253 | 8506 | 1643 | 6426 | 7.33 |
| 7.34 | 53 .8756 | 0924 | 6738 | 395 .447 | 4341 | 8696 | 2053 | 6240 | 7.34 |
| 7.35 | 54 .0225 | 1109 | 7321 | 397 .065 | 4430 | 8886 | 2462 | 6054 | 7.35 |
| 7.36 | .1696 | 1293 | 7904 | 398 .688 | 4518 | 9076 | 2871 | 5870 | 7.36 |
| 7.37 | .3169 | 1477 | 8487 | 400 .316 | 4606 | 9266 | 3280 | 5685 | 7.37 |
| 7.38 | .4644 | 1662 | 9069 | 401 .947 | 4694 | 9455 | 3689 | 5501 | 7.38 |
| 7.39 | .6121 | 1846 | 8.5 9651 | 403 .583 | 4782 | 9644 | 4097 | 5318 | 7.39 |
| **7.40** | 54 .7600 | 2.7 2029 | 8.6 0233 | 405 .224 | 1.9 4870 | 4.1 9834 | 9.0 4504 | .13 5135 | **7.40** |
| 7.41 | 54 .9081 | 2213 | 0814 | 406 .869 | 4957 | 4.2 0023 | 4911 | 4953 | 7.41 |
| 7.42 | 55 .0564 | 2397 | 1394 | 408 .518 | 5045 | 0212 | 5318 | 4771 | 7.42 |
| 7.43 | .2049 | 2580 | 1974 | 410 .172 | 5132 | 0400 | 5725 | 4590 | 7.43 |
| 7.44 | .3536 | 2764 | 2554 | 411 .831 | 5220 | 0589 | 6131 | 4409 | 7.44 |
| 7.45 | .5025 | 2947 | 3134 | 413 .494 | 5307 | 0777 | 6537 | 4228 | 7.45 |
| 7.46 | .6516 | 3130 | 3713 | 415 .161 | 5395 | 0965 | 6942 | 4048 | 7.46 |
| 7.47 | .8009 | 3313 | 4292 | 416 .833 | 5482 | 1153 | 7347 | 3869 | 7.47 |
| 7.48 | 55 .9504 | 3496 | 4870 | 418 .509 | 5569 | 1341 | 7752 | 3690 | 7.48 |
| 7.49 | 56 .1001 | 3679 | 5448 | 420 .190 | 5656 | 1529 | 8156 | 3511 | 7.49 |
| **7.50** | 56 .2500 | 2.7 3861 | 8.6 6025 | 421 .875 | 1.9 5743 | 4.2 1716 | 9.0 8560 | .13 3333 | **7.50** |

## 16. SQUARES, CUBES, ROOTS, RECIPROCALS

| N | N² | √N | √10N | N³ | ³√N | ³√10N | ³√100N | 1/N | N |
|---|---|---|---|---|---|---|---|---|---|
| **7.50** | 56 .2500 | 2.7 3861 | 8.6 6025 | 421 .875 | 1.9 5743 | 4.2 1716 | 9.0 8560 | .13 3333 | **7.50** |
| 7.51 | .4001 | 4044 | 6603 | 423 .565 | 5830 | 1904 | 8964 | 3156 | 7.51 |
| 7.52 | .5504 | 4226 | 7179 | 425 .259 | 5917 | 2091 | 9367 | 2979 | 7.52 |
| 7.53 | .7009 | 4408 | 7756 | 426 .958 | 6004 | 2278 | 9.0 9770 | 2802 | 7.53 |
| 7.54 | 56 .8516 | 4591 | 8332 | 428 .661 | 6091 | 2465 | 9.1 0173 | 2626 | 7.54 |
| 7.55 | 57 .0025 | 4773 | 8907 | 430 .369 | 6177 | 2651 | 0575 | 2450 | 7.55 |
| 7.56 | .1536 | 4955 | 8.6 9483 | 432 .081 | 6264 | 2838 | 0977 | 2275 | 7.56 |
| 7.57 | .3049 | 5136 | 8.7 0057 | 433 .798 | 6350 | 3024 | 1378 | 2100 | 7.57 |
| 7.58 | .4564 | 5318 | 0632 | 435 .520 | 6437 | 3210 | 1779 | 1926 | 7.58 |
| 7.59 | .6081 | 5500 | 1206 | 437 .245 | 6523 | 3396 | 2180 | 1752 | 7.59 |
| **7.60** | 57 .7600 | 2.7 5681 | 8.7 1780 | 438 .976 | 1.9 6610 | 4.2 3582 | 9.1 2581 | .13 1579 | **7.60** |
| 7.61 | 57 .9121 | 5862 | 2353 | 440 .711 | 6696 | 3768 | 2981 | 1406 | 7.61 |
| 7.62 | 58 .0644 | 6043 | 2926 | 442 .451 | 6782 | 3954 | 3380 | 1234 | 7.62 |
| 7.63 | .2169 | 6225 | 3499 | 444 .195 | 6868 | 4139 | 3780 | 1062 | 7.63 |
| 7.64 | .3696 | 6405 | 4071 | 445 .944 | 6954 | 4324 | 4179 | 0890 | 7.64 |
| 7.65 | .5225 | 6586 | 4643 | 447 .697 | 7040 | 4509 | 4577 | 0719 | 7.65 |
| 7.66 | .6756 | 6767 | 5214 | 449 .455 | 7126 | 4694 | 4976 | 0548 | 7.66 |
| 7.67 | .8289 | 6948 | 5785 | 451 .218 | 7211 | 4879 | 5374 | 0378 | 7.67 |
| 7.68 | 58 .9824 | 7128 | 6356 | 452 .985 | 7297 | 5063 | 5771 | 0208 | 7.68 |
| 7.69 | 59 .1361 | 7308 | 6926 | 454 .757 | 7383 | 5248 | 6169 | .13 0039 | 7.69 |
| **7.70** | 59 .2900 | 2.7 7489 | 8.7 7496 | 456 .533 | 1.9 7468 | 4.2 5432 | 9.1 6566 | .12 9870 | **7.70** |
| 7.71 | .4441 | 7669 | 8066 | 458 .314 | 7554 | 5616 | 6962 | 9702 | 7.71 |
| 7.72 | .5984 | 7849 | 8635 | 460 .100 | 7639 | 5800 | 7359 | 9534 | 7.72 |
| 7.73 | .7529 | 8029 | 9204 | 461 .890 | 7724 | 5984 | 7754 | 9366 | 7.73 |
| 7.74 | 59 .9076 | 8209 | 8.7 9773 | 463 .685 | 7809 | 6167 | 8150 | 9199 | 7.74 |
| 7.75 | 60 .0625 | 8388 | 8.8 0341 | 465 .484 | 7895 | 6351 | 8545 | 9032 | 7.75 |
| 7.76 | .2176 | 8568 | 0909 | 467 .289 | 7980 | 6534 | 8940 | 8866 | 7.76 |
| 7.77 | .3729 | 8747 | 1476 | 469 .097 | 8065 | 6717 | 9335 | 8700 | 7.77 |
| 7.78 | .5284 | 8927 | 2043 | 470 .911 | 8150 | 6900 | 9.1 9729 | 8535 | 7.78 |
| 7.79 | .6841 | 9106 | 2610 | 472 .729 | 8234 | 7083 | 9.2 0123 | 8370 | 7.79 |
| **7.80** | 60 .8400 | 2.7 9285 | 8.8 3176 | 474 .552 | 1.9 8319 | 4.2 7266 | 9.2 0516 | .12 8205 | **7.80** |
| 7.81 | 60 .9961 | 9464 | 3742 | 476 .380 | 8404 | 7448 | 0910 | 8041 | 7.81 |
| 7.82 | 61 .1524 | 9643 | 4308 | 478 .212 | 8489 | 7631 | 1303 | 7877 | 7.82 |
| 7.83 | .3089 | 2.7 9821 | 4873 | 480 .049 | 8573 | 7813 | 1695 | 7714 | 7.83 |
| 7.84 | .4656 | 2.8 0000 | 5438 | 481 .890 | 8658 | 7995 | 2087 | 7551 | 7.84 |
| 7.85 | .6225 | 0179 | 6002 | 483 .737 | 8742 | 8177 | 2479 | 7389 | 7.85 |
| 7.86 | .7796 | 0357 | 6566 | 485 .588 | 8826 | 8359 | 2871 | 7226 | 7.86 |
| 7.87 | 61 .9369 | 0535 | 7130 | 487 .443 | 8911 | 8540 | 3262 | 7065 | 7.87 |
| 7.88 | 62 .0944 | 0713 | 7694 | 489 .304 | 8995 | 8722 | 3653 | 6904 | 7.88 |
| 7.89 | .2521 | 0891 | 8257 | 491 .169 | 9079 | 8903 | 4043 | 6743 | 7.89 |
| **7.90** | 62 .4100 | 2.8 1069 | 8.8 8819 | 493 .039 | 1.9 9163 | 4.2 9084 | 9.2 4434 | .12 6582 | **7.90** |
| 7.91 | .5681 | 1247 | 9382 | 494 .914 | 9247 | 9265 | 4823 | 6422 | 7.91 |
| 7.92 | .7264 | 1425 | 8.8 9944 | 496 .793 | 9331 | 9446 | 5213 | 6263 | 7.92 |
| 7.93 | 62 .8849 | 1603 | 8.9 0505 | 498 .677 | 9415 | 9627 | 5602 | 6103 | 7.93 |
| 7.94 | 63 .0436 | 1780 | 1067 | 500 .566 | 9499 | 9807 | 5991 | 5945 | 7.94 |
| 7.95 | .2025 | 1957 | 1628 | 502 .460 | 9582 | 4.2 9987 | 6380 | 5786 | 7.95 |
| 7.96 | .3616 | 2135 | 2188 | 504 .358 | 9666 | 4.3 0168 | 6768 | 5628 | 7.96 |
| 7.97 | .5209 | 2312 | 2749 | 506 .262 | 9750 | 0348 | 7156 | 5471 | 7.97 |
| 7.98 | .6804 | 2489 | 3308 | 508 .170 | 9833 | 0528 | 7544 | 5313 | 7.98 |
| 7.99 | 63 .8401 | 2666 | 3868 | 510 .082 | 1.9 9917 | 0707 | 7931 | 5156 | 7.99 |
| **8.00** | 64 .0000 | 2.8 2843 | 8.9 4427 | 512 .000 | 2.0 0000 | 4.3 0887 | 9.2 8318 | .12 5000 | **8.00** |

## 16. SQUARES, CUBES, ROOTS, RECIPROCALS

| N | $N^2$ | $\sqrt{N}$ | $\sqrt{10N}$ | $N^3$ | $\sqrt[3]{N}$ | $\sqrt[3]{10N}$ | $\sqrt[3]{100N}$ | $1/N$ | N |
|---|---|---|---|---|---|---|---|---|---|
| 8.00 | 64 .0000 | 2.8 2843 | 8.9 4427 | 512 .000 | 2.0 0000 | 4.3 0887 | 9.2 8318 | .12 5000 | 8.00 |
| 8.01 | .1601 | 3019 | 4986 | 513 .922 | 0083 | 1066 | 8704 | 4844 | 8.01 |
| 8.02 | .3204 | 3196 | 5545 | 515 .850 | 0167 | 1246 | 9091 | 4688 | 8.02 |
| 8.03 | .4809 | 3373 | 6103 | 517 .782 | 0250 | 1425 | 9477 | 4533 | 8.03 |
| 8.04 | .6416 | 3549 | 6660 | 519 .718 | 0333 | 1604 | 9.2 9862 | 4378 | 8.04 |
| 8.05 | .8025 | 3725 | 7218 | 521 .660 | 0416 | 1783 | 9.3 0248 | 4224 | 8.05 |
| 8.06 | 64 .9636 | 3901 | 7775 | 523 .607 | 0499 | 1961 | 0633 | 4069 | 8.06 |
| 8.07 | 65 .1249 | 4077 | 8332 | 525 .558 | 0582 | 2140 | 1018 | 3916 | 8.07 |
| 8.08 | .2864 | 4253 | 8888 | 527 .514 | 0664 | 2318 | 1402 | 3762 | 8.08 |
| 8.09 | .4481 | 4429 | 8.9 9444 | 529 .475 | 0747 | 2497 | 1786 | 3609 | 8.09 |
| 8.10 | 65 .6100 | 2.8 4605 | 9.0 0000 | 531 .441 | 2.0 0830 | 4.3 2675 | 9.3 2170 | .12 3457 | 8.10 |
| 8.11 | .7721 | 4781 | 0555 | 533 .412 | 0912 | 2853 | 2553 | 3305 | 8.11 |
| 8.12 | 65 .9344 | 4956 | 1110 | 535 .387 | 0995 | 3031 | 2936 | 3153 | 8.12 |
| 8.13 | 66 .0969 | 5132 | 1665 | 537 .368 | 1078 | 3208 | 3319 | 3001 | 8.13 |
| 8.14 | .2596 | 5307 | 2219 | 539 .353 | 1160 | 3386 | 3702 | 2850 | 8.14 |
| 8.15 | .4225 | 5482 | 2774 | 541 .343 | 1242 | 3563 | 4084 | 2699 | 8.15 |
| 8.16 | .5856 | 5657 | 3327 | 543 .338 | 1325 | 3741 | 4466 | 2549 | 8.16 |
| 8.17 | .7489 | 5832 | 3881 | 545 .339 | 1407 | 3918 | 4847 | 2399 | 8.17 |
| 8.18 | 66 .9124 | 6007 | 4434 | 547 .343 | 1489 | 4095 | 5229 | 2249 | 8.18 |
| 8.19 | 67 .0761 | 6182 | 4986 | 549 .353 | 1571 | 4271 | 5610 | 2100 | 8.19 |
| 8.20 | 67 .2400 | 2.8 6356 | 9.0 5539 | 551 .368 | 2.0 1653 | 4.3 4448 | 9.3 5990 | .12 1951 | 8.20 |
| 8.21 | .4041 | 6531 | 6091 | 553 .388 | 1735 | 4625 | 6370 | 1803 | 8.21 |
| 8.22 | .5684 | 6705 | 6642 | 555 .412 | 1817 | 4801 | 6751 | 1655 | 8.22 |
| 8.23 | .7329 | 6880 | 7193 | 557 .442 | 1899 | 4977 | 7130 | 1507 | 8.23 |
| 8.24 | 67 .8976 | 7054 | 7744 | 559 .476 | 1980 | 5153 | 7510 | 1359 | 8.24 |
| 8.25 | 68 .0625 | 7228 | 8295 | 561 .516 | 2062 | 5329 | 7889 | 1212 | 8.25 |
| 8.26 | .2276 | 7402 | 8845 | 563 .560 | 2144 | 5505 | 8268 | 1065 | 8.26 |
| 8.27 | .3929 | 7576 | 9395 | 565 .609 | 2225 | 5681 | 8646 | 0919 | 8.27 |
| 8.28 | .5584 | 7750 | 9.0 9945 | 567 .664 | 2307 | 5856 | 9024 | 0773 | 8.28 |
| 8.29 | .7241 | 7924 | 9.1 0494 | 569 .723 | 2388 | 6032 | 9402 | 0627 | 8.29 |
| 8.30 | 68 .8900 | 2.8 8097 | 9.1 1043 | 571 .787 | 2.0 2469 | 4.3 6207 | 9.3 9780 | .12 0482 | 8.30 |
| 8.31 | 69 .0561 | 8271 | 1592 | 573 .856 | 2551 | 6382 | 9.4 0157 | 0337 | 8.31 |
| 8.32 | .2224 | 8444 | 2140 | 575 .930 | 2632 | 6557 | 0534 | 0192 | 8.32 |
| 8.33 | .3889 | 8617 | 2688 | 578 .010 | 2713 | 6732 | 0911 | .12 0048 | 8.33 |
| 8.34 | .5556 | 8791 | 3236 | 580 .094 | 2794 | 6907 | 1287 | .11 9904 | 8.34 |
| 8.35 | .7225 | 8964 | 3783 | 582 .183 | 2875 | 7081 | 1663 | 9760 | 8.35 |
| 8.36 | 69 .8896 | 9137 | 4330 | 584 .277 | 2956 | 7256 | 2039 | 9617 | 8.36 |
| 8.37 | 70 .0569 | 9310 | 4877 | 586 .376 | 3037 | 7430 | 2414 | 9474 | 8.37 |
| 8.38 | .2244 | 9482 | 5423 | 588 .480 | 3118 | 7604 | 2789 | 9332 | 8.38 |
| 8.39 | .3921 | 9655 | 5969 | 590 .590 | 3199 | 7778 | 3164 | 9190 | 8.39 |
| 8.40 | 70 .5600 | 2.8 9828 | 9.1 6515 | 592 .704 | 2.0 3279 | 4.3 7952 | 9.4 3539 | .11 9048 | 8.40 |
| 8.41 | .7281 | 2.9 0000 | 7061 | 594 .823 | 3360 | 8126 | 3913 | 8906 | 8.41 |
| 8.42 | 70 .8964 | 0172 | 7606 | 596 .948 | 3440 | 8299 | 4287 | 8765 | 8.42 |
| 8.43 | 71 .0649 | 0345 | 8150 | 599 .077 | 3521 | 8473 | 4661 | 8624 | 8.43 |
| 8.44 | .2336 | 0517 | 8695 | 601 .212 | 3601 | 8646 | 5034 | 8483 | 8.44 |
| 8.45 | .4025 | 0689 | 9239 | 603 .351 | 3682 | 8819 | 5407 | 8343 | 8.45 |
| 8.46 | .5716 | 0861 | 9.1 9783 | 605 .496 | 3762 | 8992 | 5780 | 8203 | 8.46 |
| 8.47 | .7409 | 1033 | 9.2 0326 | 607 .645 | 3842 | 9165 | 6152 | 8064 | 8.47 |
| 8.48 | 71 .9104 | 1204 | 0869 | 609 .800 | 3923 | 9338 | 6525 | 7925 | 8.48 |
| 8.49 | 72 .0801 | 1376 | 1412 | 611 .960 | 4003 | 9510 | 6897 | 7786 | 8.49 |
| 8.50 | 72 .2500 | 2.9 1548 | 9.2 1954 | 614 .125 | 2.0 4083 | 4.3 9683 | 9.4 7268 | .11 7647 | 8.50 |

## 16. SQUARES, CUBES, ROOTS, RECIPROCALS

| N | $N^2$ | $\sqrt{N}$ | $\sqrt{10N}$ | $N^3$ | $\sqrt[3]{N}$ | $\sqrt[3]{10N}$ | $\sqrt[3]{100N}$ | $1/N$ | N |
|---|---|---|---|---|---|---|---|---|---|
| **8.50** | 72 .2500 | 2.9 1548 | 9.2 1954 | 614 .125 | 2.0 4083 | 4.3 9683 | 9.4 7268 | .11 7647 | **8.50** |
| 8.51 | .4201 | 1719 | 2497 | 616 .295 | 4163 | 4.3 9855 | 7640 | 7509 | 8.51 |
| 8.52 | .5904 | 1890 | 3038 | 618 .470 | 4243 | 4.4 0028 | 8011 | 7371 | 8.52 |
| 8.53 | .7609 | 2062 | 3580 | 620 .650 | 4323 | 0200 | 8381 | 7233 | 8.53 |
| 8.54 | 72 .9316 | 2233 | 4121 | 622 .836 | 4402 | 0372 | 8752 | 7096 | 8.54 |
| 8.55 | 73 .1025 | 2404 | 4662 | 625 .026 | 4482 | 0543 | 9122 | 6959 | 8.55 |
| 8.56 | .2736 | 2575 | 5203 | 627 .222 | 4562 | 0715 | 9492 | 6822 | 8.56 |
| 8.57 | .4449 | 2746 | 5743 | 629 .423 | 4641 | 0887 | 9.4 9861 | 6686 | 8.57 |
| 8.58 | .6164 | 2916 | 6283 | 631 .629 | 4721 | 1058 | 9.5 0231 | 6550 | 8.58 |
| 8.59 | .7881 | 3087 | 6823 | 633 .840 | 4801 | 1229 | 0600 | 6414 | 8.59 |
| **8.60** | 73 .9600 | 2.9 3258 | 9.2 7362 | 636 .056 | 2.0 4880 | 4.4 1400 | 9.5 0969 | .11 6279 | **8.60** |
| 8.61 | 74 .1321 | 3428 | 7901 | 638 .277 | 4959 | 1572 | 1337 | 6144 | 8.61 |
| 8.62 | .3044 | 3598 | 8440 | 640 .504 | 5039 | 1742 | 1705 | 6009 | 8.62 |
| 8.63 | .4769 | 3769 | 8978 | 642 .736 | 5118 | 1913 | 2073 | 5875 | 8.63 |
| 8.64 | .6496 | 3939 | 9.2 9516 | 644 .973 | 5197 | 2084 | 2441 | 5741 | 8.64 |
| 8.65 | .8225 | 4109 | 9.3 0054 | 647 .215 | 5276 | 2254 | 2808 | 5607 | 8.65 |
| 8.66 | 74 .9956 | 4279 | 0591 | 649 .462 | 5355 | 2425 | 3175 | 5473 | 8.66 |
| 8.67 | 75 .1689 | 4449 | 1128 | 651 .714 | 5434 | 2595 | 3542 | 5340 | 8.67 |
| 8.68 | .3424 | 4618 | 1665 | 653 .972 | 5513 | 2765 | 3908 | 5207 | 8.68 |
| 8.69 | .5161 | 4788 | 2202 | 656 .235 | 5592 | 2935 | 4274 | 5075 | 8.69 |
| **8.70** | 75 .6900 | 2.9 4958 | 9.3 2738 | 658 .503 | 2.0 5671 | 4.4 3105 | 9.5 4640 | .11 4943 | **8.70** |
| 8.71 | 75 .8641 | 5127 | 3274 | 660 .776 | 5750 | 3274 | 5006 | 4811 | 8.71 |
| 8.72 | 76 .0384 | 5296 | 3809 | 663 .055 | 5828 | 3444 | 5371 | 4679 | 8.72 |
| 8.73 | .2129 | 5466 | 4345 | 665 .339 | 5907 | 3613 | 5736 | 4548 | 8.73 |
| 8.74 | .3876 | 5635 | 4880 | 667 .628 | 5986 | 3783 | 6101 | 4416 | 8.74 |
| 8.75 | .5625 | 5804 | 5414 | 669 .922 | 6064 | 3952 | 6466 | 4286 | 8.75 |
| 8.76 | .7376 | 5973 | 5949 | 672 .221 | 6143 | 4121 | 6830 | 4155 | 8.76 |
| 8.77 | 76 .9129 | 6142 | 6483 | 674 .526 | 6221 | 4290 | 7194 | 4025 | 8.77 |
| 8.78 | 77 .0884 | 6311 | 7017 | 676 .836 | 6299 | 4459 | 7557 | 3895 | 8.78 |
| 8.79 | .2641 | 6479 | 7550 | 679 .151 | 6378 | 4627 | 7921 | 3766 | 8.79 |
| **8.80** | 77 .4400 | 2.9 6648 | 9.3 8083 | 681 .472 | 2.0 6456 | 4.4 4796 | 9.5 8284 | .11 3636 | **8.80** |
| 8.81 | .6161 | 6816 | 8616 | 683 .798 | 6534 | 4964 | 8647 | 3507 | 8.81 |
| 8.82 | .7924 | 6985 | 9149 | 686 .129 | 6612 | 5133 | 9009 | 3379 | 8.82 |
| 8.83 | 77 .9689 | 7153 | 9.3 9681 | 688 .465 | 6690 | 5301 | 9372 | 3250 | 8.83 |
| 8.84 | 78 .1456 | 7321 | 9.4 0213 | 690 .807 | 6768 | 5469 | 9.5 9734 | 3122 | 8.84 |
| 8.85 | .3225 | 7489 | 0744 | 693 .154 | 6846 | 5637 | 9.6 0095 | 2994 | 8.85 |
| 8.86 | .4996 | 7658 | 1276 | 695 .506 | 6924 | 5805 | 0457 | 2867 | 8.86 |
| 8.87 | .6769 | 7825 | 1807 | 697 .864 | 7002 | 5972 | 0818 | 2740 | 8.87 |
| 8.88 | 78 .8544 | 7993 | 2338 | 700 .227 | 7080 | 6140 | 1179 | 2613 | 8.88 |
| 8.89 | 79 .0321 | 8161 | 2868 | 702 .595 | 7157 | 6307 | 1540 | 2486 | 8.89 |
| **8.90** | 79 .2100 | 2.9 8329 | 9.4 3398 | 704 .969 | 2.0 7235 | 4.4 6475 | 9.6 1900 | .11 2360 | **8.90** |
| 8.91 | .3881 | 8496 | 3928 | 707 .348 | 7313 | 6642 | 2260 | 2233 | 8.91 |
| 8.92 | .5664 | 8664 | 4458 | 709 .732 | 7390 | 6809 | 2620 | 2108 | 8.92 |
| 8.93 | .7449 | 8831 | 4987 | 712 .122 | 7468 | 6976 | 2980 | 1982 | 8.93 |
| 8.94 | 79 .9236 | 8998 | 5516 | 714 .517 | 7545 | 7142 | 3339 | 1857 | 8.94 |
| 8.95 | 80 .1025 | 9166 | 6044 | 716 .917 | 7622 | 7309 | 3698 | 1732 | 8.95 |
| 8.96 | .2816 | 9333 | 6573 | 719 .323 | 7700 | 7476 | 4057 | 1607 | 8.96 |
| 8.97 | .4609 | 9500 | 7101 | 721 .734 | 7777 | 7642 | 4415 | 1483 | 8.97 |
| 8.98 | .6404 | 9666 | 7629 | 724 .151 | 7854 | 7808 | 4774 | 1359 | 8.98 |
| 8.99 | 80 .8201 | 2.9 9833 | 8156 | 726 .573 | 7931 | 7974 | 5132 | 1235 | 8.99 |
| **9.00** | 81 .0000 | 3.0 0000 | 9.4 8683 | 729 .000 | 2.0 8008 | 4.4 8140 | 9.6 5489 | .11 1111 | **9.00** |

## 16. SQUARES, CUBES, ROOTS, RECIPROCALS

| N | $N^2$ | $\sqrt{N}$ | $\sqrt{10N}$ | $N^3$ | $\sqrt[3]{N}$ | $\sqrt[3]{10N}$ | $\sqrt[3]{100N}$ | $1/N$ | N |
|---|---|---|---|---|---|---|---|---|---|
| **9.00** | 81 .0000 | 3.0 0000 | 9.4 8683 | 729 .000 | 2.0 8008 | 4.4 8140 | 9.6 5489 | .11 1111 | **9.00** |
| 9.01 | .1801 | 0167 | 9210 | 731 .433 | 8085 | 8306 | 5847 | 0988 | 9.01 |
| 9.02 | .3604 | 0333 | 9.4 9737 | 733 .871 | 8162 | 8472 | 6204 | 0865 | 9.02 |
| 9.03 | .5409 | 0500 | 9.5 0263 | 736 .314 | 8239 | 8638 | 6561 | 0742 | 9.03 |
| 9.04 | .7216 | 0666 | 0789 | 738 .763 | 8316 | 8803 | 6918 | 0619 | 9.04 |
| 9.05 | 81 .9025 | 0832 | 1315 | 741 .218 | 8393 | 8969 | 7274 | 0497 | 9.05 |
| 9.06 | 82 .0836 | 0998 | 1840 | 743 .677 | 8470 | 9134 | 7630 | 0375 | 9.06 |
| 9.07 | .2649 | 1164 | 2365 | 746 .143 | 8546 | 9299 | 7986 | 0254 | 9.07 |
| 9.08 | .4464 | 1330 | 2890 | 748 .613 | 8623 | 9464 | 8342 | 0132 | 9.08 |
| 9.09 | .6281 | 1496 | 3415 | 751 .089 | 8699 | 9629 | 8697 | .11 0011 | 9.09 |
| **9.10** | 82 .8100 | 3.0 1662 | 9.5 3939 | 753 .571 | 2.0 8776 | 4.4 9794 | 9.6 9052 | .10 9890 | **9.10** |
| 9.11 | 82 .9921 | 1828 | 4463 | 756 .058 | 8852 | 4.4 9959 | 9407 | 9769 | 9.11 |
| 9.12 | 83 .1744 | 1993 | 4987 | 758 .551 | 8929 | 4.5 0123 | 9.6 9762 | 9649 | 9.12 |
| 9.13 | .3569 | 2159 | 5510 | 761 .048 | 9005 | 0288 | 9.7 0116 | 9529 | 9.13 |
| 9.14 | .5396 | 2324 | 6033 | 763 .552 | 9081 | 0452 | 0470 | 9409 | 9.14 |
| 9.15 | .7225 | 2490 | 6556 | 766 .061 | 9158 | 0616 | 0824 | 9290 | 9.15 |
| 9.16 | 83 .9056 | 2655 | 7079 | 768 .575 | 9234 | 0781 | 1177 | 9170 | 9.16 |
| 9.17 | 84 .0889 | 2820 | 7601 | 771 .095 | 9310 | 0945 | 1531 | 9051 | 9.17 |
| 9.18 | .2724 | 2985 | 8123 | 773 .621 | 9386 | 1108 | 1884 | 8932 | 9.18 |
| 9.19 | .4561 | 3150 | 8645 | 776 .152 | 9462 | 1272 | 2236 | 8814 | 9.19 |
| **9.20** | 84 .6400 | 3.0 3315 | 9.5 9166 | 778 .688 | 2.0 9538 | 4.5 1436 | 9.7 2589 | .10 8696 | **9.20** |
| 9.21 | 84 .8241 | 3480 | 9.5 9687 | 781 .230 | 9614 | 1599 | 2941 | 8578 | 9.21 |
| 9.22 | 85 .0084 | 3645 | 9.6 0208 | 783 .777 | 9690 | 1763 | 3293 | 8460 | 9.22 |
| 9.23 | .1929 | 3809 | 0729 | 786 .330 | 9765 | 1926 | 3645 | 8342 | 9.23 |
| 9.24 | .3776 | 3974 | 1249 | 788 .889 | 9841 | 2089 | 3996 | 8225 | 9.24 |
| 9.25 | .5625 | 4138 | 1769 | 791 .453 | 9917 | 2252 | 4348 | 8108 | 9.25 |
| 9.26 | .7476 | 4302 | 2289 | 794 .023 | 2.0 9992 | 2415 | 4699 | 7991 | 9.26 |
| 9.27 | 85 .9329 | 4467 | 2808 | 796 .598 | 2.1 0068 | 2578 | 5049 | 7875 | 9.27 |
| 9.28 | 86 .1184 | 4631 | 3328 | 799 .179 | 0144 | 2740 | 5400 | 7759 | 9.28 |
| 9.29 | .3041 | 4795 | 3846 | 801 .765 | 0219 | 2903 | 5750 | 7643 | 9.29 |
| **9.30** | 86 .4900 | 3.0 4959 | 9.6 4365 | 804 .357 | 2.1 0294 | 4.5 3065 | 9.7 6100 | .10 7527 | **9.30** |
| 9.31 | .6761 | 5123 | 4883 | 806 .954 | 0370 | 3228 | 6450 | 7411 | 9.31 |
| 9.32 | 86 .8624 | 5287 | 5401 | 809 .558 | 0445 | 3390 | 6799 | 7296 | 9.32 |
| 9.33 | 87 .0489 | 5450 | 5919 | 812 .166 | 0520 | 3552 | 7148 | 7181 | 9.33 |
| 9.34 | .2356 | 5614 | 6437 | 814 .781 | 0595 | 3714 | 7497 | 7066 | 9.34 |
| 9.35 | .4225 | 5778 | 6954 | 817 .400 | 0671 | 3876 | 7846 | 6952 | 9.35 |
| 9.36 | .6096 | 5941 | 7471 | 820 .026 | 0746 | 4038 | 8195 | 6838 | 9.36 |
| 9.37 | .7969 | 6105 | 7988 | 822 .657 | 0821 | 4199 | 8543 | 6724 | 9.37 |
| 9.38 | 87 .9844 | 6268 | 8504 | 825 .294 | 0896 | 4361 | 8891 | 6610 | 9.38 |
| 9.39 | 88 .1721 | 6431 | 9020 | 827 .936 | 0971 | 4522 | 9239 | 6496 | 9.39 |
| **9.40** | 88 .3600 | 3.0 6594 | 9.6 9536 | 830 .584 | 2.1 1045 | 4.5 4684 | 9.7 9586 | .10 6383 | **9.40** |
| 9.41 | .5481 | 6757 | 9.7 0052 | 833 .238 | 1120 | 4845 | 9.7 9933 | 6270 | 9.41 |
| 9.42 | .7364 | 6920 | 0567 | 835 .897 | 1195 | 5006 | 9.8 0280 | 6157 | 9.42 |
| 9.43 | 88 .9249 | 7083 | 1082 | 838 .562 | 1270 | 5167 | 0627 | 6045 | 9.43 |
| 9.44 | 89 .1136 | 7246 | 1597 | 841 .232 | 1344 | 5328 | 0974 | 5932 | 9.44 |
| 9.45 | .3025 | 7409 | 2111 | 843 .909 | 1419 | 5488 | 1320 | 5820 | 9.45 |
| 9.46 | .4916 | 7571 | 2625 | 846 .591 | 1494 | 5649 | 1666 | 5708 | 9.46 |
| 9.47 | .6809 | 7734 | 3139 | 849 .278 | 1568 | 5809 | 2012 | 5597 | 9.47 |
| 9.48 | 89 .8704 | 7896 | 3653 | 851 .971 | 1642 | 5970 | 2357 | 5485 | 9.48 |
| 9.49 | 90 .0601 | 8058 | 4166 | 854 .670 | 1717 | 6130 | 2703 | 5374 | 9.49 |
| **9.50** | 90 .2500 | 3.0 8221 | 9.7 4679 | 857 .375 | 2.1 1791 | 4.5 6290 | 9.8 3048 | .10 5263 | **9.50** |

## 16. SQUARES, CUBES, ROOTS, RECIPROCALS

| N | N² | √N | √10N | N³ | ³√N | ³√10N | ³√100N | 1/N | N |
|---|---|---|---|---|---|---|---|---|---|
| **9.50** | 90 .2500 | 3.0 8221 | 9.7 4679 | 857 .375 | 2.1 1791 | 4.5 6290 | 9.8 3048 | .10 5263 | **9.50** |
| 9.51 | .4401 | 8383 | 5192 | 860 .085 | 1865 | 6450 | 3392 | 5152 | 9.51 |
| 9.52 | .6304 | 8545 | 5705 | 862 .801 | 1940 | 6610 | 3737 | 5042 | 9.52 |
| 9.53 | 90 .8209 | 8707 | 6217 | 865 .523 | 2014 | 6770 | 4081 | 4932 | 9.53 |
| 9.54 | 91 .0116 | 8869 | 6729 | 868 .251 | 2088 | 6930 | 4425 | 4822 | 9.54 |
| 9.55 | .2025 | 9031 | 7241 | 870 .984 | 2162 | 7089 | 4769 | 4712 | 9.55 |
| 9.56 | .3936 | 9192 | 7753 | 873 .723 | 2236 | 7249 | 5113 | 4603 | 9.56 |
| 9.57 | .5849 | 9354 | 8264 | 876 .467 | 2310 | 7408 | 5456 | 4493 | 9.57 |
| 9.58 | .7764 | 9516 | 8775 | 879 .218 | 2384 | 7567 | 5799 | 4384 | 9.58 |
| 9.59 | 91 .9681 | 9677 | 9285 | 881 .974 | 2458 | 7727 | 6142 | 4275 | 9.59 |
| **9.60** | 92 .1600 | 3.0 9839 | 9.7 9796 | 884 .736 | 2.1 2532 | 4.5 7886 | 9.8 6485 | .10 4167 | **9.60** |
| 9.61 | .3521 | 3.1 0000 | 9.8 0306 | 887 .504 | 2605 | 8045 | 6827 | 4058 | 9.61 |
| 9.62 | .5444 | 0161 | 0816 | 890 .277 | 2679 | 8203 | 7169 | 3950 | 9.62 |
| 9.63 | .7369 | 0322 | 1326 | 893 .056 | 2753 | 8362 | 7511 | 3842 | 9.63 |
| 9.64 | 92 .9296 | 0483 | 1835 | 895 .841 | 2826 | 8521 | 7853 | 3734 | 9.64 |
| 9.65 | 93 .1225 | 0644 | 2344 | 898 .632 | 2900 | 8679 | 8195 | 3627 | 9.65 |
| 9.66 | .3156 | 0805 | 2853 | 901 .429 | 2974 | 8838 | 8536 | 3520 | 9.66 |
| 9.67 | .5089 | 0966 | 3362 | 904 .231 | 3047 | 8996 | 8877 | 3413 | 9.67 |
| 9.68 | .7024 | 1127 | 3870 | 907 .039 | 3120 | 9154 | 9217 | 3306 | 9.68 |
| 9.69 | 93 .8961 | 1288 | 4378 | 909 .853 | 3194 | 9312 | 9558 | 3199 | 9.69 |
| **9.70** | 94 .0900 | 3.1 1448 | 9.8 4886 | 912 .673 | 2.1 3267 | 4.5 9470 | 9.8 9898 | .10 3093 | **9.70** |
| 9.71 | .2841 | 1609 | 5393 | 915 .499 | 3340 | 9628 | 9.9 0238 | 2987 | 9.71 |
| 9.72 | .4784 | 1769 | 5901 | 918 .330 | 3414 | 9786 | 0578 | 2881 | 9.72 |
| 9.73 | .6729 | 1929 | 6408 | 921 .167 | 3487 | 4.5 9943 | 0918 | 2775 | 9.73 |
| 9.74 | 94 .8676 | 2090 | 6914 | 924 .010 | 3560 | 4.6 0101 | 1257 | 2669 | 9.74 |
| 9.75 | 95 .0625 | 2250 | 7421 | 926 .859 | 3633 | 0258 | 1596 | 2564 | 9.75 |
| 9.76 | .2576 | 2410 | 7927 | 929 .714 | 3706 | 0416 | 1935 | 2459 | 9.76 |
| 9.77 | .4529 | 2570 | 8433 | 932 .575 | 3779 | 0573 | 2274 | 2354 | 9.77 |
| 9.78 | .6484 | 2730 | 8939 | 935 .441 | 3852 | 0730 | 2612 | 2249 | 9.78 |
| 9.79 | 95 .8441 | 2890 | 9444 | 938 .314 | 3925 | 0887 | 2950 | 2145 | 9.79 |
| **9.80** | 96 .0400 | 3.1 3050 | 9.8 9949 | 941 .192 | 2.1 3997 | 4.6 1044 | 9.9 3288 | .10 2041 | **9.80** |
| 9.81 | .2361 | 3209 | 9.9 0454 | 944 .076 | 4070 | 1200 | 3626 | 1937 | 9.81 |
| 9.82 | .4324 | 3369 | 0959 | 946 .966 | 4143 | 1357 | 3964 | 1833 | 9.82 |
| 9.83 | .6289 | 3528 | 1464 | 949 .862 | 4216 | 1514 | 4301 | 1729 | 9.83 |
| 9.84 | 96 .8256 | 3688 | 1968 | 952 .764 | 4288 | 1670 | 4638 | 1626 | 9.84 |
| 9.85 | 97 .0225 | 3847 | 2472 | 955 .672 | 4361 | 1826 | 4975 | 1523 | 9.85 |
| 9.86 | .2196 | 4006 | 2975 | 958 .585 | 4433 | 1983 | 5311 | 1420 | 9.86 |
| 9.87 | .4169 | 4166 | 3479 | 961 .505 | 4506 | 2139 | 5648 | 1317 | 9.87 |
| 9.88 | .6144 | 4325 | 3982 | 964 .430 | 4578 | 2295 | 5984 | 1215 | 9.88 |
| 9.89 | 97 .8121 | 4484 | 4485 | 967 .362 | 4651 | 2451 | 6320 | 1112 | 9.89 |
| **9.90** | 98 .0100 | 3.1 4643 | 9.9 4987 | 970 .299 | 2.1 4723 | 4.6 2607 | 9.9 6655 | .10 1010 | **9.90** |
| 9.91 | .2081 | 4802 | 5490 | 973 .242 | 4795 | 2762 | 6991 | 0908 | 9.91 |
| 9.92 | .4064 | 4960 | 5992 | 976 .191 | 4867 | 2918 | 7326 | 0806 | 9.92 |
| 9.93 | .6049 | 5119 | 6494 | 979 .147 | 4940 | 3073 | 7661 | 0705 | 9.93 |
| 9.94 | 98 .8036 | 5278 | 6995 | 982 .108 | 5012 | 3229 | 7996 | 0604 | 9.94 |
| 9.95 | 99 .0025 | 5436 | 7497 | 985 .075 | 5084 | 3384 | 8331 | 0503 | 9.95 |
| 9.96 | .2016 | 5595 | 7998 | 988 .048 | 5156 | 3539 | 8665 | 0402 | 9.96 |
| 9.97 | .4009 | 5753 | 8499 | 991 .027 | 5228 | 3694 | 8999 | 0301 | 9.97 |
| 9.98 | .6004 | 5911 | 8999 | 994 .012 | 5300 | 3849 | 9333 | 0200 | 9.98 |
| 9.99 | 99 .8001 | 6070 | 9.9 9500 | 997 .003 | 5372 | 4004 | 9.9 9667 | 0100 | 9.99 |
| **10.00** | 10 0.000 | 3.1 6228 | 10 .0000 | 1000 .00 | 2.1 5443 | 4.6 4159 | 10 .0000 | .10 0000 | **10.00** |

## GREEK ALPHABET

| Letters | | Names | Letters | | Names | Letters | | Names |
|---|---|---|---|---|---|---|---|---|
| A | $\alpha$ | Alpha | I | $\iota$ | Iota | P | $\rho$ | Rho |
| B | $\beta$ | Beta | K | $\kappa$ | Kappa | $\Sigma$ | $\sigma$ s | Sigma |
| $\Gamma$ | $\gamma$ | Gamma | $\Lambda$ | $\lambda$ | Lambda | T | $\tau$ | Tau |
| $\Delta$ | $\delta$ | Delta | M | $\mu$ | Mu | $\Upsilon$ | $\upsilon$ | Upsilon |
| E | $\epsilon$ | Epsilon | N | $\nu$ | Nu | $\Phi$ | $\phi$ | Phi |
| Z | $\zeta$ | Zeta | $\Xi$ | $\xi$ | Xi | X | $\chi$ | Chi |
| H | $\eta$ | Eta | O | $o$ | Omicron | $\Psi$ | $\psi$ | Psi |
| $\Theta$ | $\theta$ | Theta | $\Pi$ | $\pi$ | Pi | $\Omega$ | $\omega$ | Omega |

PRINTED IN THE UNITED STATES OF AMERICA